Journal of PEDIATRIC PSYCHOLOGY

Volume 37, Number 5 • June 2012

CONTENTS

Special Section: Reimbursement with H & B Codes

479 Introduction to the Special Section: Pediatric Psychologists' Experiences in Obtaining Reimbursement for the Use of Health and Behavior Codes
Dennis Drotar

486 Commentary: The Use of Health and Behavior Codes in Pediatric Psychology: Where Are We Now?
Meghan McAuliffe Lines, W. Douglas Tynan, Gwendoline B. Angalet and Jennifer Shroff Pendley

491 Commentary: Health & Behavior Codes: Great Idea, Questionable Outcome
Danny C. Duke, Kim Guion, Kurt A. Freeman, Anna C. Wilson and Michael A. Harris

496 Commentary: Promoting Health and Well-being in Pediatric Primary Care Settings: Using Health and Behavior Codes at Routine Well-child Visits
Ayelet Talmi and Emily Fazio

503 Commentary: Medicaid Reimbursement and Utilization of Health and Behavior Codes: Year One in Oklahoma
Kristine Woods and Stephen R. Gillaspy

509 Commentary: Health and Behavior Codes in a Pediatric Headache Program: Reimbursement Data and Recommendations for Practice
Robyn Lewis Claar, Karen J. Kaczynski, Margaret Munro Lyons and Alyssa A. LeBel

514 Commentary: The Use of Health and Behavior Codes in a Pediatric Cardiology Setting
Cheryl L. Brosig

519 Commentary: Examination of Health and Behavioral Code Reimbursement From Private Payers in the Context of Clinical Multidisciplinary Pediatric Obesity Treatment
Bethany J. Sallinen and Susan J. Woolford

Section: Pediatric Eosinophilic Disorders

523 Preliminary Evaluation of Maternal Caregiver Stress in Pediatric Eosinophilic Gastrointestinal Disorders
Tiffany H. Taft, Sarah Ballou and Laurie Keefer

533 Treatment Adherence in Pediatric Eosinophilic Gastrointestinal Disorders
Kevin A. Hommel, James P. Franciosi, Elizabeth A. Hente, Annette Ahrens and Marc E. Rothenberg

543 Commentary: Psychological and Behavioral Challenges for Families of Children with Eosinophilic Gastrointestinal Disorders
Mary D. Klinnert

Section: Pediatric Pain and Distress

546 Concurrent and Longitudinal Bidirectional Relationships Between Toddlers' Chronic Pain and Mental Health: The Generation R Study
Noor J. Wolff, Anne-Sophie E. Darlington, Joke A. M. Hunfeld, Vincent W. V. Jaddoe, Albert Hofman, Hein Raat, Frank C. Verhulst, Jan Passchier and Henning Tiemeier

557 Multimethod Assessment of Children's Distress During Noninvasive Outpatient Medical Procedures: Child and Parent Attitudes and Factors
Christina M. Rodriguez, Vanessa Clough, Anjali S. Gowda and Meagan C. Tucker

567 The Role of State Anxiety in Children's Memories for Pain
Melanie Noel, Christine T. Chambers, Patrick J. McGrath, Raymond M. Klein and Sherry H. Stewart

580 A Comparison of Friendship Quality and Social Functioning Among Children With Perinatally Acquired HIV, Children With Persistent Asthma, and Healthy Children of HIV-Positive Mothers
Sarah E. Baker, Larissa N. Niec and Jill Meade

591 Friends or Foes? A Review of Peer Influence on Self-Care and Glycemic Control in Adolescents With Type 1 Diabetes
Dianne K. Palladino and Vicki S. Helgeson

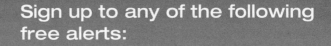

Journal of Pediatric Psychology (ISSN 0146-8693) is published ten times a year by Oxford University Press for the Society of Pediatric Psychology, P.O. Box 170231, Atlanta, GA 30317. The journal is the scientific publication of the Society of Pediatric Psychology (SSP), Division 54 of the American Psychological Association. As such, the journal publishes articles related to theory, research, and professional practice in pediatric psychology. Pediatric psychology is an interdisciplinary field addressing physical, cognitive, social, and emotional functioning and development as they relate to health and illness issues in children, adolescents, and families. The journal publishes papers on a wide variety of topics exploring the interrelationship between psychological and physical well-being of children, adolescents, and families including: psychosocial and developmental factors contributing to the etiology, course, treatment and outcome of pediatric conditions; assessment and treatment of behavioral and emotional concomitants of disease, illness, and developmental disorders; the role of psychology in healthcare settings; behavioral aspects of pediatric medicine; the promotions of health and health-related behaviors; the prevention of illness and injury among children and youth; and issues related to the training of pediatric psychologists.

Membership in Society of Pediatric Psychology
Individuals interested in becoming a member of the Society of Pediatric Psychology should contact Society of Pediatric Psychology, P.O. Box 170231, Atlanta, GA 30317. Tel/fax: 404-373-8251.

Subscriptions
A subscription to the *Journal of Pediatric Psychology* comprises 10 issues. Prices include postage; for subscribers outside the Americas, issues are sent air freight. Airmail rates are available on request.

Annual Subscription Rate (Volume 37, 10 issues, 2012)
Institutional
Print edition and site-wide online access: US$1,080/£719/€1,080
Print edition only: US$990/£659/€990
Site-wide online access only: US$900/£599/€900
Personal
Print edition and individual online access: US$239/£159/€239
Please note: US$ rate applies to US & Canada, Euros applies to Europe, UK£ applies to UK and Rest of World.

There are other subscription rates available; for a complete listing, please visit www.jpepsy.oxfordjournals.org/subscriptions.

Full prepayment in the correct currency is required for all orders. Orders are regarded as firm, and payments are not refundable. Subscriptions are accepted and entered on a complete volume basis. Claims cannot be considered more than four months after publication or date of order, whichever is later. All subscriptions in Canada are subject to GST. Subscriptions in the EU may be subject to European VAT. If registered, please supply details to avoid unnecessary charges. For subscriptions that include online versions, a proportion of the subscription price may be subject to UK VAT. Personal rates are applicable only when a subscription is for individual use and are not available if delivery is made to a corporate address.

The current year and two previous years' issues are available from Oxford Journals. Previous volumes can be obtained from the Periodicals Service Company at http://www.periodicals.com/oxford.html or from the Periodicals Service Company, 11 Main Street, Germantown, NY 12526, USA. E-mail: psc@periodicals.com. Tel: (518) 537-4700. Fax: (518) 537-5899.

Contact Information: Journals Customer Service Department, Oxford University Press, Great Clarendon Street, Oxford OX2 6DP, UK. E-mail: jnls.cust.serv@oup.com. Tel: +44 (0)1865 353907. Fax: +44(0)1865 353485. **In the Americas, please contact:** Journals Customer Service Department, Oxford University Press, 2001 Evans Road, Cary, NC 27513, USA. E-mail: jnlorders@oup.com. Tel: (800) 852-7323 (toll-free in USA/Canada) or (919) 677-0977. Fax: (919) 677-1714. **In Japan, please contact:** Journals Customer Service Department, Oxford University Press, 4-5-10-8F Shiba, Minato-ku, Tokyo, 108-8386, Japan. E-mail: custserv.jp@oup.com. Tel: +81 3 5444 5858. Fax: +81 3 3454 2929.

Methods of payment: (i) Check (payable to Oxford University Press, to Oxford University Press, Cashiers Office, Great Clarendon Street, Oxford OX2 6DP, UK) in GB£ Sterling (drawn on a UK bank), US$ Dollars (drawn on a US bank), or EU€ Euros. (ii) Bank transfer to Barclays Bank Plc, Oxford Group Office, Oxford (bank sort code 20-65-18) (UK), overseas only Swift code BARC GB 22 (GB£ Sterling to account no. 70299332, IBAN GB89BARC20651870299332; US$ Dollars to account no. 66014600, IBAN GB27BARC 20651866014600; EU€ Euros to account no. 78923655, IBAN GB16BARC20651878923 655). (iii) Credit card (Mastercard, Visa, Switch or American Express).

Oxford Journals Environmental and Ethical Policies
Oxford Journals is committed to working with the global community to bring the highest quality research to the widest possible audience. Oxford Journals will protect the environment by implementing environmentally friendly policies and practices wherever possible. Please see http://www.oxfordjournals.org/ethicalpolicies.html for further information on Oxford Journals' environmental and ethical policies.

Postal Information
Journal of Pediatric Psychology (ISSN 0146-8693) is published ten times a year, in Jan./Feb., Mar., Apr., May, June, July, Aug., Sept., Oct., and Nov./Dec., by Oxford University Press, 2001 Evans Road, Cary, NC 27513-2009. Periodical Postage Paid at Cary, NC and additional mailing offices. Postmaster: send address changes to *Journal of Pediatric Psychology*, Journals Customer Service Department, Oxford University Press, 2001 Evans Road, Cary, NC 27513-2009.

Supplements, Reprints, and Corporate Sales
For requests from industry and companies regarding supplements, bulk article reprints, sponsored subscriptions, translation opportunities for previously published material, and corporate online opportunities, please e-mail special.sales@oup.com, fax +44 (0) 1865 353774, or visit www.oxfordjournals.org/jnls/sales.

Digital Object Identifiers
For information on dois and to resolve them, please visit www.doi.org.

Permissions
For information on how to request permissions to reproduce articles or information from this journal, please visit www.oxfordjournals.org/jnls/permissions.

Advertising
Advertising, inserts, and artwork enquiries should be addressed to Advertising and Special Sales, Oxford Journals, Oxford University Press, Great Clarendon Street, Oxford, OX2 6DP, UK. Tel: +44 (0)1865 354767; Fax: +44 (0)1865 353774; E-mail: jnlsadvertising@oup.com.

Indexing and Abstracting
Journal of Pediatric Psychology is abstracted or indexed in *Beck Medical Information, Behavioral Medicine Abstracts, Biological Abstracts, Child and Youth Services, Child Development Abstracts and Bibliography, Cumulative Index to Nursing and Allied Health Literature, Current Contents, Exceptional Child Education Resources, Excerpta Medics, Family Resources Database, Health Instrument File, Index Medicus, Mental Health Abstracts, Psychological Abstracts, Referativnyi Zhurnal, Sage Family Studies Abstracts, Science Citation Index, Selected List of Tables of Contents of Psychiatric Periodicals, Social Work Research & Abstracts, Sociological Abstracts, Special Educational Needs Abstracts, The Psychological Reader's Guide,* and *Zeitschrift fur Kinder- und Jugendpsychiatrie.*

Journal of Pediatric Psychology is printed on acid-free paper that meets the minimum requirements of ANSI Standard Z39.48-1984 (Permanence of Paper), beginning with Volume 23, Number 1.

Disclaimer
Statements of fact and opinion in the articles in the *Journal of Pediatric Psychology* are those of the respective authors and contributors and not of the Society of Pediatric Psychology or Oxford University Press. Neither Oxford University Press nor the Editors, Editorial Board, or Society of Pediatric Psychology make any representation, express or implied, in respect of the accuracy of the material in this journal and cannot accept any legal responsibility or liability for any errors or omissions that may be made. The reader should make her or his own evaluation as to the appropriateness or otherwise of any experimental technique described.

Copyright © 2012 Society of Pediatric Psychology

All rights reserved; no part of this publication may be reproduced, stored in a retrieval system, or transmitted in any form or by any means, electronic, mechanical photocopying, recording or otherwise without prior written permission of the publisher or a license permitting restricted copying issued in the UK by the Copyright Licensing Agency Ltd, 90 Tottenham Court Road, London W1P 9HE.

Oxford University Press is a department of the University of Oxford. It furthers the University's objective of excellence in research, scholarship, and education by publishing worldwide.

Introduction to the Special Section: Pediatric Psychologists' Experiences in Obtaining Reimbursement for the Use of Health and Behavior Codes

Dennis Drotar, PhD

Department of Pediatrics, Cincinnati Children's Hospital Medical Center

All correspondence concerning this article should be addressed to Dennis Drotar, PhD, Division of Behavioral Medicine and Clinical Psychology, Cincinnati Children's Hospital Medical Center, 3333 Burnet Avenue, MLC 7039 Cincinnati, OH, 45229-3039, USA. E-mail: dennis.drotar@cchmc.org

Received March 29, 2012; revisions received and accepted March 29, 2012

One of the most critical influences on the growth of the practice of psychology involves reimbursement for clinical services from a range of insurers. A hallmark of clinical practice in the field of pediatric psychology is a focus of psychological services on problems associated with the management of chronic health conditions (e.g., enhancing coping, pain management, treatment adherence, and promotion of health behaviors) rather than psychopathology. For this reason, traditional methods of billing that focus on identification of mental health diagnoses based on the Diagnostic and Statistical Manual of Mental Disorders (DSM) (American Psychiatric Association, 1994) and related procedure codes for assessment and interventions do not encompass the broad scope of practice of pediatric psychology. A related problem involves insurance company policy to reimburse mental health services through a separate mechanism or carve out apart from the basic medical benefit.

For these reasons, the 2002 approval of the new health and behavior (H&B) assessment and intervention codes for inclusion in the current procedural terminology (CPT) system was heralded as an important development within clinical practice in pediatric psychology (Noll & Fischer, 2004) as well as for the field of clinical psychology in general. Within clinical psychology, the H&B codes are alive and well and used by psychologists to bill for Medicare services (394,162 outpatient visits in 2011) (R. Phelps, personal communication).

It has now been 10 years since the approval of the H&B codes for use in a range of settings and time to summarize pediatric psychologists' experiences in application of the codes (Tynan, Lutz Stehl, & Shroff Pendley, 2009). This special section of the *Journal of Pediatric Psychology* (JPP) was developed to provide a venue for practitioners from a range of settings to describe their collective experiences in application of and reimbursement for the H&B codes, to share strategies that have enhanced reimbursement, and consider approaches to advocate for policies to enhance effective use of the H&B codes. This introduction summarizes highlights from commentaries from a broad range of clinical programs that represent a cross-section of pediatric psychology services from various regions of the country, identifies implications, and clarifies next steps in future agenda for practice, advocacy, and research.

General Pediatric Psychology Services

Many pediatric psychology programs provide services to a broad range of populations with varied presenting problems and medical diagnoses. Lines, Tynan, and Angalet (2012) examined their experiences in billing with the H&B codes in a large pediatric hospital. The majority (62%) of claims were either partially or fully paid. The average rate of reimbursement was 46%. However, rate of reimbursement were quite variable depending on the insurance company: For example, commercial insurance reimbursed at 74% compared with instate Medicaid (59%) and out of state Medicaid, which reimbursed only 16% of the claims that were submitted. In addition, for reasons that were not entirely clear, interdivisional reimbursement rates were quite variable, including 37% for weight management, 44% for behavioral health, and 68% for rehabilitation.

In another example from a general pediatric psychology service, Duke, Guion, Freeman, Wilson, and Harris (2012) reported their experiences in attempting to reverse denials of the codes. In their setting, the average reimbursement rate for services was only 26% of the total fees that were billed and included a 55% rate of denials. In an interesting head to head comparison of billing for a traditional mental health services code (90801) for an initial diagnostic evaluation with a comparable H&B assessment code (96150), the authors identified a lower denial rate (39%) for the mental health services versus the H&B codes (55.5%). The overall reimbursement rate for the mental health service code was somewhat lower (53.7%) than for the H&B codes (59%). However, because the mental health services code was billed at a higher rate, it resulted in greater financial recovery. Duke et al. (2012) suggest that disparity in payment for comparable services can create significant pressure for practitioners to use traditional mental health codes and diagnoses, even if they are not as good as a fit as H&B codes in maximizing reimbursement.

Psychological Services in Primary Care

Talmi and Fazio (2012) noted the importance of integrating behavioral health services in primary care and their experiences in using H&B codes to secure reimbursement for such services in such settings. The majority of visits billed the initial assessment code (96150), which was consistent with the focus of primary care psychological services, especially one-time assessment (triage visits) to address specific behavioral health concerns. Data that were gathered for Relative Value Units (RVUs) to assess clinical productivity (Seime & Manley, 1999) yielded a sufficient number of RVUs to cover 30% of a pediatric psychologist salary. Unfortunately, because the author's hospital collected reimbursement data by encounter rather than billing code, it was not possible to obtain specific data for reimbursement rates. Talmi and Fazio (2012) also noted that the state (Colorado) in which they provided services has not reimbursed for any H&B codes because of a Medicaid rule that automatically rejects psychologists' H&B coded bills as an unauthorized provider type when billed from primary care.

State Medicaid Reimbursement

The final commentary that focused on general pediatric psychological services described the process to secure Medicaid reimbursement for the H&B codes in one state (Oklahoma) and the results of 1 year's experience with reimbursement (Woods and Gillaspy, 2012). This is an important experience given the absent or very limited reimbursement by Medicaid in many states as noted in other commentaries in this section.

The process began by contacting the behavioral unit at the Oklahoma Health Care Authority (OHCA). A series of discussions about the nature and importance of the H&B codes to patient care and the fact that other insurance companies in the state were planning to reimburse for the codes convinced the OHCA of the importance of the codes. Although reimbursement for the codes was included in the state budget, it fell below funding priorities for several years. The authors noted that the initiation of a medical home (Stille et al., 2010) model for primary care that emphasized integration of behavioral health with medical care for children with chronic health conditions may have influenced the eventual decision to fund the reimbursement for the codes. Previously, the authors had worked with the OHCA and the state board to develop a process that allowed psychology interns and fellows to bill Medicaid for services based on the traditional mental health services codes. When the H&B codes were finally approved for use by psychologists, psychology trainees were also approved to bill for the codes, while under supervision of licensed psychologists.

The reimbursement rates under Medicaid were largely consistent with that of Medicare but below that of private insurance and far below the estimated charges for the services. On the other hand, it is important to note frequent denials in Medicaid for H&B codes described by others (Brosig & Zahrt, 2006) were not noted by Woods and Gillaspy (2012).

Multidisciplinary Specialty Programs

Pediatric psychology services are often provided in the context of multidisciplinary specialty programs. Several authors described use of the H&B codes in such programs.

Pediatric Headache Program

Claar, Kaczynski, Lyons, and Abel (2012) described their experiences in obtaining reimbursement based on the H&B codes in the context of a multidisciplinary program for the evaluation and treatment of pediatric headache. This program encountered significant variation in reimbursement depending on the specific insurance company as well as a decline in reimbursement from 51% to 31% over a 2-year period (2008–2010) owing to a change in the mix of payers that reflected a greater proportion of patients with policies that did not provide reimbursement for the codes. State Medicaid and one insurance company accounted for the lion's share of poor reimbursement.

Strategies that were successful in enhancing reimbursement for the H&B codes included detailed explanation of the specific services that were provided under the codes, clarification that these services cannot be provided by local in-network providers, and are closely tied to and consistent with the patient's medical evaluation, diagnosis, and treatment. Other successful strategies included the development of relationships and consistent contacts between hospital billing staff and insurance company staff, developing a track record of services that were successfully authorized by specific companies, and highlighting these successes when attempting to obtain authorization for future patients.

Pediatric Cardiology Service

Brosig's (2012) report concerned her experience in using the H&B codes in a pediatric cardiology setting. Frequent presenting problems in this included anxiety, depression, attention problems, learning problems, and cardiac transplant-related care. Payment rates for H&B codes ranged from 42% to 79% and contrasted with payments for mental health codes (24–34%). Brosig (2012) also found that payment rates had declined over 4 years (2007–2011) from 79% to 42%. The low Medicaid reimbursement rates (8–17%) were particularly striking. Strategies that facilitated reimbursement included education of insurance company staff about the need for and specific use of the codes with cardiology populations and having specialists with experience in billing for psychological services submit the bills to insurance companies.

Multidisciplinary Pediatric Obesity Treatment

Sallinen and Woolford (2012) reported their experiences with the H&B codes in the context of a comprehensive weight management program. Psychologists provided initial assessments, reassessments, and behavioral interventions, including group and individual (Woolford, Sallinen, Clark, & Freed, 2011). Percentage collections provided by insurance companies increased from 21% to 26% over a 4-year period (2008–2011). Assessments yielded higher collection rates (35%) compared with interventions (23%). Individual interventions had a higher percentage of reimbursement (29–37%) compared with group (19%) or parent-based treatment (7%). State Medicaid (Michigan) did not reimburse for any services that were billed under the H&B codes. In order to increase reimbursement, the authors involved their hospital's administration in presentations that they made to insurers.

It is interesting and important to note that a survey conducted by the National Association of Children's Hospitals and Related Institutions indicated that lack of reimbursement for services was the most frequently reported challenge for pediatric obesity programs (Eneli et al., 2011). This suggests that Sallinen and Woolford's (2012) experience may be generalizable to other settings.

Summary and Recommendations

The experiences describe in these commentaries underscore the importance of persistent strategic efforts by the leaders, administrative, and billing staff of pediatric psychology clinical services to secure reimbursement for H&B codes, as well as continued advocacy efforts at state and national levels to enhance reimbursement. Some of these strategies are summarized in this section.

Strategies to Advocate for Increased Reimbursement for the H&B Codes

The commentaries in this section underscore the need for pediatric service and individual programs to support administrative staff's time and anticipate and manage barriers for reimbursement for services provided under the H&B codes and to provide explanations of need and the impact of services, with detailed examples. In addition, detailed follow-up on claims that are not paid, building relationships with insurance company staff, and documentation of clinical need for a service that are reimbursed the codes, by health-care providers, are relevant and potentially effective strategies.

Inconsistency of reimbursement for the H&B codes across a range of settings suggests that time and energies spent by faculty, administrators, and staff to secure reimbursement of H&B codes at local levels should be combined with collaborative advocacy at a state and national level. A maximally effective strategy will require a collaborative approach from state psychological associations, American Psychological Association (APA), and the Society of Pediatric Psychology (SPP). In order to be convinced that the H&R codes are important, policy makers may benefit from concrete, case-based examples of how psychological services have helped individual children and their families and showcase the potential negative consequences of limitations of reimbursement on the children's health and well-being. For maximum impact, it will be important for professional organizations such as SPP to partner with parents and parent advocacy groups whose children have benefitted from psychological services that were reimbursed by the H&B codes may be especially convincing.

Some Examples of Successful Advocacy Efforts and Novel Strategies to Maximize Reimbursement for the H&B Codes

Several of the commentaries provide excellent examples of advocacy efforts to secure reimbursement in specific settings that may have broader generalizability. For example, Lines et al. (2012) describe the importance of working with state of Delaware Medicaid to advocate for changes to open the H&B codes for reimbursement by pediatric psychologists. In addition, their work with local school districts to arrange for mental health services to be provided by a credentialed pediatric psychologist provider to Medicaid-enrolled students at two local elementary schools is an excellent example of creative advocacy.

Another excellent example is Duke et al.'s (2012) developing partnership with Oregon state Medicaid program to provide intensive behavioral health services to adolescents and young adults whose hospitalization for chronic health problems such as diabetes were attributable to psychological problems that could be successfully managed and/or prevented by behavioral health interventions reimbursed by H&B codes. This partnership represents a potential "win–win" situation for both insurers and hospital for the following reasons: Private insurance companies (or Medicaid) who are responsible for covering the costs of hospitalizations for preventable conditions (e.g., diabetic ketoacidosis) can reduce costs. Hospitals stand to gain because hospitalized patients with problems that can be prevented by behavioral health "interventions" occupy beds that could be filled by patients with higher levels of acuity of medical problems that warrant greater reimbursement.

Talmi and Fazio (2012) suggested a number of potentially useful strategies to enhance reimbursement of behavioral health services delivered by pediatric psychologists in primary care. These include: (a) developing capitated funding contracts with insurers to integrate qualified, experienced behavioral health practitioners in primary care (Cummings, O'Donohue & Ferguson, 2002); (b) restructuring models of service delivery in primary care to integrate services for medical and behavioral health problems under the structure of the medical home (Stille et al., 2010); and (c) developing innovative mechanisms to sustain and support behavioral health billing and reimbursement in primary care (e.g., creating access to behavioral health services for parental caregivers in pediatric settings (Golden & Fortuny, 2011).

A final strategy that has promise to enhance reimbursement for the H&B codes that was not represented in these commentaries but is worth noting involves higher level negotiations by hospitals for insurance contracts that place all providers including psychologists on a level playing field. For example, at Cincinnati Children's Hospital Medical Center (CCHMC), the Division of Payor Relations has negotiated contracts in which H&B codes are reimbursed at the same rate of reimbursement as other medical codes (Stark, 2007). This strategy puts pressure on insurers to find ways to fund behavioral health services if they want to develop or continue large contracts with the hospital. This has resulted in high rates (84%) of reimbursement rates of H&B codes, as well as mental health codes (80%) by private insurers (2011). On the other hand, this has not affected Medicaid reimbursement for the H&B codes in the state of Ohio which remains nonexistent based on state-level policy.

It should also be noted that the generalizability of this negotiation strategy is limited by local market forces. For example, in order for a hospital to be successful with such an approach, they need to have a very favorable share of the health-care market in their region. This is true for CCHMC but is not the case with Rainbow Babies and Children's Hospital in the same state, which faces stiff city-wide and regional competition (from the Cleveland Clinic and Akron Children's Hospital), which was reflected in reimbursement rates of 40% for mental health codes for 2011.

Implications for Service Development in the Field of Pediatric Psychology

Taken together, the contributions to the special issue clearly indicate that while the H&B codes provide some reimbursement for psychological services, it is by no means sufficient to cover the costs of delivering psychological services in pediatric settings. These data can be taken as a cause for concern in that they reflect significant threats to the fiscal viability of pediatric psychology clinical services (at least as a stand-alone source of outcome) for all but programs with exceptional circumstances (e.g., excellent local market share and capacity to negotiate reimbursement rates). For this reason, the future economic potential of psychological services delivered in pediatric settings that are based on the H&B codes will continue to require concerted and persistent local and national advocacy. From a pragmatic standpoint, pediatric psychology service programs will need to leverage other sources of funding (e.g., from hospital or medical subspecialty budgets) in order to sustain support for service development (Drotar, 2004; Rae, 2004). This was already happening in many of the settings represented in these commentaries and is a testimony to the value that many pediatric hospitals and subspecialty programs place on the importance of services delivered by pediatric psychologists. However, this assumes that hospitals are doing sufficiently well in their economic bottom line to support such services.

Implications for Strategies of Data Gathering and Research
Tracking Reimbursement Rates

The commentaries that have been presented in this section have relevant implications for future directions in developing systematic strategies for tracking the use of and reimbursement for the H&B codes in a wide range of settings and for research that could enhance reimbursement by insurers. The findings reported in several of the commentaries indicated change over time and different reimbursement rates for H&B codes across different insurance companies and specialties who submit the claims. For this reason, it will be important for clinical service programs to develop ongoing methods to track reimbursement rates for the codes in order to monitor progress in reimbursement, to identify barriers that need to be addressed in order in enhance reimbursement, and strategies to surmount them. Such data can be used to summarize experiences with reimbursement with specific insurers, specific codes, or across specialty groups in order to identify gaps in reimbursement, set goals for advocacy efforts, and plan for the development of new services.

Demonstration of Cost Effectiveness and Cost Offset of Behavioral Health Services That Are Reimbursed by the Codes

A continuing and critical challenge for future research in pediatric psychology concerns the need for empirical demonstration that psychological services that are reimbursed by the H&B codes can ameliorate negative medical outcomes and health-care utilization and reduce health-care costs. There are any number of potential demonstration projects that could be potentially convincing to insurers (e.g., reduction in costs related to visits to physicians and diagnostic procedures owing to more effective pain management, reduction of frequency of physical symptoms, hospitalizations, and health-related complications (e.g., graft loss in transplantation based on improved adherence to medical treatment).

Unfortunately, at this point in time, to my knowledge there are no recent systematic studies that have demonstrated the cost offset or cost effectiveness of delivery of psychological services to pediatric populations that are reimbursed by the H&B codes. Evidence does support cost offset of behavioral health services with adults (Blount et al., 2007; Elliot, Barber & Horne 2005), including Pallak and Cummings' report (1992) of the cost offset of intensive outpatient psychological service on health-care utilization in a large Midwestern HMO. Unfortunately, none of this work pertains directly to demonstration of cost offset for the H&B codes in various populations. For this reason, a critical future challenge for the field of pediatric psychology is to develop such evidence for a range of pediatric chronic health problems and psychological services (Nelson & Steele, 2009).

Potential Implications of the Patient Protection and Affordable Care Act for the Delivery and Reimbursement of Pediatric Psychological Services

One of the most interesting and important new directions in health-care reimbursement in the United States that may have an impact on reimbursement for behavioral health services is the Patient Protection and Affordable Care Act (PPACA). The PPACA is designed to bring health insurance to millions of previously uninsured Americans by expanding Medicaid and establishing state-based health plan exchanges to offer health insurance plans to individuals and small businesses (Clay, 2011; Nordal, 2012). Coverage of mental and substance use treatment services under PPACA are expected to be on par with medical services. New structures such as patient-centered health homes and accountable care organizations will be developed. It is anticipated that reimbursement mechanisms under the PPACA will increasingly shift from fee for service to alternative models that reward providers for good outcomes, bundle payments for comprehensive services or pay for episodes of care (Clay, 2011). The PPACA is expected to result in opportunities for psychologists to join interdisciplinary teams to provide integrated care in the context of patient-centered health homes and greater investment in prevention.

On the face of it, the PPACA would appear to offer considerable potential to enhance optimal delivery and reimbursement for psychological services that are integrated with medical, including pediatric care. However, as the case with many broad and sweeping policy changes, the devil will be in the details of how the principles of the PPACA are implemented in specific states. Implementation begins in 2014 and is stated to be completed in 2019 (assuming an increasing number of state-level legal challenges are not upheld). Apart from legal challenges, there are any number of potential barriers to the PPACA support of behavioral health services. These include the fact that psychologists are not included in Medicare's definition of health-care providers and state-level corporate practices of medicine statutes that prohibit psychologists from forming integrated practice corporations with physicians (Clay, 2011).

The opportunities and challenges to practice and reimbursement that will be posed by the PPACA are a top priority for APA which is working closely together with the newly formed State Implementation of Health Care Reform Initiative of the APA practice organization (Clay, 2011; Nordal, 2012). Examples of specific goals of state-level advocacy efforts include development of mental health bundled payments (Arkansas), integration of children's services with quality assessment measures (Massachusetts), integration of behavioral health services in patient-centered medical homes and accountable care organizational demonstration projects (New York), and psychologists' participation in integrated care models (Nordal, 2012). The recent 29th APA state leadership conference had the theme: "Bringing psychology to the table; state leadership in health-care reform."

It will be most important that pediatric psychologists in various states and the SPP join APA and state-level efforts and advocate for children and families to receive the behavioral health services that best fit their needs. There is a formidable agenda of future challenges for the field of pediatric psychology that relates to the delivery and reimbursement of psychological services, including the H&B Codes. Pediatric psychologists have always been good at rising to such challenges. My hope is that the contributions to this special section will inspire dialog, critique, and submissions of research and creative strategies of clinical care and advocacy to enhance the delivery and reimbursement of pediatric psychology services in a range of settings.

Conflicts of interest: None declared.

References

American Psychological Association. (1994). *Diagnostic and Statistical Manual of Mental Disorders* (4th edn.). Washington, DC: American Psychiatric Association.

Blount, A., Kathol, R., Thomas, M., Schoenbaum, M., Rollman, B. L., O'Donohue, W., & Peek, C. J. (2007). The economics of behavioral health services in medical settings: A summary of the evidence. *Professional Psychology, 38*(3), 290–297.

Brosig, C. L. (2012). Commentary: The use of health and behavioral codes in a pediatric cardiology setting. *Journal of Pediatric Psychology*. Advance online publication. doi:10.1093/jpepsy/jsr125

Brosig, C. L., & Zahrt, D. M. (2006). Evolution of an inpatient pediatric psychology consultation service: Issues related to reimbursement and the use of health and behavior codes. *Journal of Clinical Psychology in Medical Settings, 13*, 425–429.

Claar, R. R., Kacyuski, K., Lyons, K., & Lebel, A. (2012). Commentary: Health and behavior codes in pediatric headache program: Reimbursement data and recommendation for practice. *Journal of Pediatric Psychology*. Advance online publication. doi:10.1093/jpepsy/jsr109

Clay, R. A. (2011). Health-care reform 2.0: APA and psychologists across the country are working to ensure psychology's place in the nation's new health-care system. *Monitor on Psychology, 42*(10), 46–51.

Cummings, N. A. (1990). The biodyne model of brief intermittent therapy throughout the life cycle. In N. A. Cummings, H. Dorken, M. S. Pallack, & C. J. Henke (Eds.), *The Impact of Psychological Intervention on Healthcare Utilization and Costs* (Tech. Rep. No. 11-C-9834419, Appendix II, pp. 152–177). San Francisco: Foundation for Behavioral Health.

Cummings, N. A., O'Donohue, W., & Ferguson, K. (Eds.), (2002). *The impact of medical cost offset on the practice and research: Making it Work for You*. Reno, NV: Context Press.

Drotar, D. (2004). Commentary: We can make our own dime or two, Help children and their families, and advance science while doing so. *Journal of Pediatric Psychology, 29*(1), 61–63.

Duke, D., Guion, K., Freeman, K. A., Wilson, A. C., & Harris, M. A. (2012). Commentary: Health & behavior codes: Great idea, questionable outcome. *Journal of Pediatric Psychology*. Advance online publication. doi:10.1093/jpepsy/jsr126

Elliot, R. A., Barber, N., & Horne, R. (2005). Cost-effectiveness of adherence-enhancing interventions: A quality assessment of the evidence. *The Annals of Pharmacotherapy, 39*(3), 508–515.

Eneli, I., Norwood, V., Hampl, S., Ferris, M., Hibbeln, T., Patterson, J., ... Hassink, S. (2011). Perspectives on obesity programs at children's hospitals: Insights from senior program administrators. *Pediatrics, 128*, S86–S90.

Golden, O., & Fortuny, K. (2011). Brief 4: Improving the lives of young children: Meetings parents' health and mental health needs through medicaid and CHIP so children can thrive. *Urban Institute*, 1–21.

Lines, M. M., Tynan, W. D., & Angalet, G. B. (2012). Commentary: The use of health and behavior codes in pediatric psychology: Where are we now? *Journal of Pediatric Psychology*. Advance online publication. doi:10.1093/jpepsy/jss045

Nelson, T. D., & Steele, R. G. (2009). Evidence-based practice in pediatric psychology. In M. C. Roberts, & R. G. Steele (Eds.), *Handbook of Pediatric Psychology*

(4th edn., pp. 99–117). New York: The Guilford Press.

Noll, R. B., & Fisher, S. (2004). Commentary. Health and behavior CPT codes: An opportunity to revolutionize reimbursement in pediatric psychology. *Journal of Pediatric Psychology, 29*(7), 571–578.

Nordal, K. C. (2012). State leadership in health care reform. *Monitor on Psychology, 43*(10), 21.

Pallak, M. S., & Cummings, N. A. (1992). Inpatient and outpatient psychiatric treatment: The effect of matching patients to appropriate level of treatment on psychiatric and medical-surgical hospital days. *Applied and Preventive Psychology: Current Scientific Perspectives, 1*, 83–87.

Rae, W. A. (2004). Financing pediatric psychology services: Buddy, can you spare a dime? *Journal of Pediatric Psychology, 29*(1), 47–52.

Sallinen, B. J., & Woolford, S. J. (2012). Commentary: Examination of health and behavioral code reimbursement from private payers in the context of clinical multidisciplinary pediatric obesity treatment. *Journal of Pediatric Psychology*. Advance online publication. doi:10.1093/jpepsy/jss008

Seime, R. J., & Manley, C. R. (1999). Relative value units: Using the new "currency" for measuring clinical productivity in a productivity/incentive plan. *Journal of Clinical Psychology in Medical Settings, 6*(2), 183–201.

Stark, L. (2007). Successful implementation of the health and behavior codes in a pediatric setting. Presented as annual meeting of the American Psychological Association, San Francisco, CA.

Stille, C., Turchi, R., Antonelli, R., Cabana, M., Cheng, T., Laraque, D., & Perrin, J. (2010). The family-centered medical home: Specific considerations for child health research and policy. *Academic Pediatrics, 10*, 211–217.

Talmi, A., & Fazio, E. (2012). Commentary: Promoting health and well-being in pediatric primary care settings: Using health and behavior codes at routine well child visits. *Journal of Pediatric Psychology*. Advance online publication. doi:10.1093/jpepsy/jss047

Tynan, W. D., Lutz Stehl, M., & Shroff Pendley, J. (2009). Health insurance and pediatric psychology services. In S. Roberts, & R. G. (Eds.), *Handbook of Pediatric Psychology* (Vol. 4th ed., pp. 71–88). New York: The Guilford Press.

Woolford, S. J., Sallinen, B. J., Clark, S. J., & Freed, G. L. (2011). Results from a clinical multidisciplinary weight management program. *Clinical Pediatrics, 50*, 187–191.

Woods, K., & Gillaspy, S. (2012). Medical reimbursement and utilization of health and behavior codes. *Journal of Pediatric Psychology*. Advance online publication. doi:10.1093/jpepsy/jss039

Commentary: The Use of Health and Behavior Codes in Pediatric Psychology: Where Are We Now?

Meghan McAuliffe Lines,[1,2] PhD, W. Douglas Tynan,[1,2] PhD, Gwendoline B. Angalet,[2] PhD, and Jennifer Shroff Pendley,[1] PhD

[1]Nemours/A.I. duPont Hospital for Children and [2]Nemours Health and Prevention Services

All correspondence concerning this article should be addressed to Meghan McAuliffe Lines. E-mail: mmlines@nemours.org

Received December 19, 2011; revisions received January 19, 2012; accepted February 14, 2012

This article focuses on the current status of the use of Health and Behavior (H&B) codes by pediatric psychologists. We address the rationale for the use of these codes in a pediatric psychology setting, practice updates since the codes were initiated, and our experience with utilizing these codes in one pediatric hospital. We conclude with a summary of our assertions and future directions for policy and practice.

History of the H&B Codes

The Current Procedural Terminology (CPT) codes were developed in 1966 by the American Medical Association (AMA) as a way to define and document medical procedures and services. Today, these codes are utilized not only for documentation, but also as the primary method by which third-party reimbursement for services is obtained. Psychologists have historically used Mental Health (MH) CPT codes to bill for the therapy and assessment services that they provide. While these codes are certainly relevant to the practice of pediatric psychologists in a healthcare setting, they are not sufficient for documenting all of the work that these providers do. Pediatric psychologists are often involved in behavioral procedures for the treatment of physical health problems, and this treatment differs significantly from traditional psychotherapy (Table I). In these cases, the role of the psychologist is to treat issues related to a patient's medical condition rather than treating mental illness. Examples include adherence to treatment regimen, management of medical symptoms, adjustment to medical illness, or distress related specifically to medical procedures.

To address this type of practice, the American Psychological Association (APA) proposed, in 1998, a set of "Health & Behavior" (H&B) codes to address the gap between documentation and practice. The H&B codes are a set of codes intended for use by nonphysician practitioners to identify assessment and treatment for biopsychosocial factors related to a patient's physical health problems (APA, 2004; see Table II). These codes may be reported by, but are not limited to, psychologists, advanced practice nurses, and licensed clinical social workers. The APA Practice Directorate was a strong advocate for the adoption of these codes and petitioned the AMA CPT Coding Committee to approve them for use. In 2002, the H&B codes were published in the CPT manual, and the Centers for Medicare and Medicaid Services (CMS) approved payment for the codes.

The Relevance of H&B Codes in Integrated Care

An important consideration for the use of H&B codes is that psychologists using the codes are associating a medical diagnosis, rather than a psychological diagnosis, with their billing. However, the scope of practice for a psychologist prohibits the diagnosis of a physical health condition. Therefore, the medical diagnosis made by a physician will be used when reporting health behavior services provided by a psychologist (APA, 2006). This suggests a relationship between medical and psychological services that is inherent to integrated care models. The benefits of integrated care have been documented for many decades, but an appropriate billing structure to support this practice was not in effect prior to the advent of H&B codes.

Table I. *How Health and Behavior Services Differ From Traditional Psychotherapy*

	Psychotherapy	H&B services
Diagnosis	Mental illness and behavior disturbances	Physical illness or injury
Primary focus	Affective relief, insight, decision-making, and resolving emotional condition	Psychological factors that affect or interfere with physical functioning and recovery
Goal	To alleviate emotional disturbance and behavior change	Improve health and well-being
Collaboration	Emphasis on privacy and confidentiality	Encourage collaboration and cotreatment with primary care team

Source: Casciani, 2004

Table II. *H&B CPT Codes 96,150–96,155*

Code	Definition
96150	Initial assessment of the patient to determine the biological, psychological, and social factors affecting the patient's physical health and any treatment problems.
96151	Reassessment of the patient to evaluate the patient's condition and determine the need for further treatment.
96152	Intervention service provided to an individual to modify the psychological, behavioral, cognitive, and social factors affecting the patient's physical health and well being.
96153	Intervention service provided to a group.
96154	Intervention service provided to a family with the patient present.
96155	Intervention service provided to a family without the patient present.

Source: Casciani, 2004

Without effective coding, psychologists practicing in integrated care settings either provide services as part of the medical practice without billing for them, or use MH codes to bill for behavioral health services. Diagnoses from the Diagnostic and Statistical Manual of Mental Disorders, Fourth Edition, Text Revision (DSM-IV-TR) such as Adjustment Disorder in which the stressor is a serious general medical condition, Psychological Factors Affecting a General Medical Condition, and Disorder (e.g., Anxiety, Depression) Due to a General Medical Condition are MH codes that are often used when billing for behavioral health services (American Psychiatric Association, 2000). However, none of these codes accurately reflects the medical condition as the primary reason for treatment. Moreover, the use of these codes purports that a mental health condition is present, which often is not the case and presents a serious ethical quandary for psychologists.

The workarounds that have been used in the past have not been effective in accurately reflecting the role of the psychologist practicing in an integrated care setting. Thus the adoption of H&B codes represents a formal step toward recognition of the broad role of psychologists in the healthcare setting (Shigaki, 2004). The recent release of the APA *Guidelines for Psychological Practice in Health Care Delivery Systems* (APA, 2011), which indicate that "psychologists have special expertise in communication, behavioral issues, patient decision making, human interaction and systems that is relevant to the full spectrum of health and mental health issues and settings," represents an additional effort to recognize and elevate the work of psychologists in this setting.

Payer Adoption and Reimbursement

Over the past 9 years, there has been a gradual uptake of this new H&B coding system. From the beginning, Medicare agreed to cover five of the six codes (96150–96154), excluding coverage for the 96155 code in which the family is seen without the patient present. By October 2004, Medicaid was reimbursing these codes in two states (Dittman, 2004), and this has been increasing over time. As others (e.g., Kessler, 2008) have documented, it is difficult to gather a definitive list of insurance carriers that are currently reimbursing this service. Therefore, direct contact with state payers is recommended. In the state of Delaware, Medicaid reimbursement rates for codes 96150–96154 are competitive (Table III).

While it has been documented that many payers now accept these codes and reimbursement for H&B codes is generally higher than reimbursement for MH codes, success with obtaining reimbursement varies. In 2004, Delamater reported results of a national survey in which the majority of psychologists who were using H&B codes at the time reported a low (less than 50%) reimbursement rate. When claims were denied, the majority (73%) of the time it was due to "the use of a medical diagnosis by a psychologist." In 2006, Brosig and Zahart reported on the use of these codes in a pediatric hospital and found that 69% of claims were reimbursed. For claims that were paid, the reimbursement varied from 58% to 85%.

Reimbursement of H&B Codes in a Pediatric Hospital

In order to examine the progress that has been made since these data were reported, we have examined the 2011 H&B claims in a pediatric hospital in the Mid-Atlantic. Within our hospital, we have 11 psychologists in the Division of Behavioral Health, three of whom have joint appointments with a medical division as well. With the Division of Rehabilitation, we have one neuropsychologist. H&B codes have been used sporadically for over 5 years; utilization has increased significantly over the past year as reimbursement rates have improved.

In this setting between January and October of 2011, 1,614 claims were submitted and approximately 62% of these claims were either partially or fully paid. The majority (1,466) of the claims submitted were for outpatient treatment. Payments varied widely with an average rate of reimbursement of 46% for claims that were paid.

An examination of breakdown across settings within the hospital revealed that outpatient claims were covered more frequently than inpatient claims (64% vs. 44%). We also examined these claims in three separate pediatric divisions to determine if there were differences in rate of payment between claims submitted through the Division of Behavioral Health and integrated medical divisions. The findings were mixed: 68% of claims submitted through the Rehabilitation division were covered, versus 44% of claims for Behavioral Health and 37% of claims from the Weight Management clinic within the Division of Consultative Pediatrics. The reason for this discrepancy across divisions is unclear and further examination is necessary. The Division of Rehabilitation may have a higher rate of reimbursement due to the sheer volume of claims submitted. During the time period assessed, approximately 73% of all claims were submitted by the Division of Rehabilitation. It is also possible that the specific diagnoses coded by this division or other factors may have affected rate of reimbursement.

Finally, we examined the rate of payment across payers. Not surprisingly, out-of-state Medicaid demonstrated the highest rate of denial, reimbursing only 16% of the claims submitted. With few exceptions, the claims reimbursed for out-of-state Medicaid were submitted by

Table III. *Delaware Medicaid Reimbursement Rates for H&B Codes*

Code	Reimbursement rate per 15 min of service
96150	$20.88
96151	$20.22
96152	$19.19
96153	$4.64
96154	$18.86
96155	Limited to Part C Social Worker Taxonomy with provider-specific pricing

the neuropsychologist in the Division of Rehabilitation. Further exploration regarding the relative success of this provider is warranted. In-state Medicaid and commercial insurance providers had much lower denial rates (59% and 74% of claims reimbursed, respectively), though still not ideal. A breakdown of reimbursement rates for each of the six H&B codes is provided in Table IV.

As a relatively new process, no set procedures are in place for rebilling or advocating for reimbursement of the H&B codes in our hospital. It has been challenging to garner support for allocation of significant billing staff time for advocating for the H&B codes due to the relatively small revenue stream for Behavioral Health as opposed to other specialties. However, the coding staff has begun to advocate internally for the use of these codes and we are hopeful that this will influence billing.

Importance of Open Codes

Historically, psychologists have been advised by the APA and other professional organizations to use the H&B codes when they bill Medicaid and private payers for the health behavior services they provide. If they do not get reimbursement, they have been guided to appeal those denials (e.g., APA, 2006). However, appeals will be unsuccessful if the insurers in the state have not "opened" the H&B codes for billing by mental health providers in their provider panels. "Opening a code" means that Medicaid through their policy, or private insurers through their contracts, have authorized the use of designated codes for billing for specified health behavior services which are covered benefits under their plans. These are administrative decisions that cannot be done by simply appealing a denial of charges. The insurance provider then needs to ensure that the psychologists are credentialed on their medical panel. In addition, the providers must correctly specify whether the health behavior service they have provided to individuals was in one-on-one or group modalities, and that they

Table IV. *Reimbursement Rates by CPT Code and Payer*

Code	DE Medicaid (%)	Out-of-state Medicaid (%)	Commercial (%)
96150	49	16	79
96151	83	0	77
96152	41	7	66
96153	67	20	63
96154	40	25	65
96155	0	0	100[a]
Total	59	16	74

[a]Although 100% of claims were reimbursed, this was a very low sample size ($n = 3$) so may not be representative.

are providing it in a setting in which they are authorized to perform the service.

If Medicaid has not opened an H&B code in a state, providers through their professional organizations may advocate with the Medicaid leadership for the code to be opened for use by licensed mental health professionals, demonstrating the rationale and benefits to be derived for better compliance with medical treatment protocols and improved health outcomes for patients. It has been shown that when Medicaid opens a code to add a covered service, private insurers tend to follow the precedent that has been established to continue to be competitive in that marketplace.

As an illustration of how the process to advocate for policy change could be used, several of the authors worked with a local school district to arrange for mental health services to be provided by a credentialed provider to Medicaid-enrolled students at two local elementary schools. The services were covered in the Medicaid benefit available to the students if those services were provided in a traditional office, but not in a school setting. The authors contacted Medicaid officials requesting the ability to offer the services in the school setting as a means to increase access to the service for children who had demonstrated need and were having difficulty getting the services. Medicaid recognized the need and facilitated contact with the senior leadership of the two Managed Care organizations under contract with Medicaid to manage the outpatient mental health benefits for eligible Medicaid clients. The authors then convened a meeting with representatives of Medicaid, Managed Care organizations, the school district, the mental health provider who was a member of the Managed Care organizations' provider networks, and the one selected to provide the services in the school settings. After much discussion about the need for the service to be accessible in the school setting and how the requirements for an eligible service site could be met, Medicaid and the Managed Care organizations agreed to approve a formal request from the mental health provider to add the school setting to their office site as service sites for their work. After approval was received, the mental health provider worked with the Managed Care organizations to test actual billings for services to make sure that the reimbursement process worked. Then the Managed Care organizations changed their policy to add a code for schools to be an authorized service site and wrote a formal protocol for the members of their provider networks to bill for services provided in school settings. Based upon this experience, we believe that a similar process could be followed for H&B codes.

Conclusions and Future Directions

Where are we now? At this stage of the journey, it is safe to say that we are no longer where we once were but have not yet arrived at where we are going. Over the past decade, the field has begun a paradigm shift in which psychologists are beginning to garner recognition for their vital role in medical care. The advent of the H&B codes mark a critical juncture in the road, and the use of these codes is steadily increasing over time. However, many remain reticent to bill with the H&B codes due to the variability in reimbursement to date. Our current data suggest that progress is evident but slow, and we have not yet reached a point at which reimbursement of these codes has become common practice. Despite the many challenges, it is critical for psychologists to use the codes, as they may be discontinued if they are not utilized (Dittman, 2004; Noll & Fischer, 2004).

In many states, the 96155 code (family therapy with the patient not present), in particular, is not open for psychologists. However, there is a strong rationale for the provision of treatment to parents and families, especially in the case of very young children with chronic illness. Moreover, in our experience the open codes are not consistently being reimbursed with reason codes such as "Provider may not bill this service" and "Noncovered charges" atop the list, suggesting that there are additional barriers to appropriate reimbursement in place. It is recommended that psychologists work with their state Medicaid office, State Insurance Commissioner, as well as insurance providers to advocate for the proper reimbursement for these codes. Moreover, the Society for Pediatric Psychology, APA, and state psychological associations may be able to work with payers to increase reimbursement rates.

There are exciting future possibilities with H&B codes as well. The individual assessment and intervention H&B

codes (96150–96152) have been approved by Medicare for telehealth services (APA, 2009). There is a growing movement towards the provision of telehealth for serving patients in rural and underserved areas, and the H&B codes may make reimbursement for this service possible. Additionally, while preventive services are not typically covered for psychologists, the H&B codes do allow billing for services aimed at the prevention of problems associated with an existing medical illness. This may open the door for future possibilities to reimburse for preventive services.

Conflicts of interest: None declared.

References

American Psychiatric Association. (2000). *Diagnostic and Statistical Manual of Mental Disorders* (4th ed., text rev.). Washington, DC: Author.

American Psychological Association. (2004). *Health and Behavior CPT® Codes*. Retrieved from http://www.apapracticecentral.org/reimbursement/billing/secure/new-codes.aspx

American Psychological Association. (2006). *FAQs on the Health and Behavior CPT Codes*. Retrieved from http://www.apapracticecentral.org/reimbursement/billing/cpt/secure/faq.aspx

American Psychological Association. (2009). *Practice Update: Final Medicare Fee Schedule Rule is a Mixed Bag for Psychology*. Retrieved from http://www.apapracticecentral.org/update/2009/11-23/secure/final-medicare-fee.apsx

American Psychological Association. (2011). *Guidelines for Psychological Practice in Health Care Delivery Systems*. Retrieved from http://www.apa.org/about/governance/council/policy/hospital-privileges.pdf

Brosig, C. L., & Zahart, D. M. (2006). Evolution of an inpatient pediatric psychology consultation service: Issues related to reimbursement and the use of health and behavior codes. *Journal of Clinical Psychology in Medical Settings, 13*(4), 425–529.

Casciani, J. M. (2004). How health and behavior services differ from traditional psychotherapy. *APA Monitor on Psychology, 35*(9), 59.

Delamater, A. (2004). *Health and behavior code surveys*. Honolulu, HI: Paper presented at the American Psychological Association Annual Meeting.

Dittman, M. (2004). CPT codes: Use them or lose them. *APA Monitor, 35*(9), 58.

Kessler, R. (2008). Integration of care is about money too: The health and behavior codes as an element of a new financial paradigm. *Families, Systems, and Health, 26*(2), 207–216.

Noll, R. B., & Fischer, S. (2004). Commentary: Health and behavior CPT codes: An opportunity to revolutionize reimbursement in pediatric psychology. *Journal of Pediatric Psychology, 29*, 571–578.

Shigaki, C. L. (2004). *Psychologists Working With Patients Who Have Physical Health Problems Can Benefit from Using the New CPT Health and Behavior Codes*. Retrieved from http://www.public-health.uiowa.edu/icmha/PsychotherapyServices.DOC

Commentary: Health & Behavior Codes: Great Idea, Questionable Outcome

Danny C. Duke, PHD, Kim Guion, PHD, Kurt A. Freeman, PHD, Anna C. Wilson, PHD, and Michael A. Harris, PHD

Child Development and Rehabilitation Center, Oregon Health & Science University

All correspondence concerning this article should be addressed to Michael A. Harris, PHD, Associate Professor, Pediatrics, Oregon Health & Science University, 707 SW Gaines Street, Portland, OR, 97239, USA. E-mail: harrismi@ohsu.edu

Received December 13, 2011; revisions received December 19, 2011; accepted December 22, 2011

Operating a successful pediatric psychology service in a hospital setting requires attention to three primary domains of professional practice: the clinical, operational, and financial (Kessler, 2008). Even an optimally provided service in the clinical and operational domains is unlikely to be sustainable if not also financially viable. One major challenge to financial viability is that overhead expenses charged to pediatric psychology services are typically similar to charges made to medical services, which receive considerably more money per unit of service and thus generate significantly more revenue. This disparity in income potential has contributed to placing considerable financial pressure and time demands on providers of hospital-based pediatric psychology services.

The financial challenges associated with the successful practice of pediatric psychology in hospital settings highlights the importance of optimizing billing practices as a necessary component of sustainable practice. Providing behavioral health services to patients with primary medical conditions has been demonstrated as an an important aspect of medical care, but can only become a standard of care when psychologists are adequately compensated for providing the service. In this commentary, we briefly review the potential economic benefits of using Health and Behavior (H&B) codes, describe the use of these codes in our practice, and discuss current pragmatic barriers and problems associated with their use.

Economic Value of Behavioral Health Services

Based on the statistics from the Agency for Healthcare Research and Quality (2011), the average Medicaid patient stay in 2008 was $6,900 and about the same for an uninsured patient, compared to $8,400 for a patient stay covered by private insurance, adjusted for inflation. For children with complex medical conditions, a hospital stay is rarely just a single day, but more often becomes a week or more. Frequently, these patients require stabilization services rather than intensive medical care. As such, they can be financially costly both to insurance companies and to healthcare systems. Many hospitalizations could be avoided or abbreviated if patients and their families received behavioral health services, as hospitalizations and length of stay are often associated with behaviorally based barriers such as nonadherence, pain management difficulty, or other domains for which behavioral interventions are especially effective.

Integrating behavioral health services into health care has distinct financial advantages (e.g., Chiles, Lambert, & Hatch, 1999; Harris & Mertlich, 2003). In fact, behavioral healthcare services have been shown to be cost-effective. For example, consider the care provided to individuals with diabetes. In 2003, the average national cost of one hospitalization for diabetic ketoacidosis (DKA) is approximately $11,000 (Maldonado, Chong, Oehl, & Balasubramanyam, 2003). Approximately 100,000 hospitalizations for DKA occur in the United States each year (Fishbein & Palumbo, 1995), with associated costs that exceed $1 billion per year (Kitabchi, Umpierrrez, & Murphy, 2001). Given that participation in behavioral healthcare services focused on improving adherence to treatment has been shown to result in fewer hospitalizations of youth with poorly controlled diabetes (Harris & Mertlich, 2003), improved access to such care represents a cost-effective intervention.

Mental Health Versus H&B Codes

Historically, licensed psychologists who delivered clinical assessment and treatment in medical settings relied primarily on the use of Current Procedural Terminology (CPT) codes 90801 (Psychiatric Diagnostic Interview), 90804 (Individual Psychotherapy, 20–30 min), 90806 (Individual Psychotherapy, 45–50 min), and 90847 (Family Psychotherapy) to designate the care provided. To receive reimbursement for services billed under these codes, third-party insurers require that they be associated with a mental health diagnosis derived from the *Diagnostic and Statistical Manual of Mental Disorders* (DSM-IV-TR; APA, 2000; Noll & Fischer, 2004) or the World Health Organization's *International Classification of Diseases* (World Health Organization ICD-10; 2004). This requirement has placed significant pressure on psychologists to provide a mental health diagnosis (Carter et al., 2003), even when the primary referral was for assessment, preventative services, or behavioral health care of individuals with acute or chronic health conditions, focused on assisting people with those health conditions.

Although the economic value of behavioral health services has been well established (e.g., Blount et al., 2007; Chiles et al., 1999; Harris & Mertlich, 2003), and significant efforts have been undertaken by national organizations to increase appropriate behavioral/mental health care in pediatrics (Meschan Foy, Kelleher, & Laraque, 2010), it continues to be challenging to use behavioral health services to screen for and provide appropriate early intervention services to patients. The growth of behavioral medicine provided expanded roles and opportunities for psychologists to collaborate with other healthcare professionals to address important health issues (Brown et al., 2002). The introduction of H&B codes, developed by the American Psychological Association Practice Directorate and approved by the American Medical Association for use in integrated medical settings, was expected to change how billing occurred for patients presenting with a primary medical diagnosis when behavioral health care was provided (Miyamoto, 2006). This change in billing practice had potential to improve the quality of care delivered by psychologists serving these patients. Examples of services appropriately captured using these codes has included improving patient adherence to medical treatment, symptom management (e.g., pain), promoting improved health-related behaviors (e.g., exercise), reducing health-related risk-taking behaviors (e.g., smoking), and improving adjustment and coping with physical illness or disability (Miyamoto, 2006). Behavioral healthcare services, best captured with H&B codes, has the potential to offer the most appropriate care (and cost-effective care, as noted previously) given that the majority of the challenges of adhering to treatment regimens for complex medical conditions are behavioral, psychological, and social.

Our Service Experience: Great Idea, Questionable Outcomes

The advent of H&B codes created a sense of optimism among pediatric psychologists that more comprehensive and preventative behavioral health services could be provided to patients with primary medical diagnoses, and that insurance payment would be at rates similar to other comparable psychological services. Unfortunately, the reality has not lived up to the optimism in our medical setting.

In our pediatric psychology service, we have faced an ongoing struggle to obtain adequate authorization and reimbursement for both inpatient and outpatient services that have been appropriately captured using H&B codes. Anecdotally, our billing specialists have reported that when insurance company case managers learn that a psychologist has provided behavioral and/or psychological services, the authorization is frequently denied due to limits to mental health coverage or a lack or preauthorization. This is in direct contrast to the intent of the H&B codes, which should be covered by medical benefits and should not require preauthorization. When authorization for care under H&B codes has been denied under the insurance company's assumption that services by a psychologist should be billed under the mental health arm of coverage, both the billing staff and treating psychologists have contacted the insurance agency to educate them about the proper use of H&B codes; however, upward of 75% of those attempts to obtain coverage under H&B codes were still denied. In many of these cases, an in-depth appeal letter was sent outlining the proper use of H&B codes accompanied by citing outcome research supporting psychological and behavioral interventions for youth with complex medical conditions. Unfortunately, our experiences have been that evidence regarding the cost-saving benefit of service captured with H&B codes is largely insufficient to reverse insurance denials.

In an effort to empirically evaluate the use of H&B codes in our setting, we examined clinical billing data from our inpatient pediatric psychology practice within a large tertiary medical care center in the Pacific Northwest. We also generated an estimate of cost-effectiveness for our services. The inpatient consultation service is available to all other services within a 350-bed university children's hospital, which provide approximately 20,000 admissions each year. The medical teams most frequently using our services have included general pediatrics, endocrinology, and hematology/oncology. The most frequent referral concerns have included adjustment to medical diagnoses, pain management, adherence, and anxiety.

Analysis of H&B Code Reimbursement in Our Inpatient Program

During a trial period that emphasized increased use of H&B code billing as the most appropriate code for the provided services, our practice billed for similar assessment services using both the traditional mental health code 90801 and H&B code 96150 (H&B Assessment, 15-min units) for a total of 101 patients seen. We analyzed the use of code 96150 to capture behavioral assessment services provided to 45 children hospitalized for an acute or chronic health condition over a period of approximately 6 months. When considering all services billed, our analysis showed that the mean reimbursement rate was approximately 26% of the total fees billed (Table I). Denial of coverage occurred for 25 patients, representing a greater than 55% denial rate. When considering the remaining 20 patients for whom we received reimbursement for services, the rate of return was approximately 59% of the total amount billed (Table I).

During the same time period, providers utilized traditional CPT evaluation code 90801 to capture the services provided to 56 children hospitalized for similar reasons. Considering all services billed using 90801, our total reimbursement rate was almost 33% (Table I). However, third-party insurers denied coverage for 22 of these patients, or a 39% denial rate. When considering only the services reimbursed, our return rate was 53.7% of the amount billed (Table I). While this was lower than the reimbursement for the H&B code (59%), because 90801 was billed at a higher rate, it resulted in a 2.5 times higher financial return per encounter. Thus, while percentage of the billed amount paid by insurance (when reimbursed) was greater for H&B codes (59% vs. 53.7%), the lower denial rate for traditional CPT codes (39.3% vs. 55.5%; Table I) and the higher rate billed resulted in significantly greater financial recovery for services.

Table I. *Amount Paid by CPT Code*

CPT Code	Sessions	Paid	Denied	Percent paid per session	Percent paid for all sessions
90801	45	34	22	53.70	26.23
96150	56	20	25	59.03	32.60

We further investigated our experience using H&B codes within the context of inpatient care as it relates to overall costs associated with adherence problems. The mean duration of stays for pediatric inpatients in our hospital has been at 4.5 days over the recent past. Using the mean daily cost of hospitalization based on the most conservative statistics from the Agency for Healthcare Research and Quality in 2008, the total mean cost of hospitalization for our patients can be estimated to be $31,050 per patient. Approximately 10% of the 101 services we provided were for problems related to nonadherence to treatment, which suggests approximately $310,500 in potential healthcare expenses for nonadherence alone. Given that appropriate behavioral health care can significantly reduce future health risks, including reduced hospitalizations (e.g., Harris & Mertlich, 2003), this analysis illustrates the pragmatic value of the services represented by H&B codes. Given the potential financial savings and benefits to healthcare systems, we submit that it is in the best interests of third-party payers to adequately reimburse for behavioral health care for patients presenting with primary medical conditions.

Our data suggest that the lower reimbursement rate for assessments billed for using H&B code 96150 makes its use financially less desirable if an appropriate mental health diagnosis can be identified and the encounter billed using CPT code 90801. The significant disparity in reimbursement rates and actual dollars received between 90801 and 96150 codes is striking. While children hospitalized with acute or chronic health conditions often have co-existing mental health conditions, this disparity in payment for similar services likely creates pressure for practitioners to identify mental health diagnoses to maximize financial return for services provided (Carter et al., 2003).

Recommendations and Future Directions

The ethical quandary for our pediatric psychology practice and the use of H&B codes is exemplified in the disconnect between our financial data, our service data, and the empirical evidence supporting the value of providing the highest level and the most cost-effective care for youth with complex medical conditions. Specifically, H&B codes often represent the most appropriate CPT code for the delivery of evidence-supported behavioral health care to youth struggling to manage their health; however, in our institution, it also results in the greatest financial losses and renders our pediatric psychology services unsustainable without alternative funding. Although the introduction of H&B codes was a step in the right direction, appropriate reimbursement of these codes remains problematic. Below we present recommendations and encourage ongoing individual and collaborative efforts to address these issues.

Advocacy and Financial Reforms

Payment for H&B assessments using H&B code 96150 should be comparable to other similar services (90801). In our experience, this has not been the case and remains a barrier to providing optimal services. The need for preapproval for services best captured with H&B codes is contrary to their intent. H&B codes were developed for use in busy hospital and clinic settings where preauthorization is often difficult and at times impossible. Additionally, both payment rate and percentage of return have been inadequate and do not sufficiently compensate for services provided, are not enough to sustain H&B services, and cannot sustain the practice of pediatric psychology in a medical setting.

It is our responsibility to advocate individually and as members of larger organizations, such as APA, to eliminate the preauthorization requirement for insurance payment for H&B services. The common practice of denying coverage following delivery of the service is unacceptable when a physician referral for the service has been made appropriately. Advocacy also occurs on a case-by-case basis, and thus we agree with the recommendations of Noll and Fischer (2004) regarding lobbying third-party payers or the medical director of a specific carrier for improved acceptance of these codes. Individual cases should be appealed and parent and pediatric medical provider advocacy encouraged. Joint efforts to inform medical providers, patients, and third-party insurance companies about H&B services have the potential to improve patient access to optimal care (Noll & Fischer, 2004), and improve reimbursement rates and procedures.

Research

Updated research is needed to further demonstrate the financial value of preventative behavioral health care and early intervention services in medical settings. Growing evidence supports satisfaction with, and effectiveness of, inpatient and outpatient behavioral health consultative services (e.g., Carter et al., 2003). However, the reality in which we function as pediatric psychologists is that third-party payers are only likely to reimburse for services that are demonstrably cost-effective and in their economic benefit. Thus, continued efforts to empirically demonstrate the cost-savings values of both inpatient and outpatient behavioral health care for patients with acute and chronic health conditions is critical. With increasing research evidence, efforts at advocacy and education will likely be more effective.

Glimmers of Hope: Demonstration Project to Avoid Repeated Hospitalizations

Recently, our division has partnered with the area's Medicaid program to provide intensive behavioral health to young people with complex medical conditions who have been repeatedly hospitalized for health issues related to nonadherence to treatment. These individuals are financially costly to insurance companies due to avoidable hospitalizations (e.g., five DKA hospitalizations in 1 year). In addition, our hospital loses a great deal of money when these young people are hospitalized in that they are taking up beds that could be occupied by patients with a much higher level of acuity. Besides being funded to develop the infrastructure to support this intervention, our regional Medicaid has approved our use of billing for our services using H&B codes. We see this partnership as an exciting opportunity to establish the benefit of services using H&B codes, and are hopeful that outcomes will be useful in discussions with other insurance carriers.

Conclusion

In conclusion, although the focus of our commentary has been primarily on the financial aspects of H&B code use, the delivery of optimal patient care should always underlie decision-making; this approach has guided our continued provision of inpatient consultative services, despite being unprofitable. Unfortunately, in the world of modern health care, the financial and the clinical aspects of care are inextricably linked. Although pediatric psychologists have made tremendous strides in the past decade, we submit that financial systems of authorization and payment remain barriers to providing efficient and effective delivery of behavioral health care for youth in hospital settings. Much work needs to be done at both the individual practitioner and professional levesl to address these barriers. We remain optimistic that our collective efforts in the face of these challenges will improve service delivery and the sustainability of pediatric psychology services in medical settings.

Funding

Dr. Anna Wilson's contribution to this project was supported by the Eunice Kennedy Shriver National Institute of Child Health and Human Development (NIH/NICHD K23HD064705; PI: Wilson).

Conflicts of interest: None declared.

References

American Psychiatric Association. (2000). *Diagnostic and Statistical Manual of Mental Disorders,* 4th ed (Text Revision). Washington, DC: American Psychiatric Association.

Agency for Healthcare Research and Quality. (2011). *Growth in Medicaid Patient Hospital Admissions Outpace Those for Privately Insured Patients.* Rockville, MD: AHRQ News and Numbers, January 19, 2011. Retrieved from http://www.ahrq.gov/news/nn/nn011911.htm

Blount, A., Schoenbaum, M., Kathol, R., Rollman, B. L., Thomas, M., & O'Donohue, W. (2007). The economics of behavioral health services in medical settings: A summary of the evidence. *Professional Psychology: Research and Practice, 38,* 290–297.

Brown, R. T., Freeman, W. S., Brown, R., Belar, C., Hersch, L., Hornyak, L. M., ... Reed, G. (2002). The role of psychology in health care delivery. *Professional Psychology: Research and Practice, 33,* 536–545.

Carter, B. D., Kronenberger, W. G., Baker, J., Grimes, L. M., Crabtree, V. M., Smith, C., & McGraw, K. (2003). Inpatient pediatric consultation-liaison: A case-controlled study. *Journal of Pediatric Psychology, 28,* 423–432.

Chiles, J. A., Lambert, M. J., & Hatch, A. L. (1999). The impact of psychological interventions on medical cost offset: A meta-analytic review. *Clinical Psychology: Science and Practice, 6,* 204–220.

Fishbein, H., & Palumbo, P. J. (1995). *Acute metabolic complications in diabetes.* (pp. #NIH 95–1468). Bethesda (MD): National Institutes of Health.

Harris, M. A., & Mertlich, D. (2003). Piloting home-based behavioral family systems therapy for adolescents with poorly controlled diabetes. *Children's Health Care, 32,* 65–79.

Kessler, R. (2008). Integration of care is about money too: The health and behavior codes as an element of the new financial paradigm. *Families, Systems, and Health, 26,* 207–216.

Kitabchi, A. E., Umpierrez, G. E., Murphy, M. B., Barrett, E. J., Kreisberg, R. A., Malone, J. I., & Wall, B. M. (2001). Management of hyperglycemic crises in patients with diabetes. *Diabetes Care, 24,* 131–153.

Maldonado, M. R., Chong, E. R., Oehl, M. A., & Balasubramanyam, A. (2003). Economic impact of diabetic ketoacidosis in a multiethnic indigent population: analysis of costs based on the precipitating cause. *Diabetes Care, 26*(4), 1265–1269.

Meschan Foy, J., Kelleher, K. J., & Laraque, D., for the American Academy of Pediatrics Task Force on Mental Health. (2010). Enhancing pediatric mental health care: Strategies for preparing a primary care practice. *Pediatrics, 125*(Suppl 3), S87–S108.

Miyamoto, R. E. S. (2006). Billing effectively with the new health and behavior current procedural terminology codes in primary care and specialty clinics. *Journal of Clinical Psychology, 62,* 1221–1229.

Noll, R. B., & Fischer, S. (2004). Health and behavior codes: An opportunity to revolutionize reimbursement in pediatric psychology. *Journal of Pediatric Psychology, 29,* 571–578.

World Health Organization. International Classification of Diseases-10th revision ICD-10; 2004. Retrieved from http://www.who.int/classifications/icd/en/

Commentary: Promoting Health and Well-being in Pediatric Primary Care Settings: Using Health and Behavior Codes at Routine Well-child Visits

Ayelet Talmi,[1,2] PHD, and Emily Fazio,[3] PHD

[1]Department of Psychiatry, [2]Department of Pediatrics, University of Colorado Denver, and [3]Children's Hospital Colorado

All correspondence concerning this article should be addressed to Ayelet Talmi, PHD, Departments of Psychiatry and Pediatrics, University of Colorado School of Medicine, 13123 E. 16th Avenue, B130, Aurora, CO, 80045, USA. E-mail: ayelet.talmi@ucdenver.edu

Received February 10, 2012; revisions received February 16, 2012; accepted February 17, 2012

Pediatric primary care provides an optimal setting for the practice of pediatric psychology and the use of health and behavior codes to capture this practice. Pediatric primary care settings provide continuous and comprehensive medical services that are readily accessible to the vast majority of children in the United States and their families (Centers for Disease Control, 2004). These settings are ideally suited to promote optimal development and well-being through the provision of expanded services that address parental concerns, developmental tasks, psychosocial factors, and behavioral health issues in the context of trusting relationships with familiar providers. Pediatric psychologists integrated into primary care settings are able to promote health and well-being of children and families in a manner directly aligned with the mandates and guidelines of the practice of pediatric primary care (American Academy of Child and Adolescent Psychiatry and American Academy of Pediatrics, 2009).

Pediatric primary care is often the only available port of entry into service systems for vulnerable children and their families. Although the American Academy of Pediatrics (AAP) and Bright Futures provide systematic guidelines and outline methods for comprehensive surveillance and screening during well-child checks, most pediatric practices and providers are overwhelmed by the complex risk factors presented during "routine" visits lasting an average of 18 min (Olson et al., 2004) and may be reluctant to solicit information about behavioral and psychosocial matters because they are unable to adequately address them or receive reimbursement for treating them (American Academy of Child and Adolescent Psychiatry and American Academy of Pediatrics, 2009).

Consequently, children facing significant risk factors that impinge upon development and profoundly impact family functioning remain unidentified. Even when risk or early disturbance is identified, families often have difficulty accessing necessary community resources.

Pediatric psychologists in primary care engage in activities that "improve the health-related quality of life of children and their families" (Noll & Fischer, 2004). Such activities include: (a) promoting health and well-being and providing anticipatory guidance during routine well-child visits; (b) screening, early identification, and referral around developmental and behavioral health issues; (c) providing early treatment for issues that, left untreated, could lead to significant impairment; and (d) triaging, referring to, and coordinating with community resources when higher levels of care are necessary. Pediatric psychologists help improve adherence, promote healthy behaviors and reduce behaviors that increase health risks, and improve communication between healthcare providers and the children and families they serve (Noll & Fischer, 2004).

Barriers to Behavioral Health in Primary Care

Unfortunately, substantial barriers exist to creating sustainable behavioral health programs in primary-care settings. Foremost among these are the significant challenges surrounding reimbursement for behavioral health services. In a report on reimbursement of mental health services in primary care, Mauch, Kautz, and Smith (2008) identified seven barriers: (a) insurer limitations on the same-day billing for physical health and mental health services, (b) nonreimbursable time spent in collaborative care and case management activities, (c) no reimbursement for nonphysician providers, (d) insurer denials of primary care provider bills when mental health diagnosis and treatment are listed, (e) differential reimbursement rates in rural and urban settings, (f) challenges in obtaining reimbursement for behavioral health services in school-based clinics, and (g) lack of incentives for behavioral health screening and prevention efforts. These barriers limit both access to behavioral health services and integrated behavioral health program sustainability.

Children and families receiving behavioral health services in primary-care settings may be seen by medical providers for *medical* diagnoses often without comorbid mental health diagnoses that could be billed under the purview of mental health (Kessler, 2008; Mauch et al., 2008; Miyamoto, 2006). When behavioral health providers bill health and behavior codes in primary-care settings, they generate considerably lower relative value units (RVUs) than if they billed evaluation and management (E&M) or traditional mental health codes (American Academy of Child and Adolescent Psychiatry and American Academy of Pediatrics, 2009). As a result, behavioral health consultations (e.g., assessment, feedback, and collaborative treatment planning) yield lower reimbursement or RVUs despite being integral to patient health and well-being.

Models of Successful Behavioral Health Care in Pediatric Primary Care: Project CLIMB

Project CLIMB (Consultation Liaison in Mental health and Behavior), an integrated mental health program, has successfully served the behavioral health needs of an at-risk population in a high-volume pediatric primary-care clinic and residency training site housed within a large teaching hospital affiliated with a university school of medicine (see http://www.aap.org/mentalhealth/mh3co.html#Colorado). Project CLIMB is co-led by a pediatric psychologist and a triple-boarded child, adolescent, and adult psychiatrist. Families served in this clinic have access to seamless and comprehensive care that spans physical and behavioral health in the context of a medical home. Our team also refers and coordinates care with community agencies and resources, when more intensive services are needed. In addition to providing access to mental health services, our team has worked diligently to increase primary care providers' capacity to treat children and families with complex needs in the context of pediatric primary care through educational offerings, training, case collaboration, and precepting (Bunik, Stafford, Rosenberg, & Talmi, 2008).

Health and Behavior Codes in Pediatric Primary Care

Our use of health and behavior codes typically involves associating services with the medical diagnosis of "Routine infant or child health check" (ICD-9 Code V20.2). Many of the children and families with whom our behavioral health team is asked to consult do not have existing mental health diagnoses and would not meet criteria upon further evaluation. However, pediatric providers frequently request consultations to help address behavioral or developmental difficulties that are interfering with a child's ability to optimally engage in age-appropriate activities. Behavioral health services for well-child visits, acute illness visits, and management of chronic disease (e.g., obesity, asthma) include psycho-education, anticipatory guidance, promoting adherence and compliance, and enhancing the relationship between pediatric primary care providers and the children and families they serve. A case study illustrating behavioral health consultations with an infant and his mother during well-child visits may be accessed online.

Medical chart reviews were completed on all patients seen by a behavioral health provider during a 1-year period (2010) using an existing, de-identified dataset with IRB approval. Additionally, we reviewed financial and billing records from 2010 through 2011. Medical record abstraction yielded detailed information related to health and behavior code usage and medical diagnoses assigned for each visit. In 2010, of the ~20,000 total clinic visits, 2,018 included behavioral health consultations (10%). Of these behavioral health consultations, 987 (49%) were conducted during "routine" visits (i.e., well-child checks) and 51% during medical visits, with medical diagnoses of failure to thrive, unspecified disturbance of conduct, and asthma listed most frequently. The psychiatrist saw 17% of the behavioral health patients, of whom 46% carried an ADHD diagnosis.

Table I details health and behavior code billing and finance data for 2010 and 2011, including RVU equivalents, units billed, RVUs generated, and FTE (full-time equivalent) calculations by code. Clinical productivity (RVUs) is based on an institutional standard of 2,100 RVUs annually for a full-time pediatric psychologist. The national standard is 2,300 RVUs (Academic Psychiatric Benchmarking Survey, 2011). As can be seen from these data, the majority of visits in 2010 (77%) and 2011 (69%) were for initial assessment (CPT code 96150). In our clinic, patients receive an average of 1.8 behavioral health consultations. Many consultations are one-time assessment and triage visits for specific behavioral health concerns.

Table I. Health and Behavior RVU and FTE Data for 2010 and 2011

CPT codes (RVU value)	2010			2011		
	Units billed	Total RVU	FTE	Units billed	Total RVU	FTE
96150 (0.5)	917	458.5	0.22	841	420.5	0.20
96151 (0.58)	241	139.8	0.07	1	0.6	0.00
96152 (0.46)	14	6.4	0.00	346	159.2	0.08
96154 (0.45)	18	8.1	0.00	24	10.8	0.01
Total	1,190	612.8	0.29	1,211	591.0	0.28

Each year, health and behavior code billing yielded sufficient RVUs to cover ~30% of a pediatric psychologist's salary.

In our institution, code-based reimbursement data are not available. The hospital collects reimbursement data by encounter (i.e., clinic visit), not by billing code. At present, it is not possible to determine how much actual revenue is generated when health and behavior codes are billed in the context of pediatric primary-care encounters. According to preliminary reports from the Colorado State Department of Health Care Policy and Finance (HCPF), it appears as though the State has not reimbursed any health and behavior code billing through Medicaid. This is likely due to a Colorado Medicaid rule that automatically rejects psychologist health and behavior code bills as "unauthorized provider type" when billed in pediatric primary care because psychologists are not physicians and, therefore, are not "authorized" providers within a primary-care setting.

Policy Recommendations to Promote Reimbursement

Advocate for systems changes where health and behavior codes are: (a) routinely used by behavioral health professionals to document the services provided in pediatric primary care and (b) universally covered benefits in pediatric health insurance plans. Although the development and implementation of health and behavior codes has created a mechanism by which to bill for behavioral health services provided in medical settings, numerous barriers to billing and reimbursement significantly limit their utility. Mental health benefits are often "carved out," and medical providers are excluded from the network of professionals able to bill for mental health services (Mauch et al., 2008). Health and behavior billing enables pediatric psychologists to document their efforts at integrating physical and mental health, but actual reimbursement for such efforts is inadequate or nonexistent. Mental health services that are reimbursable by private insurers in the primary-care setting generally include screening, assessment, and/or medication management; however, only 60% of Medicaid programs reimburse for screening and assessment and a very limited number of insurers reimburse nonphysician providers for these services (National Institute for Health Care Management, 2009; National Governor's Association, 2005).

Use capitated funding mechanisms to negotiate contracts with behavioral health entities to embed qualified and experienced behavioral health clinicians in primary care. Behavioral health managed care entities with capitated contracts have a vested interest in maintaining or increasing their penetration rates to serve the targeted number of individuals in their catchment areas. Pediatric primary-care settings provide access to large numbers of children and families who can be counted as receiving services under capitated behavioral health plans. Moreover, behavioral health clinicians working in primary-care settings are often highly productive, serving many more children and families than traditional outpatient behavioral health providers can serve.

In Colorado, several behavioral health organizations fund clinicians to deliver integrated mental health services in primary-care settings with rapid expansion of such models over the last few years. For example, the community mental health center designated to provide Medicaid mental health benefits in our county funds a full-time licensed clinician to see patients in our pediatric primary care clinic. By integrating a full-time clinician into our program, the mental health center can serve its target population (county), increase penetration rates, and, thereby, fulfill contractual requirements with Medicaid. Additionally, the on-site clinician creates greater access to care for a population facing considerable barriers to behavioral health services and who would need to access these services through the mental health center.

Reorganize managed care services to reintegrate physical and behavioral health under the auspice of medical home. Health-care reform presents an important opportunity to reconsider how health services are being delivered. In Colorado, the Accountable Care Collaborative (ACC), a Medicaid program developed to improve client health and reduce healthcare costs, assigns members (people insured by Medicaid) to one of seven Regional Care

Collaborative Organizations (RCCOs) statewide and to a primary care medical provider (PCMP; Colorado Department of Health Care Policy and Financing, 2011a). RCCOs provide care coordination, medical management of complex cases, and provider support for resources, referrals, and quality improvement (Colorado Department of Health Care Policy and Financing, 2011b). Medicaid incentivizes RCCOs with a per member/per month rate that is contingent upon the RCCOs ability to deliver coordinated, comprehensive, and cost-effective services.

In order to meet members' needs, RCCOs must continually develop partnerships, streamline services, and create new programs and service delivery models to optimize health and well-being of their members. Individuals struggling with behavioral health issues typically have to access services and resources across two separate systems of care (i.e., physical and mental health) and often have greater and more costly health system utilization. RCCOs that successfully manage both physical and behavioral health services are well-positioned to address the comprehensive needs of their members, improve communication among providers, and ultimately deliver integrated services within a medical home. Since member data are tracked within a single system, these programs could also yield invaluable data on health outcomes in relation to behavioral health services. To date, such data have been difficult to obtain because of the silos in which physical and behavioral health information exist.

Mounting evidence linking behavioral health supports to improved health outcomes and reduced health costs in combination with the RCCOs' focus on creating medical homes and delivering coordinated, comprehensive services may be a catalyst for broad integration of behavioral health services into medical settings. Having RCCOs as the single payers and managers of both physical and behavioral health benefits would eliminate several barriers: (a) reimbursement for behavioral health services would not require preauthorization; (b) all providers would be in network; and (c) billing and reimbursement processes would be internal to the system and not contingent upon external, cross-system approvals, and lengthy waiting periods between billing and collecting revenue. If RCCOs offered integrated behavioral health services as a covered benefit, these services would be sustainable for children insured by Medicaid.

Promote the medical home approach to increase integration of behavioral health services. A medical home is one in which a pediatric provider works in partnership with the family/patient to ensure that all of the medical and nonmedical needs of the patient are met. Through this partnership, the pediatric provider helps the family/patient access and coordinate specialty care, educational services, out-of-home care, family support, and other public and private community services that are important to the overall health of the child and family (Stille et al., 2010). The medical home approach is a promising framework for incorporating mental health care into primary care, establishing stronger partnerships with families, and improving cross-sector case collaboration (National Institute for Health Care Management, 2009). Behavioral health is an integral component of the medical home approach and as such should be a fundable component.

In Colorado, Family Voices Colorado (see www.familyvoicesco.org) and the Colorado Children's Healthcare Access Program (CCHAP; see www.cchap.org) work together to designate primary care settings as medical homes using site visits, provider and patient surveys, and assessments of practice characteristics. Medical homes are supposed to provide access to and coordination among medical, oral, and mental health services. Those primary-care settings with a medical home designation receive a per member financial incentive from Medicaid. Practices with high patient volumes may consider pooling per member incentives to hire on-site behavioral health providers. Revenue generated from screening efforts (e.g., developmental screening and depression screening) can also be used to fund expanded behavioral health services within a medical home.

Use innovative funding mechanisms to sustain and support behavioral health billing in pediatric primary care. In a recent report, The Urban Institute described two-generation Medicaid billing under which strategies including treating caregiver mental health issues (e.g., perinatal mood and anxiety disorders), creating access to behavioral health services for caregivers in pediatric settings, and increasing insurance options for caregivers and their children are employed to benefit child well-being (Golden & Fortuny, 2011). Initiatives like "Money Follows the Person" (U.S. Department of Health & Human Services, 2011; National Conference of State Legislatures, 2011) also expand the potential for treating behavioral health issues wherever they emerge instead of relying exclusively on traditional mental health service systems. This approach reduces restrictions on the types of services that can be provided in particular settings (e.g., mental health services only at community mental health centers) and enables clients to access services and supports from qualified professionals in settings where they are typically seen (e.g., primary care). Providers, in turn, can get reimbursed for services rendered.

Implications for Pediatric Psychology Practice
Health Promotion and Prevention
The hallmark of pediatric practice is anticipatory guidance, which includes conveying information that assists parents in understanding current and future developmentally salient issues with the aim of preventing future disturbance. Recommended topics include injury and violence prevention, family well-being, parent–child relationship issues, sleep issues, school adjustment, and fostering optimal development, all of which can fall under the purview of behavioral health consultation provided during well-child visits (Hagan, Shaw, & Duncan, 2008).

Serving the Early Childhood Population
Research suggests that parents are more likely to turn to their healthcare provider for information regarding parenting and child development than to another specialist (Inkelas, Schuster, Newacheck, Olsen, & Halfon, 2002; Inkelas et al., 2002). Capitalizing on the close succession of visits in the first year, pediatric psychologists working in primary care settings are in a unique position to enhance infant and early childhood mental health by developing strong relationships with caregivers, supporting young children and their families, and providing critical information about development and well-being (Talmi, Buchholz, & Stafford, 2009). Without behavioral health services in primary care, many young children and their families would not be seen or identified until significant disturbance emerged later in development and when they met criteria for mental health diagnoses. Moreover, the comfort, safety, and familiarity of pediatric primary care settings in which caregivers routinely raise concerns and obtain information and resources to address these concerns increases the potential of primary care settings to function as gateways to behavioral health services.

Training Transdisciplinary Professionals to Assess and Address Behavioral Health in Pediatric Populations
The shortage of pediatric behavioral health providers, particularly in rural areas, places an even greater burden on pediatric primary care settings to provide behavioral health services. A competent, high-quality workforce will ensure that the services provided in the context of primary care can appropriately meet the needs of a population whose only access to health and mental health services may be in primary care. Since its inception, our team has developed numerous education and training opportunities for pediatric primary care providers, allied health professionals, and integrated mental health-service providers. CLIMB clinicians teach preclinic didactics and noon conferences to residents and medical trainees on various topics related to mental health, behavior, and development. These and other presentations are distributed to pediatric and behavioral health providers statewide.

Directions for Future Research
The AAP task force on children's mental health (AAP, 2002) includes among its goals: identifying mental health competencies required for pediatric primary-care clinicians, providing skill building and educational opportunities, changing medical education curricula, and developing new clinical tools (National Institute for Health Care Management, 2009). More research is needed to scientifically validate the outcomes associated with increased training and education about behavioral health on providers' knowledge, attitudes, and practice.

Pediatric primary care providers would benefit from tools and algorithms that promote mental health, identify problems, engage patients and families, determine need for further assessment/evaluation, and assess care options and resources for children with identified problems (AAP, 2008). The AAP policy statement focused on identifying developmental disorders in children 0–3 provides a framework for identification of specific screening tools and information on how to select appropriate tools and CPT codes to use for billing purposes (Council on Children with Disabilities, 2006).

Research efforts must focus on exploring the costs and benefits of integrated models in order to determine the most effective and efficient approach to services. Additionally, more research is needed to empirically compare child and family outcomes for patients served in integrated versus traditional mental health settings. Finally, much of the research and literature has focused primarily on integrative initiatives for adults, for whom mental health and substance use disorders are more prevalent (National Institute for Health Care Management, 2008). Pediatric psychologists are uniquely positioned to demonstrate the benefits of preventive efforts and promotion of development and well-being within integrated pediatric primary-care settings.

Conclusions
Integration of behavioral health services into routine health maintenance activities is critical in providing comprehensive services that include early identification, amelioration

of distress, triage and referral, and the creation of a medical home (AAP, 2002). Although to date, reimbursement for behavioral health services in pediatric settings is negligible, documenting services provided, access to care, and utilization rates is essential in raising awareness and creating momentum for policy changes. In combination with research and policy efforts, routine use of health and behavior codes has the potential to transform models of behavioral and physical health services in the pediatric population. A comprehensive behavioral health approach in pediatric primary care could provide: (a) access to culturally responsive, family-centered resources once issues are identified through screening processes; (b) access to onsite integrated care for those patients who cannot access community services; and (c) continual interaction with primary care providers to enhance case management and care coordination. Using this approach, pediatric psychologists can collaboratively meet the needs of children and families and ultimately improve their health and well-being.

Conflicts of interest: None declared.

Acknowledgment

We are grateful to our collaborators in the Child Health Clinic, Maya Bunik, MD, MSPH, Mary Navin, MSN, RN, NE-BC, to Project CLIMB team members, and to the faculty, residents, trainees, staff, and families who support our work.

Funding

Funding for this work is generously provided by Rose Community Foundation, The Colorado Health Foundation, and Children's Hospital Colorado, Departments of Pediatrics and Psychiatry and Behavioral Sciences.

References

Academic Psychiatric Benchmarking Survey. (2011). Retrieved from http://www.adminpsych.org

American Academy of Pediatrics. (2002). Center for Medical Home Implementation. Retrieved from www.medicalhomeinfo.org

American Academy of Pediatrics. (2008). Task force on mental health fact sheet. Retrieved from www.aap.org/commpeds/dochs/mental health/docs/TFOMH%Fact%20Sheet%202%2008.pdf

American Academy of Child and Adolescent Psychiatry Committee on Health Care Access and Economics. (2009). American Academy of Pediatrics Task Force on Mental Health. (2009). Improving mental health services in primary care: Reducing administrative and financial barriers to access and collaboration. *Pediatrics*. 123(4), 1248–1251.

Bunik, M., Stafford, B., Talmi, A., & Rosenberg, A. (2008). Integration of mental health into the academic primary care setting: Attitudes, skill, knowledge and support. *Ambulatory Pediatrics*, 8(2), e7.

Centers for Disease Control. (2004). Table 2. Annual rate of ambulatory care visits with corresponding standard errors, by setting type and selected patient and provider characteristics: United States, 2004. Retrieved from www.cdc.gov/nchs/data/hestat/estimates2004_tables.pdf#02

Colorado Department of Health Care Policy and Financing. (2011a). Colorado Accountable Care Collaborative Program. Retrieved from http://www.colorado.gov

Colorado Department of Health Care Policy and Financing. (2011b). Your Guide to Medicaid's Accountable Care Collaborative Program. Retrieved from http://www.healthcolorado.net

Council on Children with Disabilities. (2006). Identifying infants and young children with developmental disorders in the medical home: An algorithm for developmental surveillance and screening. American Academy of Pediatrics Policy Statement. *Pediatrics*, 118, 405–420.

Golden, O., & Fortuny, K. (2011). *Brief 4: Improving the lives of young children: Meeting parents' health and mental health needs through Medicaid and CHIP so children can thrive*. Urban Institute.

Hagan, J. F., Shaw, J. S., & Duncan, P. (Eds.), (2008). *Bright Futures: Guidelines for Health Supervision of Infants, Children, and Adolescents* (3rd ed., pp. 648). Elk Grove Village, IL: American Academy of Pediatrics.

Inkelas, M., Schuster, M. A., Newacheck, P. W., Olsen, L. M., & Halfon, N. (2002, May). *Having a particular clinician for well child care and quality of early childhood health care*. Baltimore, MD: Paper presented at the annual meeting of the Pediatric Academic Societies.

Inkelas, M., Glascoe, F. P., Regalado, M., Peck, C., Bethell, C., Mistry, R., & Halfon, N. (2002, May). *National patterns and disparities in parent concerns about child development*. Baltimore, MD: Paper presented at the annual meeting of the Pediatric Academic Societies.

Kessler, R. (2008). Integration of care is about money too: The health and behavior codes as an element of a new financial paradigm. *Families, Systems, & Health, 26*(2), 207–216.

Mauch, D., Kautz, C., & Smith, S. A. (2008). *Reimbursement of mental health services in primary care settings* (HHS Pub. No. SMA-08-4324). Rockville, MD: Center for Mental Health Services, Substance Abuse and Mental Health Services Administration.

Miyamoto, R. (2006). Billing effectively with the new health and behavior current procedural terminology codes in primary care and specialty clinics. *Journal of Clinical Psychology, 62*(10), 1221–1229.

National Conference of State Legislatures. (2011). A guide to long-term care for state policy makers: Money follows the person initiatives. *Issue Brief.* Retrieved from www.ncsl.org/issues-research/health/archive-money-follows-the-person-initiatives.aspx

National Institute for Health Care Management. (2008). Understanding the uninsured: Tailoring policy solutions for different subpopulations. *Issue Brief.* Retrieved from www.nihcm.org

National Institute for Health Care Management. (2009). Strategies to support the integration of mental health into pediatric primary care. *Issue Paper.* Retrieved from www.nihcm.org

National Govenors Association. (2005). Funding for children's mental health services: Making the most of Medicaid. *Issue Brief.* Retrieved from www.nga.org

Noll, R. B., & Fischer, S. (2004). Commentary. Health and behavior CPT codes: An opportunity to revolutionize reimbursement in pediatric psychology. *Journal of Pediatric Psychology, 29,* 571–578.

Olson, L., Inkelas, M., Halfon, N., Schuster, M., O'Connor, K., & Mistry, R. (2004). Overview of the content of health supervision for young children: Reports from parents and pediatricians. *Pediatrics, 113,* 1907–1916.

Stille, C., Turchi, R., Antonelli, R., Cabana, M., Cheng, T., Laraque, D., & Perrin, J. (2010). The family-centered medical home: Specific considerations for child health research and policy. *Academic Pediatrics, 10,* 211–217.

Talmi, A., Stafford, B., & Buchholz, M. (2009). Providing perinatal mental health services in pediatric primary care. *Zero to Three, May 2009,* 10–16.

U.S. Department of Health & Human Services. (2011). Affordable care act supports states in strengthening community living. *News Release.* Retrieved from http://www.hhs.gov/news

Commentary: Medicaid Reimbursement and Utilization of Health and Behavior Codes: Year One in Oklahoma

Kristine Woods, PsyD, and Stephen R. Gillaspy, PhD

Department of Pediatrics, University of Oklahoma Health Sciences Center

All correspondence concerning this article should be addressed to Stephen R. Gillaspy, PhD, University of Oklahoma Health Sciences Center, 1200 N. Children's Drive, Suite 12400, Oklahoma City, OK, 73104, USA. E-mail: stephen-gillaspy@ouhsc.edu

Received December 15, 2011; revisions received January 23, 2012; accepted January 24, 2012

Introduction

In 2002, the Centers for Medicaid and Medicare Services (CMS) approved and activated the health and behavior Current Procedural Terminology (CPT) codes (H&B codes) with the purpose of improving services delivered to patients within the medical system (Foxhall, 2000). The implementation of H&B codes for use by licensed clinical psychologists was the culmination of efforts by the American Psychological Association (APA) Practice Directorate and the Interdivisional Healthcare Committee starting in 1997.

The APA has been continually working with Medicare and private insurance companies to improve access and reimbursement of the codes, but Mullins, Ambrosino, Duncan, Smith, and Phelps (2010) noted that adoption and reimbursement from Medicaid continues to lag behind. These authors reported on results of a survey of success with Medicaid reimbursement for pediatric psychologists and the typical process for psychologists pursuing reimbursement for the codes. Unfortunately, the majority of respondents either did not have Medicaid reimbursement or were unaware of the source of the funds (e.g., State Medicaid office, Health Care Authority, the Behavioral Health Division).Currently, no data have been published on the number of states that provide Medicaid reimbursement for H&B codes. Since Medicaid is administered at the state level, monitoring of successful Medicaid reimbursement remains a challenge.

Few articles have been published since Noll and Fischer's (2004) commentary on the H&B codes, and it remains unclear how accessible the codes are across the country, in part because of the variability in reimbursement across states, and the lack of a systematic way to track this information. The purpose of this commentary is to provide an overview of the process of obtaining Medicaid reimbursement for the H&B codes in Oklahoma and to report on the data compiled by the state's Medicaid program on the utilization and reimbursement of the codes during their first year of implementation. Additionally, in Oklahoma postdoctoral fellows and predoctoral interns enrolled in accredited training programs are permitted to bill Medicaid for services while under the supervision of a licensed psychologist; therefore, the process of opening up the codes for use by psychology trainee as well as utilization of H&B codes are reported in addition to services provided by licensed psychologists.

Why is Medicaid Reimbursement for the H&B Codes Critical?

It is estimated that approximately 60 million people are currently enrolled in the national Medicaid program (Kaiser Family Foundation, 2011a), which equates to roughly one in five Americans. Furthermore, in June 2010, over 26 million children were enrolled in the Medicaid program (Kaiser Family Foundation, 2011b). In order to qualify for Medicaid, the family income is compared to the federal poverty level (Centers for Medicare and Medicaid Services, 2011b); thus, the majority of children with Medicaid coverage come from families of lower socioeconomic status (SES). Research has indicated a positive association between SES and health outcome, and access to optimal health care is limited with lower SES (Fuemmeler, Moriarty, & Brown, 2009).

Examination of 2010 census data revealed that over 3,751,000 people resided in the state of Oklahoma, with roughly 25% being under the age of 18 years. For the fiscal year of July 2010 to June 2011, the Oklahoma Health Care Authority (OHCA; Russel, 2011) reported an average enrollment of 487,396 children in the state Medicaid program, which translates into 59% of all Oklahoma children receiving insurance coverage from the state Medicaid program. Therefore, Medicaid is the predominant insurance provider for the vast majority of children in Oklahoma.

The passage of the Affordable Care Act in 2010 has the potential to greatly influence the role that psychologists play and the types of services patients and families will receive. Specifically, health care reform brings a new focus to the integration of mental and physical health care services, an investment in prevention, the expectation of collaboration between behavioral health providers and primary care and other medical providers, and the establishment of patient-centered health homes and accountable care organizations. Psychologists have the unique biopsychosocial skill set necessary to provide integrated care and the H&B codes provide a reimbursable mechanism to provide such care. Moreover, it is expected that health care reform will expand Medicaid eligibility, underscoring the importance of Medicaid reimbursement of H&B codes.

Process for Obtaining Medicaid Reimbursement for H&B Codes in Oklahoma

In 2005, the secondary author made contact with the Behavioral Health Unit at the OHCA regarding reimbursement for the H&B codes. At that time, the OHCA was unaware of the codes and had no plans to open the codes for use. This initial contact was followed by subsequent emails and face to face meetings with the Director of the Behavioral Health Unit. The secondary author and three other psychologists in the state (two pediatric psychologists and one health psychologist) began informal and formal discussions with the Behavioral Health Unit regarding the codes and their positive impact on health conditions. During these discussions, the Behavioral Health Unit was provided with literature on the intent of the codes, and they were informed of Medicare reimbursement and a movement for the majority of private insurance companies to reimburse the codes. The state association was also educated about the H&B codes and was asked to support the need for Medicaid reimbursement.

The OHCA staff was receptive to the concept of the codes, but reported a budget request would have to be approved in order to open the codes for use. In 2007, the Behavioral Health Unit of the OHCA proposed reimbursement for the H&B codes and submitted a budget request for the state fiscal year of 2009 (July 1, 2008–June 30, 2009). Although funding for the H&B codes was added to the annual budget request, it was not a priority, and was typically included with other behavioral health initiatives. Each year the H&B codes fell below the funding priority. During that time, the OHCA Behavioral Health Director participated in a presentation on the H&B codes at the 2008 Oklahoma Psychological Association annual meeting (Mullins et al., 2008) and encouraged psychologists to lobby the state legislature for increased behavioral health funding and reimbursement of H&B codes. In 2010, the H&B codes were included with several other behavioral health initiatives focused on increased access to care and the codes were approved through the OHCA emergency rules. From 2005 to 2010, the OHCA initiated a medical home model for primary care, emphasizing integration of behavioral health and a biopsychosocial perspective to primary care. It is believed that the OHCA focus on integration of care and increased access for behavioral health services influenced the decision to provide reimbursement for the H&B codes.

Oklahoma Medicaid began reimbursing for the H&B codes in July of 2010, and reimbursement for the H&B codes was and continues to be paid from the behavioral health budget rather than the medical budget as proposed. Despite this discrepancy from the intended funding source for the codes, it does not appear to have had an impact on reimbursement rates or success. Medicaid reimbursement for H&B codes was restricted to only those services provided by licensed clinical psychologists, and currently, Oklahoma Medicaid only provides reimbursement to psychologists for services provided to children under 21 years of age, restricting reimbursement for the codes to children and adolescents. Additionally, the OHCA specified that the codes are to be used for children with chronic and terminal illnesses, which is inconsistent with the current CPT manual which states "Codes 96150-96155 describe services offered to patients who present with primary physical illnesses, diagnoses, or symptoms and may benefit from assessments and interventions that focus on the biopsychosocial factors related to the patient's health status," (American Medical Association, 2011, p. 517).

In 2008, the secondary author worked with the OHCA and the state licensing board to develop a formal process to allow psychology interns and fellows to bill Medicaid for trainee-provided services using the traditional CPT codes. This agreement stipulates that only psychology interns and fellows participating in formal training programs are permitted to bill Medicaid and receive reimbursement under their clinical supervisor for clinical services provided to patients and families. The reimbursement schedule for trainee-provided services was negotiated at the same rate as services provided by licensed psychologists. When the H&B codes were approved for use for licensed psychologists, psychology interns and fellows in formal training programs were also approved to bill for the codes while under supervision.

Oklahoma Medicaid Reimbursement Statistics

The data included in this report were extracted by the OHCA and includes all H&B codes reimbursable by psychologists (96150–91655). Medicaid claims were extracted from July 1, 2010 to September 30, 2011 in order to capture all claims submitted during the state's fiscal year.

Number of Encounters and Units of Service

Data provided by the OHCA indicates that a total of 448 encounters were submitted to Medicaid using H&B codes between July 2010 and June 2011 (T. Russell, OHCA, personal communications, November–December 2011). Of these 448 encounters, only 44 encounters were denied reimbursement (9.8%). Of note, however, is the fact that substantially more claims were initially denied reimbursement, but were later reimbursed after being resubmitted. Licensed psychologists utilized the H&B codes for a total of 197 encounters, comprised of 355 units of service, at both the inpatient and outpatient levels. Of these 197 encounters, 108 were billed under the assessment codes (96150-initial assessment and 96151-reassessment) and 89 encounters were billed under the intervention codes (95152-individual, 96154-family with patient present, and 96155-family without patient present). Psychology interns and fellows billed for a total of 243 encounters, which was comprised of 526 units. Of these 243 encounters, 127 were billed under the assessment codes whereas 11 were billed under the intervention codes.

Children between the ages of 5 and 12 received the majority of services billed through the H&B codes (188 total encounters) followed by 174 total encounters for adolescents 13 to 18 years old. The most commonly used primary medical diagnoses included sickle cell disease (76 encounters), cancer (62 encounters), weight-related diagnoses (49 encounters), pain conditions (31 encounters), hemophilia (22 encounters), and cystic fibrosis (12 encounters).

Reimbursement Rates

Currently, Medicaid reimbursement rates in Oklahoma are approximately equal to the reported reimbursement rates for Medicare across all codes. Importantly, the average reimbursement rate for the five largest private insurance companies in Oklahoma remains substantially above the national Medicare rates (J. Hayes, personal communication, November–December 2011). See Table I for more information. Noll and Fischer (2004) cautioned that underuse of the codes by psychologists could potentially result in loss of control over the codes as well as decreased reimbursement values for the codes. Compared to national Medicare rates published by Noll and Fischer (2004), the national average for Medicare reimbursement of H&B codes has declined over the years (Centers for Medicare and Medicaid Services, 2011a). See Table II for more information. Information generated from the CMS indicates that Medicare reimbursement of H&B codes has decreased in Oklahoma from 2004 to 2011, and this overall decrease has been gradual over the years (Table III). What is unclear, however, is whether the rates have decreased due to lack of use, economic decline across the country, or some other factor.

Table I. Average Reimbursement Rates by Insurance Type

CPT Code	Oklahoma Medicare	Oklahoma Medicaid	Average Private[a]	Estimated Charge[b]
96150-Initial assessment	$20.68	$20.01	$30.66	$62.04
96151-Reassessment	$20.00	$19.35	$29.66	$60.00
96152-Individual	$19.01	$18.39	$28.29	$57.03
96153-Group	$4.57	$4.42	$6.66	$13.71
96154-Family w/patient	$18.67	$18.06	$27.79	$56.01
96155-Family w/o patient	–	$21.22	$29.22	$58.00

Note. Amounts are for one unit of service
[a]Rates were included from the five largest private insurance carriers in the state, and reimbursement rates were specific to the rate for the authors' institution
[b]Estimated charge is based on 200% of Medicare. Specific charge data not publicly available, but typical methodology for determining charges is initially based on setting the charge floor at 200% of Medicare.

Conclusions

Implementation of the H&B codes for pediatric psychologists has allowed for greater integration of psychosocial functioning within the medical system, thus allowing for utilization of the biopsychosocial model of care. Despite the presence of psychosocial stressors, many of the children receiving services under these codes would not be eligible for psychological services because they do not have a diagnosable mental health disorder. Thus, the H&B codes allow psychologists to assist the medical team in providing comprehensive care within the context of the child's medical condition (Kessler, 2008).

Table II. *2011 National Average Reimbursement Rates for Medicare*

CPT Code	2011 Rate	Rate Reported in Noll & Fischer (2004)
96150-Initial assessment	$21.07	$26
96151-Reassessment	$20.39	$26
96152-Individual	$19.37	$25
96153-Group	$4.76	$5
96154-Family w/patient	$19.03	$24
96155-Family w/o patient	–	$23

Table III. *Medicare Reimbursement Rates for Oklahoma 2004–2011*

Year	96150	96151	96152	95153	96154
2004	25.19	24.12	23.04	5.20	22.67
2005	24.99	24.24	23.15	5.25	22.77
2006	24.92	24.16	23.08	5.23	22.70
2007	22.39	21.63	20.55	4.85	20.17
2008	21.50	20.74	20.03	4.59	19.65
2009	21.94	21.22	20.19	4.75	19.47
2010a	21.94	21.22	20.16	4.84	19.47
2010b	22.42	21.68	20.60	4.94	20.23
2011	20.68	20.00	19.01	4.57	18.69

Note. Amounts are for 1 unit of service. Retrieved from www.cms/hhs.gov/apps/pfslookup/

A review of the process for obtaining Medicaid reimbursement for H&B codes in Oklahoma and examination of the first year of utilization data revealed several important findings. First, it is commendable that Oklahoma has one of only a few state Medicaid programs to reimburse for the H&B codes. The reimbursement data reveal that previously cited issues with denials for H&B codes (e.g., noncovered service, no prior authorization, ineligible provider; Brosig & Zahrt, 2006) has not been a significant problem during this first year. Additionally, the fact that a significant portion of the reimbursed encounters were provided by psychology interns and fellows demonstrates that our trainees are actively engaged in using the H&B codes. This active engagement should help to promote the use of the H&B codes and suggests that we are slowly making improvements in the area of workforce development for integrated healthcare.

Although the Oklahoma Medicaid agency is supportive of the H&B codes, the fact that reimbursement is from the behavioral health budget versus the medical budget suggests a continued division between behavioral and medical health and a need for further integration at the administrative and funding level in Medicaid agencies. This is further evidenced by the addition of language assigned to the codes referring to the provision of services for chronically and terminally ill patients. As healthcare reform calls for increased integration of services and removal of the medical versus behavioral health approach (Clay, 2011), it is hoped that the H&B codes will be better appreciated and seen as applicable to all patients where psychological, behavioral, emotional, cognitive, and social factors impact the management of physical health problems. Lastly, although Oklahoma Medicaid reimburses for H&B codes at approximately the same rate as Medicare, the current reimbursement is significantly less than private insurance companies. This parity with Medicare reimbursement should be concerning given that Medicare reimbursement for H&B codes has declined since 2004 (Centers for Medicare and Medicaid Services, 2011a).

Future Directions

It will continue to be important for psychologists to advocate for proper use and reimbursement of the H&B codes by their state Medicaid programs (Clay, 2011). Recommendations drawn by Mullins et al. (2010) on ways to further the successful reimbursement of H&B codes included having the background and education about the codes to properly bill for services, using the codes when appropriate to do so and appealing claims that are denied, working with the financial department of one's institution, enlisting support from state psychological associations, and seeking support from the children and families being served under the codes. Families can directly lobby state Medicaid agencies and their state legislators to emphasize the importance of the H&B codes and the need for increased reimbursement. This can take the form of emails, letters, phone calls, or face to face interactions. Families may also request to have their medical provider lobby on behalf of the H&B codes. Many pediatricians appreciate the value of pediatric psychology and because of the medical hierarchy and perceived leadership, can often provide more influence than psychologists or individual families. Additionally, support at the state level from physician organizations can have a substantial impact on insurance companies' willingness to reimburse the codes, particularly as physicians are able to attest to the value of psychological services in the management of chronic illnesses.

Regarding seeking Medicaid reimbursement, we would add that it is essential to determine the rule-making process within the state Medicaid agency and what Medicaid personnel psychologists should work with to advocate for H&B codes. Furthermore, as each state Medicaid program is either in the planning stages or already making preparations for healthcare reform, psychologists are urged to advocate for the H&B codes in the context healthcare reform (Nordal, 2011). Psychologists also play an important role in educating Medicaid personnel on how utilization of the H&B codes is congruent with integrated care and allows for a truly biopsychosocial approach to healthcare. As each state modifies its Medicaid program to comply with the Affordable Care Act of 2010, it will be important to monitor Medicaid reimbursement for H&B codes across all states as currently there is no way to track this information in one uniform manner.

In Oklahoma, we will continue to promote the H&B codes and the role psychologists can play in the new healthcare system. We will lobby for increased reimbursement for H&B codes and provide feedback on utilization to date. Although, reimbursement has not been denied for clinical services provided to patients outside the definition of chronically and terminally ill, we will lobby for removal of this language. This change in the language will be increasingly important with health care reform's focus on early intervention and prevention services.

Acknowledgments

The authors would like to acknowledge the Oklahoma Health Care Authority Reporting and Statistics Unit for providing descriptive statistics on Medicaid utilization and reimbursement of the Health and Behavior CPT codes. The authors would like to specifically thank Tony Russell for his assistance. The authors would also like to thank Drs Larry Mullins, Rhonda Johnson, and Teri Bourdeau for their efforts in lobbying the OHCA for reimbursement of the H&B codes.

Conflicts of interest: None declared.

References

American Medical Association. (2011). *2012 CPT: Current procedural terminology professional edition* (p. 517). Chicago, IL: American Medical Association.

Brosig, C. L., & Zahrt, D. M. (2006). Evolution of an inpatient pediatric psychology consultation service: Issues related to reimbursement and the use of health and behavior codes. *Journal of Clinical Psychology in Medical Settings, 13*, 425–429.

Centers for Medicare and Medicaid Services. (2011a). *Physician fee schedule*. Retrieved from http://www.cms.hhs.gov/apps/pfslookup/

Centers for Medicare and Medicaid Services. (2011b). *Medicaid eligibility: Overview*. Retrieved from https://www.cms.gov/MedicaidEligibility/

Clay, R. A. (2011). Health-care reform 2.0: APA and psychologists across the country are working to ensure psychology's place in the nation's new health-care system. *Monitor on Psychology, 42*(10), Retrieved from http://www.apa.org/monitor/2011/11/health-care-reform.aspx

Dittmann, M. (2004). CPT codes: Use them or lose them. *Monitor on Psychology, 35*(9), Retrieved from http://www.apa.org/monitor/oct04/cpt.aspx

Foxhall, K. (2000). New CPT codes will recognize psychologists' work with physical health problems. *Monitor on Psychology, 31*(10), Retrieved from http://www.apa.org/monitor/nov00/codes.aspx

Fuemmeler, B. F., Moriarty, L., & Brown, R. T. (2009). Racial and ethnic health disparities and access to care. In M. C. Roberts, & R. G. Steele (Eds.), *Handbook of pediatric psychology* (Vol. 4, pp. 575–585). New York: Guilford.

Kaiser Family Foundation. (2011a). *Faces of Medicaid*. Retrieved from http://facesofmedicaid.kff.org/facesofmedicaid.aspx

Kaiser Family Foundation. (2011b). *Medicaid enrollment: June 2010 data snapshot*. Retrieved from http://www.kff.org/medicaid/upload/8050-03.pdf

Kessler, R. (2008). Integration of care is about money too: The health and behavior codes as an element of a new financial paradigm. *Families, Systems, & Health, 26*, 207–216.

Miyamoto, R. E. S. (2006). Billing effectively with the new health and behavior current procedural terminology codes in primary care and specialty clinics. *Journal of Clinical Psychology, 62*, 1221–1229.

Mullins, L. L., Ambrosino, J. M., Duncan, C., Smith, K. C., & Phelps, R. E. (2010). Using health and behavior codes to help sustain practice in pediatric psychology. Paper presented at the American Psychological Association Annual Meeting, San Diego, CA.

Mullins, L. L., Gillaspy, S. R., Spaeth, D., & Jonhson, R. (2008). Health and behavior CPT codes: New opportunities for the professional practice of health psychology. Paper presented at the Oklahoma Psychological Association Annual Conference, Oklahoma City, OK.

Noll, R. B., & Fischer, S. (2004). Commentary. Health and behavior CPT codes: An opportunity to revolutionize reimbursement in pediatric psychology. *Journal of Pediatric Psychology, 29*(7), 571–578.

Nordall, K. C. (2011). Health-care reform begins at home. *Monitor on Psychology, 42*(7), Retrieved from http://www.apa.org/monitor/2011/07-08/perspectives.aspx

Russel, T. *Behavioral health fast facts*. (June 2011). [Data file]. Oklahoma City, OK: Oklahoma Health Care Authority.

Commentary: Health and Behavior Codes in a Pediatric Headache Program: Reimbursement Data and Recommendations for Practice

Robyn Lewis Claar,[1,2] PHD, Karen J. Kaczynski,[1,2] PHD, Margaret Munro Lyons,[1] BA, and Alyssa A. LeBel,[1,3] MD

[1]*Division of Pain Medicine, Department of Anesthesiology, Perioperative and Pain Medicine,* [2]*Department of Psychiatry, and* [3]*Department of Neurology, Children's Hospital Boston and Harvard Medical School*

All correspondence concerning this article should be addressed to Robyn Claar, PhD, Pain Treatment Service, Children's Hospital Boston, 333 Longwood Ave, Boston, MA, 02115, USA. E-mail: robyn.claar@childrens.harvard.edu

Received November 10, 2011; revisions received November 22, 2011; accepted November 23, 2011

Pediatric psychologists play an important role in pediatric hospitals as independent providers, consultants, and members of multidisciplinary teams in both inpatient and outpatient settings (Aylward, Bender, Graves, & Roberts, 2009). Psychological assessment and treatment often focus on psychosocial factors that contribute to a chronic or acute medical condition. Pediatric psychologists address child and family adjustment in the context of a child's medical diagnosis in many ways, including by teaching coping skills for managing illness, pain, and associated emotional distress; helping patients improve adherence to medical regimens; and helping families support optimal child functioning despite illness. Thus, the primary presenting issue and focus of treatment is the child's medical condition, and a mental health diagnosis may not be appropriate or justified in many children who are treated by pediatric psychologists.

This shift in focus toward health behaviors and coping with medical illness, and away from traditional mental health diagnoses, has led to difficulties with reimbursement for pediatric psychology services (Mitchell & Roberts, 2004). Specifically, in the past, pediatric psychologists were required to bill for services using Diagnostic and Statistical Manual of Mental Disorders codes, resulting in a significant increase in the prevalence of "adjustment disorders" due to the use of this diagnosis to bill for pediatric psychology services (Rabasca, 1999). Health and behavior (H&B) codes were developed in order to address this issue by allowing pediatric psychologists to bill for assessments and interventions based on the child's medical diagnosis. Pediatric psychologists in medical settings have been strongly encouraged to use H&B codes (see http://www.apa.org/practice/cpt2002.html, http://www.apa.org/monitor/may06/codes.aspx, and www.apa.org/practice/cpt faq.html) to more accurately reflect the nature of services provided and to improve billing and reimbursement. Medical services are often covered by insurance, but psychology services, even as a component of a multidisciplinary team, are often covered by mental health carve outs if they are covered at all, resulting in lower rates of reimbursement. Billing an H&B code with a medical diagnosis sometimes allows for coverage within a patient's medical benefits. Additionally, patients and their families may be more open to pediatric psychology services billed under a medical diagnosis, as opposed to a potentially stigmatizing and inaccurate mental health disorder.

H&B codes became active in 2002, and it is unclear whether the use of these codes has improved reimbursement for pediatric psychology services, as anticipated. In 2004, the Society of Pediatric Psychology created a Task Force on Access for Patients to Clinical Services to evaluate reimbursement rates with H&B codes. Delamater, one of the chairs of the task force, conducted a web-based survey of pediatric and adult health psychologists in the United States regarding their knowledge and use of H&B codes (Delameter, 2004). Results indicated that although 90% of respondents reported knowing about H&B codes, only 44% used them at that time. Of those using the codes, the majority reported less than 50% reimbursement. Reimbursement was improved when the use of H&B codes was specifically explained to insurance companies. Denials were often due to the lack of pre-authorization for services and the use of a medical diagnosis by a psychologist.

Limited additional research has been conducted to examine whether psychologists have been successfully reimbursed using these codes. Noll and Fischer (2004) reported that most private insurers in their local region provided from 70% to 100% reimbursement for H&B codes, although reimbursement was considerably lower for public insurers. It appears that these reimbursement rates were reported by insurance companies, however, and the actual rate of reimbursement to hospitals and clinics is unclear. Brosig and Zahrt (2006) documented somewhat lower rates of reimbursement for a pediatric psychology consultation service but noted improvements in their H&B reimbursement rates from 58% in fiscal year 2001–2002 to 85% in fiscal year 2004–2005. In addition, they noted that these reimbursement rates were higher than rates for mental health CPT codes. However, they also reported that H&B codes were rejected in 31% of cases due to lack of coverage of these services by Medicaid, lack of prior authorization, or the provider being out of network.

It has been proposed that integrating pediatric psychologists into multidisciplinary outpatient medical clinics (Koocher, 2004) and educating third-party payers about the use of H&B codes for pediatric psychology services (Brosig & Zahrt, 2006) should result in improved reimbursement. In addition, it may be that developing expertise in providing pediatric psychology assessment and interventions within a specific population may improve reimbursement by demonstrating efficacy and providing a consistent model of care that is recognized by insurance companies. Thus, we propose to evaluate reimbursement rates for pediatric psychology services with H&B codes at a pediatric headache clinic, a multidisciplinary outpatient clinic in which psychology is well-integrated, and patients exhibit limited variability in presenting medical problems, allowing psychologists to develop expertise in evaluating and treating these conditions, while also allowing insurers to become familiar with the billing model.

When the Pediatric Headache Program at Children's Hospital Boston opened in January 2008, we opted to bill all our multidisciplinary psychological evaluations with H&B codes to most accurately reflect the nature of our services in evaluating patients with chronic headaches. Thus, we prepared insurance companies in advance for H&B codes by obtaining prior authorizations for the use of these codes and stressing the importance of psychological evaluations as an integral component to the multidisciplinary evaluations we provide in our clinic. We expected to receive higher levels of reimbursement

Table I. *H&B Code Insurance Reimbursement for New Patient Psychological Evaluations (NE) and Follow-Up Treatment (FU)*

Year	Number of NE	Percent Reimbursement	Number of FU	Percent Reimbursement
2008	217	43.80	80	50.95
2009	258	45.95	113	39.02
2010	206	43.81	141	31.04

from insurance carriers using H&B codes. In the event that a patient's medical insurance would not authorize an evaluation under H&B codes, we then obtained authorizations to bill using mental health codes. Over the past 3 years, we have been unable to use H&B codes for 13 new patient evaluations (2 in 2008, 1 in 2009, and 10 in 2010). In our program, we conducted 219 new patient evaluations in 2008, 259 new patient evaluations in 2010, and 216 new patient evaluations in 2010. These multidisciplinary evaluations include comprehensive evaluations with both a neurologist and a pediatric psychologist with expertise in pain management. The psychologist bills under the same medical diagnosis assigned by the neurologist, typically tension headache (307.81), common migraine (346.10), classic migraine (346.00), and/or new daily persistent headache (339.42). Our program also includes a practice administrator who is well-versed in the insurance authorization and billing process who obtains pre-authorizations when necessary for all new patient evaluations prior to their initial appointments.

We analyzed our rates of reimbursement for each of the past 3 years since our clinic opened in January 2008. As can be seen in Table I, our rates of reimbursement are not as favorable as those documented by Brosig and Zahrt (2006) and Noll and Fischer (2004), and are consistently around 44% when averaged over the greater than 60 insurance companies that we have billed each year for new patient multidisciplinary evaluations. From 2008 to 2010, our H&B rates have been billed between $115 and $117 per unit, as set and approved by our hospital's physicians' organization. New patient evaluations, typically billed at 4 units for a 1 hr new patient psychological evaluation, were billed between $460 and $468. Therefore, our reimbursement rates were approximately $200 for new patient evaluations.

A percentage of our patients participate in follow-up psychological treatment for pain management with a psychologist in our program; the majority of our patients participate in treatment with local psychologists in the community due to geographical barriers and limited provider availability. Table I also includes our rates of reimbursement for follow-up psychological treatment visits per

Table II. *New Evaluation (NE) and Follow-Up (FU) Reimbursement by Top 6 Insurance Companies*

Insurer	Year	Number of NE	NE Percent Reimbursement	Number of FU	FU Percent Reimbursement
Company A	2008	88	14.46	33	7.89
	2009	131	28.96	87	26.51
	2010	73	25.75	105	24.69
Company B	2008	42	84.81	22	86.79
	2009	21	88.83	6	92.30
	2010	19	75.70	0	N/A
Company C	2008	19	72.86	4	83.70
	2009	28	79.10	7	85.04
	2010	15	80.37	5	84.93
Company D	2008	13	83.70	13	85.06
	2009	14	80.74	0	N/A
	2010	10	85.56	1	84.91
Company E	2008	6	80.46	1	90.23
	2009	8	75.81	12	80.61
	2010	1	100	0	N/A
Company F	2008	6	72.78	0	N/A
	2009	10	83.74	0	N/A
	2010	12	88.66	0	N/A
State Medicaid	2008	13	0	2	0
	2009	15	0	0	N/A
	2010	23	0	10	0

calendar year. Although the number of outpatient return visits for psychological treatment has increased each year, our rate of reimbursement declined from approximately 51% in 2008 to 31% in 2010. We typically bill 3 units for outpatient psychological treatment; thus we billed between $345 and $351 per appointment and were reimbursed approximately $175 per patient in 2008, which declined to $106 in 2010. Although our percentage of reimbursements is lower than we would like, our collections are within the lower range of what psychologists in the community typically charge and collect.

We sought to understand why our reimbursement declined over time and examined our rates of reimbursement by insurance company for our top insurance companies (in terms of number of patients covered by these companies) as well as for our state Medicaid; these data are presented in Table II. We found that over time, we have treated more patients with insurance that does not reimburse us well (e.g., insurance company A and state Medicaid) and have treated fewer patients with insurances that reimburse well (insurance companies B, C, D, E, and F).

Thus, we also decided to analyze our rates of reimbursement for H&B codes for our top 6 insurance companies when removing patients with the top low paying insurance company (insurance company A), when removing patients with state Medicaid, and when removing both of these groups of patients; these data are presented in Table III. We found that when we removed insurance company A from consideration of our top insurance companies, our rates of reimbursement for new patient evaluations from 2008 to 2010 increased from 43–46% to 59–72% and our rates of reimbursement for follow-up psychological treatment increased from 26–52% to 33–87%. Unfortunately, our rates of reimbursement for both new evaluations and follow-up treatment decreased from 2008 to 2010, with better collections in 2008 (72% and 87%, respectively) than in 2010 (59% and 33%, respectively). When patients with both insurance company A or state Medicaid were eliminated from analyses, our insurance reimbursement rates for both new patient evaluations and follow-up appointments was consistently above 80%.

Results of our analyses indicate that overall, we have been successful in using H&B codes to bill for our multidisciplinary evaluations within the headache program at Children's Hospital Boston. However, there is significant variability by insurance companies. Unfortunately, the greatest number of patients treated in our clinic are covered by insurance company A that does not reimburse us as well as our other top companies. In addition, despite APA's advocacy efforts in facilitating reimbursement from Medicaid (see http://www.apapracticecentral.org/reimbursement/billing/update.aspx, http://www.apapracticecentral.org/reimbursement/billing/cpt/secure/faq.aspx for further details), we do not receive reimbursement from our state Medicaid for H&B codes, and we have seen more of these patients each calendar year.

Table III. *New Evaluation (NE) and Follow-Up (FU) Reimbursement by Top Six Insurers and Eliminating Company A and State Medicaid*

Year	Insurer	Number of NE	NE Percent Reimbursement	Number of FU	FU Percent Reimbursement
2008					
	Top 6	187	44.75	75	51.96
	Top minus Company A	99	71.75	42	86.77
	Top minus Medicaid	174	47.65	72	50.51
	Top minus Company A and State Medicaid	86	81.14	40	86.04
2009					
	Top 6	227	45.62	112	39.35
	Top minus Company A	96	67.89	25	84.40
	Top minus Medicaid	204	49.26	112	39.35
	Top minus Company A and State Medicaid	93	82.00	25	84.40
2010					
	Top 6	153	42.86	121	25.87
	Top minus Company A	80	58.66	16	32.80
	Top minus Medicaid	130	50.27	111	28.40
	Top minus Company A and State Medicaid	57	81.85	6	84.92

Our results indicate that H&B codes can be used successfully for reimbursement of psychological evaluations in a multidisciplinary evaluation. However, rates of reimbursement vary considerably by insurance companies. In addition, our experience with reimbursement is influenced by the rates set by our organization that are considerably higher than those in the community and insurance companies may reimburse us at a rate they consider typical for psychologists in the community, which in turn, makes our rate of reimbursement appear artificially low. We also are required to evaluate patients in our clinic regardless of their insurance and unfortunately our volume of patients with lower paying insurance companies has increased significantly over the past 3 years that our clinic has been open. Although some programs and practitioners may experience a decline in their reimbursement rates due to competition from other local hospitals, we have not found that our reimbursement rates are affected in this way, as we are the only tertiary care center in the northeast providing comprehensive multidisciplinary headache evaluations

Our practice administrator has developed a number of successful strategies for obtaining pre-authorizations when necessary that allow us to obtain reimbursement using H&B codes. These tips are summarized below:

1. When requesting special authorization for a patient to be seen by a provider who is out of network or noncovered, always explain that the evaluation is a one-time service and that if follow-up care is needed, the patient will be referred to a local in-network provider. If the service is out-of-network, explain why the psychological evaluation cannot be performed by a local, in-network provider, and that it is integral component of the evaluation. We have found these strategies to be the most helpful in receiving successful, one-time authorizations for H&B codes.
2. Explain how the psychological evaluation is tied to, and crucial to, the patient's medical evaluation and/or treatment. In our clinic, evaluation by a psychologist is a requirement for the multidisciplinary evaluation, and patients cannot undergo evaluation with the physician without also undergoing evaluation with the psychologist.
3. When possible and allowed by the insurance company, develop consistent insurance company contacts who know who you are and what you are requesting. It helps to have a person who has authorized the service before in obtaining additional authorizations.
4. Remember the names of past patients who have had services successfully authorized by the insurance company to use as an example for the insurance contact person in obtaining future authorizations for other patients.
5. Know that insurance plans and contracts are constantly changing and that a company that previously has reimbursed for H&B codes without prior authorization may suddenly require authorizations in the future.

The development of H&B codes has improved pediatric psychology services by more accurately reflecting the nature of the services provided. In addition, many insurance companies in our area do reimburse adequately for services billed with H&B codes. However, clearly more effort needs to be directed at improving reimbursement rates, particularly by our largest private third party payers and state Medicaid. With both the insurance companies and the hospital, we may also require more advocacy for the benefit and value of pediatric psychology services. We also have considered charging our services at a bundled rate to gain more consistency in our reimbursements and have begun a preliminary investigation within our department regarding the possibility of using these bundled rates. Future efforts will be directed at evaluating the cost benefit of pediatric psychology interventions, in terms of improving health outcomes and prevention. We as a field must be able to demonstrate that our interventions are worth paying for because they result in decreased costs in the long run. With that knowledge, reimbursement rates will likely increase.

Funding

The authors acknowledge the support of Sara Page Mayo Endowment for Pediatric Pain Research and Treatment in the preparation of this article.

Conflicts of interest: None declared.

References

Aylward, B. S., Bender, J. A., Graves, M. M., & Roberts, M. C. (2009). Historical developments and trends in pediatric psychology. In M. C. Roberts, & R. G. Steele (Eds.), *Handbook of pediatric psychology* (4th ed., pp. 3–18). New York, NY: Guilford Press.

Brosig, C. L., & Zahrt, D. M. (2006). Evolution of an inpatient pediatric psychology consultation service: issues related to reimbursement and the use of health and behavior codes. *Journal of Clinical Psychology in Medical Settings, 13*, 425–429.

Demamater, A. (2004, July). Health and behavior code surveys. Paper presented at the American Psychological Association Annual Meeting. Honolulu, HI.

Koocher, G. P. (2004). Commentary: First, AIDE for pediatric psychology. *Journal of Pediatric Psychology, 29*, 53–54.

Mitchell, M. C., & Roberts, M. C. (2004). Commentary: Financing pediatric psychology services: "Look what they've done to my song, ma" or "The sun'll come out tomorrow"? *Journal of Pediatric Psychology, 29*, 55–59.

Noll, R. B., & Fischer, S. (2004). Commentary. Health and behavior CPT codes: An opportunity to revolutionize reimbursement in pediatric psychology. *Journal of Pediatric Psychology, 29*, 571–578.

Rabasca, L. (1999). Cancer patients find anxiety not covered under managed care [Electronic version]. *APA Monitor, 30*, 26.

Commentary: The Use of Health and Behavior Codes in a Pediatric Cardiology Setting

Cheryl L. Brosig, PhD
Medical College of Wisconsin

All correspondence concerning this article should be addressed to Cheryl L. Brosig, PhD, Medical College of Wisconsin, Department of Pediatrics, 8701 Watertown Plank Road, Milwaukee, WI, 53201, USA E-mail: cbrosig@chw.org

Received December 8, 2011; revisions received December 19, 2011; accepted December 22, 2011

Congenital heart disease (CHD) is the most common birth defect, occurring in approximately 6 in 1,000 live-births (Hoffman & Kaplan, 2002). Due to advances in diagnostic and surgical techniques and postoperative management strategies, the majority of children with CHD are surviving (Tweddell et al., 2009). However, these children are at increased risk for neurodevelopmental and psychosocial problems, likely due to multiple factors including abnormal prenatal brain development, perioperative management strategies, altered cerebral blood flow and oxygen delivery, and genetic syndromes (Wernovsky Shillingford, & Gaynor, 2005). Children with CHD have lower cognitive functioning and higher rates of attentional, behavioral, and emotional problems when compared to the normal population (Brosig, Mussatto, Kuhn, & Tweddell, 2007a,b; Karsdorp, Everaerd, Kindt, & Mulder, 2007; Snookes et al., 2010). In addition, increased parental stress, as well as impaired quality of life for both children with CHD and their parents has been reported (Brosig et al., 2007b; Landolt, Valsangiacomo Buechel, & Latal, 2008; Lawoko & Soares, 2003; Uzark & Jones, 2003).

Given the aforementioned problems in this patient population, in July 2007, the Pediatric Cardiology Division at our institution employed a full-time pediatric psychologist to help address the neurodevelopmental and psychosocial concerns of these children and families. Cardiologists and nurses asked families about the child's emotional, behavioral, and academic functioning during routine cardiac follow-up clinic visits. If there were concerns in any of these areas, a referral was made to the pediatric psychologist. Based on the clinical information provided, the psychologist determined whether a separate visit with the psychologist was needed, and what type of intervention was required (e.g., psychological testing, individual therapy, health and behavior intervention, etc.).

The current report summarizes our experience with financial reimbursement for pediatric psychology services in the outpatient pediatric cardiology setting over the past 4 years. We have been using the health and behavior codes at our institution since 2002, and have reported on our experience using them for inpatient pediatric psychology consultation previously (Brosig & Zahrt, 2006). We were interested to learn about reimbursement rates for health and behavior codes as well as mental health codes in the outpatient pediatric cardiology setting, as both types of services are utilized by children with CHD and their families. Results will be used to inform strategies to improve reimbursement rates for pediatric psychology services for this population.

Methods
Procedure

Charts and billing records of all outpatients seen by the pediatric psychologist in the outpatient cardiology setting over the past 4 years (FY 2007–2008 through FY 2010–2011) were reviewed for this study. The study was approved by the hospital Institutional Review Board (IRB). Parents provided consent and children (if age appropriate) provided assent to have their records included in this review.

When a new cardiology patient was referred to the pediatric psychologist for evaluation, an insurance verification specialist contacted the insurance company to verify benefits (including whether the company acknowledged health and behavior codes), and obtained prior authorization for the patient to be seen. Information about which billing codes were authorized was provided to the psychologist before the patient's visit. Based on the data from the initial assessment, the psychologist determined whether a mental health or health and behavior code was billed.

Charts were reviewed for referral date and referral question. Financial data were calculated by staff in the billing office of the institution, and included information regarding type of insurance (Medicaid vs. Commercial), billing code used (mental health vs. health and behavior), and payment rate. Charges for new patient visits as well as follow-up visits were included.

Results

During the study period, 165 new outpatients were seen; 98% of patients had a cardiac diagnosis (3 patients were siblings of a child with a cardiac diagnosis). Patients ranged in age from 6 months to 27 years old. Reasons for referral to psychology included: anxiety/depression ($n=49$, 29.7%); attention problems ($n=32$, 19.4%); learning problems ($n=24$, 14.5%); transplant-related care ($n=20$, 12.1%); behavior problems ($n=19$, 11.5%); coping with chronic illness ($n=11$; 6.7%); and developmental delay ($n=10$; 6.1%).

The most frequently used CPT codes by year are depicted in Table I. In general, the focus of the practice was on initial evaluations (90801—Diagnostic Evaluation; 96101—Psychological Testing; and 96150—Health and Behavior Assessment). Since many families lived a significant distance from the hospital, follow-up psychology services were often coordinated with a provider located closer to where the families resided. When follow-up services were provided, a majority of them focused on family interventions rather than individual therapy.

Payment rates for all outpatient psychology services provided in the pediatric cardiology clinic (including follow-up visits) were calculated by year, with separate analyses for health and behavior codes (CPT codes: 96150, 96151, 96152, 96154, and 96155) versus mental health codes (CPT codes: 90801, 90804, 90806, 90808, 90812, 90846, 90847, and 96101); these payment rates are reported in Figure 1. Overall payment rates for mental health CPT codes have ranged from 24% to 34% over the past 4 years, whereas payment rates for health and behavior CPT codes have ranged from 42% to 79%. While payment rates for health and behavior CPT codes have been consistently higher than payment rates for mental health CPT codes, it is important to note that payment rates for health and behavior codes have declined over the years. As the percent of charges based on health and behavior CPT codes has increased (from 8% of charges in FY 2007–2008 to 62% of charges in FY 2010–2011), the payment rate has decreased (from 79% in FY 2007–2008 to 42% in FY 2010–2011).

To further explore the reimbursement rate patterns, payments were also analyzed based on payer type (Medicaid or other government funded insurance programs vs. commercial/HMO/PPO insurance programs). These results are reported in Figure 2. Not surprisingly, commercial payers reimbursed at higher rates when compared to Medicaid or other government funded program, for both mental health and health and behavior CPT codes. However, it is concerning that Medicaid reimbursement rates for health and behavior codes ranged from only 8% to 17% (which is even lower than the Medicaid reimbursement rates for mental health codes), given that many children with chronic health conditions have Medicaid as their primary insurance. In our study, the percentage of charges to Medicaid varied by year: 54% in FY 2007–2008; 35% in FY 2008–2009; 50% in FY 2009–2010; and 41% in FY 2010–2011.

Conclusions/Implications

There are several limitations to the current study. It is based on a single psychologist's experience at one institution, practicing within a very specialized setting (pediatric cardiology outpatient clinic). Therefore, it is not clear whether the findings are representative of what other pediatric psychologists, who work with different pediatric

Table I. *Most Frequently Used CPT Codes by Year*

CPT Code	FY 2007–2008 (%)	FY 2008–2009 (%)	FY 2009–2010 (%)	FY 2010–2011 (%)
90801 Diagnostic Evaluation	28	21	22	22
90806 Individual Therapy (45–50 min)	13	14	1	2
90847 Family Therapy	22	26	33	11
96101 Psychological Testing	25	8	12	11
96150 Health and Behavior Assessment	3	9	13	24
96152 Health and Behavior Intervention (Individual)	2	0	7	6
96154 Health and Behavior Intervention (Family with patient)	0	6	4	17

Note. FY = fiscal year.

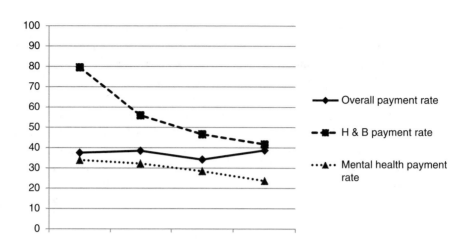

Figure 1. Payment rate by year.

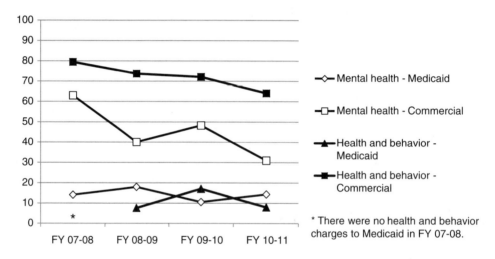

Figure 2. Yearly payment rate based on payer and CPT code.

populations, and practice in other states, have experienced when utilizing health and behavior or mental health codes.

Nevertheless, the results of this report do highlight a number of important issues. While the hope was that using health and behavior codes would result in improved reimbursement rates for pediatric psychology services (Noll & Fischer, 2004), this only was the case for children who had commercial insurance. A significant problem remains in that Medicaid's reimbursement of these codes in our state was less than 20%. Despite concerted efforts to improve reimbursement rates (by hiring an insurance verification specialist, getting preauthorization for services, and verifying what types of codes are billable), it has been our experience that if a significant portion of the patients seen by the pediatric psychologist have Medicaid as their primary insurance (and this number is increasing, given current economic conditions), the revenue generated will not be sufficient to offset the costs of the psychologist's salary. Thus, increased access to psychology services for patients with chronic health conditions will only be possible if there are outsides sources of revenue (besides billing) to offset the cost of hiring (and retaining) psychologists.

An additional proposed advantage of the health and behavior codes is that they come out of the patient's medical benefits, and are not supposed to require preauthorization. We have not found this to be the case. We continue to need to get prior authorization to use these codes, and some insurance companies still do not recognize them, even though they have now been active for nearly 10 years.

It is concerning that reimbursement rates for psychology services have declined over the four year period. Part of this may relate to the increase in the percent of patients who have Medicaid; because Medicaid's reimbursement rates are so low, particularly for health and behavior codes, this lowers the overall payment rate. The decrease in payment rates may also reflect changes in contracts with commercial payers. On average, we have increased our charges by approximately 5% per year, but our contracted payment rates have not increased at this rate. Many insurance companies have a set amount that they will reimburse for a particular code, regardless of our charge.

Finally, it is important to recognize that using health and behavior codes will not be appropriate in all circumstances. Even though a majority of the patients in this study had a medical diagnosis, over 80% of them were referred for a mental health reason. Many pediatric psychologists provide traditional mental health services, such as psychological testing, in additional to behavioral health interventions; thus adequate reimbursement for all types of services that psychologists provide is critical.

It appears that there is much work that remains to be done in order to improve patient access to psychology services and improve reimbursement for these services. In our experience, it has been helpful to have an insurance verification specialist to get information about patient benefits and determine which CPT codes are authorized prior to the patient's appointment. In some circumstances, the insurance verification specialist has been able to educate insurance companies about the health and behavior codes and why they are appropriate to use in certain cases. It has also been important to have designated people in our billing and collections office who are specialists in psychology billing, as billing codes used by psychologists differ significantly from those used by physicians. These billing specialists provide the psychologists at our institution with annual training regarding changes in CPT codes. In addition, they periodically audit our charts to make sure that documentation meets standards to capture charges at the highest rates.

Puente (2011) suggests that in order to remain economically viable as a profession, psychology needs to embrace not only "mental health", but "health" in general; pediatric psychology already does this. Going forward, psychologists need to be active in forming public policy with respect to how "quality health care" is defined (DeLeon & Kazdin, 2010; Levant, Tanner House, May, & Smith, 2006; Tovian, 2004). With the Patient Protection and Affordable Care Act (2010), there will be increased emphasis on improving access to comprehensive health care services, including services provided by psychologists. As there will also be increased emphasis on reducing health care costs, psychologists need to continue to demonstrate effectiveness as a profession in reducing health care costs and improving health outcomes. It is likely that payment for all health care services, including those for psychologists, will change from the fee-for-service system that we know. There is discussion of "global payments" to interdisciplinary teams who provide services (Nutting et al., 2011). Psychologists need to be involved when team-based reimbursement rates are outlined (Rozensky, 2011). This is a time of great change in health care; it is critical that we continue to advocate for ourselves and our patients as these changes unfold.

Acknowledgments

I would like to acknowledge Pam Dorna and Kristen Andersen for their assistance with preparation of this manuscript.

Conflicts of interest: None declared.

References

Brosig, C. L., Mussatto, K. A., Kuhn, E. M., & Tweddell, J. S. (2007a). Neurodevelopmental outcome in preschool survivors of complex congenital heart disease: Implications for clinical practice. *Journal of Pediatric Health Care, 21*, 3–12.

Brosig, C. L., Mussatto, K. A., Kuhn, E. M., & Tweddell, J. S. (2007b). Psychosocial outcomes for preschool children and families after surgery for complex congenital heart disease. *Pediatric Cardiology, 28*, 255–262.

Brosig, C. L., & Zahrt, D. M. (2006). Evolution of an inpatient pediatric psychology consultation service: Issues related to reimbursement and the use of health and behavior codes. *Journal of Clinical Psychology in Medical Settings, 13*, 425–429.

DeLeon, P. H., & Kazdin, A. E. (2010). Public policy: Extending psychology's contributions to national priorities. *Rehabilitation Psychology, 55*, 311–319.

Hoffman, J. I., & Kaplan, S. (2002). The incidence of congenital heart disease. *Journal of the American College of Cardiology, 39*, 1890–1900.

Karsdorp, P. A., Everaerd, W., Kindt, M., & Mulder, B. J. (2007). Psychological and cognitive functioning in children and adolescents with congenital heart disease: a meta-analysis. *Journal of Pediatric Psychology, 32*, 527–554.

Landolt, M. A., Valsangiacomo Buechel, E. R., & Latal, B. (2008). Health-related quality of life in children and adolescents after open-heart surgery. *Journal of Pediatrics, 152*, 349–355.

Lawoko, S., & Soares, J. (2003). Quality of life among parents of children with congenital heart disease, parents of children with other diseases and parents of healthy children. *Quality of Life Research, 12,* 655–666.

Levant, R. F., Tanner House, A., May, S., & Smith, R. (2006). Cost offset: Past, present, and future. *Psychological Services, 3,* 195–207.

Noll, R. B., & Fischer, S. (2004). Commentary. Health and behavior CPT codes: An opportunity to revolutionize reimbursement in pediatric psychology. *Journal of Pediatric Psychology, 29,* 571–578.

Nutting, P. A., Crabtree, B. F., Miller, W. L., Stange, K. C., Stewart, E., & Jaen, C. (2011). Transforming physician practices to patient-centered medical homes: lessons from the national demonstration project. *Health Affairs, 30,* 439–445.

Puente, A. E. (2011). Psychology as a health care profession. *American Psychologist, 66,* 781–792.

Rozensky, R. H. (2011). The institution of the institutional practice of psychology: Health care reform and psychology's future workforce. *American Psychologist, 66,* 797–808.

Snookes, S. H., Gunn, J. K., Eldridge, B. J., Donath, S. M., Hunt, R. W., Galea, M. P., & Shekerdemian, L. (2010). A systematic review of motor and cognitive outcomes after early surgery for congenital heart disease. *Pediatrics, 125,* e818–e827.

Tovian, S. M. (2004). Health services and health care economics: The health psychology marketplace. *Health Psychology, 23,* 138–141.

Tweddell, J. S., Nersesian, M., Mussatto, K. A., Nugent, M., Simpson, P., Mitchell, M. E., ... Hoffman, G. M. (2009). Fontan palliation in the modern era: Factors impacting mortality and morbidity. *Annals of Thoracic Surgery, 88,* 1291–1299.

Uzark, K., & Jones, K. (2003). Parenting stress and children with heart disease. *Journal of Pediatric Health Care, 17,* 163–168.

Wernovsky, G., Shillingford, A. J., & Gaynor, J. W. (2005). Central nervous system outcomes in children with complex congenital heart disease. *Current Opinions in Cardioogy, 20,* 94–99.

Commentary: Examination of Health and Behavioral Code Reimbursement From Private Payers in the Context of Clinical Multidisciplinary Pediatric Obesity Treatment

Bethany J. Sallinen,[1] PhD, and Susan J. Woolford,[1,2] MD, MPH

[1]Department of Pediatrics and Communicable Diseases and [2]Child Health Evaluation and Research (CHEAR) Unit, University of Michigan

All correspondence concerning this article should be addressed to Bethany J. Sallinen, PhD, Department of Pediatrics and Communicable Diseases, University of Michigan, Division of Child Behavioral Health, 1500 E. Medical, Center Drive, SPC 5318, Ann Arbor, MI, 48109-5318, USA. E-mail: bsalline@med.umich.edu

Received December 15, 2011; revisions received and accepted January 20, 2012

In response to the epidemic of childhood obesity, the University of Michigan Health System developed the Pediatric Comprehensive Weight Management Center (PCWMC). Due to a large demand for obesity services across the economic spectrum, but particularly for low-income adolescents, our health system determined that clinical multidisciplinary weight management services should be accessible to all potential patients without regard to their ability to pay. Subsequently, the PCWMC obtained approval to use the charity care screening exception which allows care to be provided using a sliding scale (starting at zero for low income patients). The charity care screening exception is an institutional policy for patients who do not have insurance and who have an inability to pay for healthcare as determined primarily by the United States federal poverty level guidelines. As such, patients in the program are screened by financial counsellors prior to entry to determine the amount they will be responsible for based on the sliding scale, over and above their insurance copays and deductibles. For example, patients may qualify for 100% adjustment of charges if their household income does not exceed 250% of the federal poverty level guidelines, and 55% adjustment if their household income is between 250% and 400% of the guidelines.

Following financial screening, all patients are scheduled for a comprehensive multidisciplinary initial assessment in the PCWMC. The multidisciplinary team includes a medical director (i.e., pediatrician), pediatric psychologist, exercise physiologist, dietitian, and social worker. Following a feedback session to review results obtained from the initial assessment, a decision is then made about joining a 6-month behavioral family-based weight management program. The adolescent program (Michigan Pediatric Outpatient Weight Evaluation and Reduction; MPOWER), described elsewhere (Woolford, Sallinen, Clark, & Freed, 2011), first started accepting patients in April 2007. Briefly, patients currently attend weekly 2-hr sessions for six months. One hour always includes group exercise for adolescents, led by an exercise physiologist. The second hour of the program includes a rotating schedule of group visits, with the monthly family nutrition group led by the dietitian, the parent behavioral group led by the psychologist, and the youth behavioral group led by the social worker. Families also participate in two 45-min individual sessions per month where they meet with two of the following providers: psychologist, exercise physiologist, dietitian, and social worker. In 2008, the PCWMC expanded its services by implementing the MPOWER JR program for patients 7 to 11 years old. This program is also six months in duration with weekly 2-hr sessions. The program is held at the local YMCA, which allows for parents to also exercise during the first hour with their children. The second hour of the session rotates between groups (i.e., separate for parents and children) and individual sessions. A comprehensive assessment of patients' progress (including repeat laboratory tests, psychological measures, exercise testing, and determination of body composition) is performed by the team at three and six months to provide feedback for families and to inform treatment decisions.

When the PCWMC was first created, it was decided that health and behavior codes would be the most appropriate way to bill for behavioral health services provided by the psychologist. This was informed in part by the seminal commentary by Noll and Fischer (2004) about use of health and behavior Current Procedural Terminology (CPT) codes in pediatric psychology. The medical diagnoses billed are typically abnormal weight gain and obesity. The psychologist provides initial assessments to all patients entering the program (charged as CPT 96150) and reassessments after three and six months of program participation (charged as CPT 96151). Interventions provided by the psychologist include behavioral group sessions once per month for each age group (charged as CPT 96153), and individual sessions with patients and/or their families to assist with tailoring behavior change techniques to promote achievement of healthy weight status (charged as CPT 96152, 96154, or 961155, depending on who is present).

Health and Behavior Code Collection Results From One Pediatric Psychologist

For the purpose of this commentary, data about collection for services billed by the pediatric psychologist using health and behavior codes was obtained for financial years 2008 through 2011. Michigan Medicaid (fee-for-service) does not enroll pediatric psychologists as health care professionals and thus does not reimburse health and behavior codes. As a result, description of collection obtained from health and behavior codes will be limited to private insurance carriers only, and will not include Medicaid (managed care or fee-for-service).

Figure 1 shows that total charges for all health and behavior codes combined (96150–96155) increased from Financial Year 2008 through 2011. Percent collection from private insurance for health and behavior codes also increased over the 4 years, from 21% in 2008 to 26% in 2011. Figure 2 shows the average percent collection from private insurance carriers for each CPT code charged across the 2008–2011 financial period. Percent collection was calculated by dividing the amount charged by the amount collected. On average, assessments had higher collection rates (35%) compared to interventions (23%) during this time period. It is unclear why we collected more from reassessments (40%) than initial assessments (30%). With respect to intervention, inspection of CPT codes reveal differences based on type of intervention. Overall, a lower percentage of charges were collected for groups (CPT code 96153) and interventions with parents alone (CPT code 96155), compared to individual interventions including patients (either CPT code 96152 or 96154). Interestingly, much of the empirical support for behavioral family-based weight management treatment grew out of randomized controlled trials examining group interventions (Epstein, Myers, Raynor, & Saelens, 1998). There is also emerging evidence to suggest that intervening with parents alone as the agent of change provides meaningful improvements in child weight status (Golan & Crow, 2004; Golan, Kaufman, & Shahar, 2006; Janicke et al., 2008; Janicke et al., 2009). Despite evidence for these approaches, reimbursement is lower compared to individual interventions including either predominately the patient (CPT 96152) or the patient and his/her family (CPT 96154).

Future Directions
Private Insurance Carriers

Overall, the rates of collection for health and behavior codes were higher than expected. Our pediatric weight management center does not currently obtain preauthorization for services. It is possible that enacting this practice would increase the percentage of charges

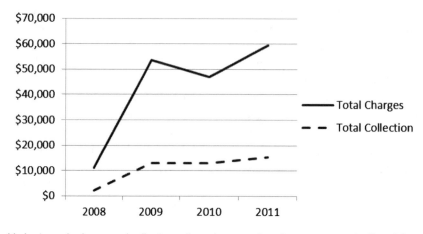

Figure 1. Total health and behavior code charges and collection collapsed across private insurance payor for financial years 2008–2011.

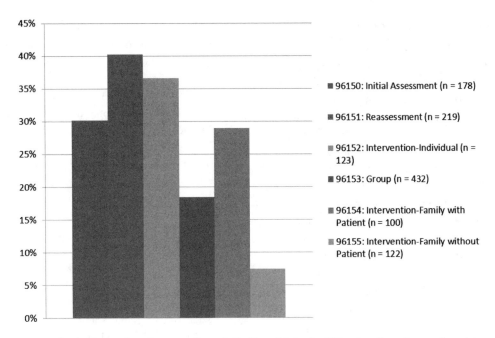

Figure 2. Average percent collection from private insurance for each Health and Behavior CBT code collapsed across financial year (2008–2011).

collected; however, the extent to which this would be impacted by payer mix and other factors such as benefit restrictions, patient cost share, copays, and deductibles is unknown. We plan to explore this moving forward.

Medicaid

The state of Michigan does not reimburse health and behavior codes to PhD level providers, such as psychologists. In light of the fact that obesity disproportionately affects low income populations, there is certainly a need for psychologists and other leaders to support efforts for reimbursement of behavioral health services for obese children who are recipients of Medicaid. This will likely require presentation of data to Medicaid. Efforts may be bolstered by involving and partnering with the American Psychological Association (APA) Practice Directorate, as similar advocacy campaigns are underway. Specifically, their website offers a section dedicated to health and behavior codes. Included in this section is a sample letter to insurance companies to assist with advocating for reimbursement. Similarly, psychologists are encouraged to contact the APA Practice Directorate's Government Relations Office with any difficulties experienced with billing these codes.

Health and Behavior CPT Codes

Collection rates appear to vary in our weight management center for different types of assessments and interventions. It is interesting that our 3- and 6-month reassessments obtained greater rates of collection compared to our initial assessment. The next step would be to examine rates of collection at the individual insurance carrier level to determine if rates of collection differ by carrier and are thus driving this result. With respect to treatment, it is disappointing that we received relatively low rates of collection for groups and provision of individual intervention with parents alone. These treatment approaches are included in the 2007 Expert Committee recommendations for the prevention, assessment, and treatment of childhood obesity (Barlow & The Expert Committee, 2007). Insurers should be encouraged to cover these recommended services. As pediatric psychologists we need to promote these specific mechanisms through which to deliver evidenced-based treatment. This may include educating insurance carriers about different models of treatment delivery and presenting data to support delivering obesity treatment via groups and sessions with parents alone. Education may occur via letters to insurance companies and/or scheduling meetings where data can be presented. If these attempts are unsuccessful, administrators within large institutions where pediatric psychologists are working, such as medical centers, may be able to facilitate efforts to connect with insurance companies. In fact, when our PCWMC was first being developed, the administration at our institution was involved with presentations made to insurers in an effort to increase coverage. Although rates of collection were higher for individual interventions involving patients, rates could clearly improve and thus may benefit from similar advocacy efforts.

Pediatric Obesity Multidisciplinary Treatment

As part of FOCUS on a Fitter Future, convened by the National Association of Children's Hospitals and Related Institutions (NACHRI), senior administrators of member hospitals were surveyed about their pediatric obesity programs. The most frequently cited challenge was lack of reimbursement (Eneli et al., 2011). This challenge is echoed by many others involved in the treatment of obese youth (Edwards & Schwarzenberg, 2009; Griffith, Gantz, Lowry, Dai, & Bada, 2007; Simpson & Cooper, 2009; Tershakovec, Watson, Wenner, & Marx, 1999), although most research is aimed at examining reimbursement for medical services rather than psychological services. Limited data is available about reimbursement for behavioral health services provided by psychologists in weight management. Pediatric psychologists, as experts in health behavior change, play an important role in the assessment and treatment of obese youth, and are an integral part of clinical multidisciplinary obesity treatment teams. In order for pediatric psychologists to continue their presence in multidisciplinary treatment, collection for services provided needs to be demonstrated. Using health and behavior codes to bill for weight management services provided by a pediatric psychologist appears to be a viable option. As psychologists we need to get involved in advocacy efforts with insurance companies in order to increase acceptance and reimbursement for health and behavior codes. This will ultimately provide more children with access to behavioral health services that have been demonstrated to have a significant positive impact on their health and quality of life.

Acknowledgments

The author expresses appreciation to Pam Egbert for providing data about the use and reimbursement of health and behavior codes by third-party payors in the Pediatric Comprehensive Weight Management Center, and to Ilene Phillips for her thoughts regarding the interpretation of the data.

Conflicts of interest: None declared.

References

Barlow, S. E.; The Expert Committee. (2007). Expert committee recommendations regarding the prevention, assessment, and treatment of child and adolescent overweight and obesity: Summary report. *Pediatrics, 120*, S164–S192.

Edwards, N. M., & Schwarzenberg, S. J. (2009). Designing and implementing an effective pediatric weight management program. *Reviews in Endocrine and Metabolic Disorders, 10*, 197–203.

Eneli, I., Norwood, V., Hampl, S., Ferris, M., Hibbeln, T., Patterson, K., ... Hassink, S. (2011). Perspectives on obesity programs at children's hospitals: Insights from senior program administrators. *Pediatrics, 128*, S86–S90.

Epstein, L. H., Myers, M. D., Raynor, H. A., & Saelens, B. E. (1998). Treatment of pediatric obesity. *Pediatrics, 101*, 554–570.

Golan, M., & Crow, S. (2004). Targeting parents exclusively in the treatment of childhood obesity: Long-term results. *Obesity Research, 12*, 357–361.

Golan, M., Kaufman, V., & Shahar, D. R. (2006). Childhood obesity treatment: Targeting parents exclusively v. parents and children. *British Journal of Nutrition, 95*, 1008–1015.

Griffith, J., Gantz, S., Lowry, J., Dai, H., & Bada, H. (2007). Insurance reimbursement in a university-based pediatric weight management clinic. *Journal of the National Medical Association, 99*, 1037–1041.

Janicke, D. M., Sallinen, B. J., Perri, M. G., Lutes, L. D., Huerta, M., Silverstein, J. H., & Brumback, B. (2008). Comparison of parent-only vs family-based interventions for overweight children in underserved rural settings: Outcomes from project STORY. *Archives of Pediatric and Adolescent Medicine, 162*, 1119–1125.

Janicke, D. M., Sallinen, B. J., Perri, M. G., Lutes, L. D., Silverstein, J. H., & Brumback, B. (2009). Comparison of program costs for parent-only and family-based interventions for pediatric obesity in medically underserved rural settings. *Journal of Rural Health, 25*, 326–330.

Noll, R. B., & Fischer, S. (2004). Commentary. Health and behavior CPT codes: An opportunity to revolutionize reimbursement in pediatric psychology. *Journal of Pediatric Psychology, 29*(7), 571–578.

Simpson, L. A., & Cooper, J. (2009). Paying for obesity: A changing landscape. *Pediatrics, 123*, S301–S307.

Tershakovec, A. M., Watson, M. H., Wenner, W. J., & Marx, A. L. (1999). Insurance reimbursement for the treatment of obesity in children. *Journal of Pediatrics, 134*, 573–578.

Woolford, S. J., Sallinen, B. J., Clark, S. J., & Freed, G. L. (2011). Results from a clinical multidisciplinary weight management program. *Clinical Pediatrics, 50*, 187–191.

Preliminary Evaluation of Maternal Caregiver Stress in Pediatric Eosinophilic Gastrointestinal Disorders

Tiffany H. Taft, PsyD, Sarah Ballou, BA, and Laurie Keefer, PhD
Division of Gastroenterology, Northwestern University Feinberg School of Medicine

All correspondence concerning this article should be addressed to Tiffany Taft, PsyD, Division of Gastroenterology, 676 N. Saint Clair Street, Suite 1400, Chicago, IL, 60611, USA.
E-mail: ttaft@northwestern.edu

Received April 22, 2011; revisions received December 12, 2011; accepted December 14, 2011

Objective To characterize caregiver stress (CS) in parents of children with Eosinophilic Gastrointestinal Disorders (EGIDs) and understand relationships with psychological functioning and child behavior. **Methods** Caregivers with a child (0–17 years) with EGID completed questionnaires for demographics, EGID severity, treatments, CS, psychological distress, self-efficacy, and child behaviors. **Results** A total of 163 caregivers (98% mother, 94% Caucasian) participated. CS correlated with psychological distress, income, child behavioral problems, treatments, and disease severity. Children were rated higher than age-specific norms for emotional difficulties. Behavioral difficulties associated with gender, age, EGID severity, and duration. Parent psychological distress was most strongly associated with CS. Parental self-efficacy, dietary treatments, and child emotional difficulties were also related to stress. **Conclusions** Mothers reported stress and psychological distress from caring for a child with EGID. The relationship between these variables suggests these parents may benefit from supportive psychotherapy interventions. Evaluation of parental self-efficacy and child behavior is also warranted.

Key words child behavior; eosinophilic gastrointestinal disorders; parental caregiver stress; psychological functioning.

Introduction

Eosinophilic Gastrointestinal Disorders (EGIDs) are chronic diseases of the digestive system, characterized by inflammation due to an increase in the number of *eosinophils* (white blood cells) in the mucosal lining of the gastrointestinal tract. When there is a disruption to the gastrointestinal environment, eosinophils engulf and kill harmful bacteria. In EGID patients, eosinophils fail to die off after they complete this process and instead permeate the mucosal lining of the gut, leading to gastrointestinal symptoms, tissue damage and chronic inflammation. Variations of eosinophilic disorders depend on the location of eosinophil infiltration and include: Esophagitis (esophagus), Gastritis (stomach/intestinal tract), Enteritis (small intestine), Gastroenteritis (diffuse throughout GI tract), and Colitis (large intestine) (Oh & Chetty, 2008; Verheijden & Ennecker-Jans, 2010). Some common EGID symptoms are abdominal pain, diarrhea, acid reflux, dysphagia (difficulty swallowing), nausea, and vomiting (Kelly & Hewson, 2000). Symptoms vary depending on the location of the disease as well as the age of the patient (Eroglu et al., 2009; Liacouras, 2003; Spergel et al., 2009).

Over the past decade, EGIDs have gained increasing attention due to steadily rising global prevalence (Franciosi, 2009; Noel, Putnam, & Rothenberg, 2004). The majority of these data are for Eosinophilic Esophagitis (EoE), with considerably less information available for the other EGID subtypes. Pediatric EoE occurs in approximately four out of every 10,000 children (Noel et al., 2004). The age of initial diagnosis varies widely (0–18 years, mean 6.2 years), with higher rates in Caucasians (84%) and males (75%). (Assa'ad et al., 2007;

Eroglu et al., 2009; Franciosi, Tam, Liacouras, & Spergel, 2009; Spergel et al., 2009). Accurate EGID diagnosis can be challenging, often requiring patients to undergo several invasive procedures including food allergy testing, colonoscopy, or upper endoscopy.

Current EGID treatments are intensive, require significant parental monitoring, and are not always satisfactorily effective (Liacouras, 2003; Liacouras et al., 2011). These aim to reduce exposure to antigens that would disrupt the gastrointestinal environment and cause eosinophils to proliferate. Given the high incidence of food sensitivities in EGID patients, many treatments target inflammatory reactions to food antigens. Corticosteroid treatment or steroid-sparing agents directly target the inflammation in the gut (Liacouras, 2003; Oh & Chetty, 2008). Dietary treatments include food elimination, formula-based diets, and gastric tube feedings (Assa'ad, 2009; Pratt, Demain, & Rathkopf, 2008). Food introduction trials involve elimination of the top eight allergy-producing foods (dairy, soy, eggs, wheat/gluten, peanuts, tree nuts, fish, and shellfish) for a period of several weeks followed by a systematic reintroduction of one food at a time to the child's diet. In some children, additional foods are involved in invoking inflammatory responses, creating a longer and more complicated reintroduction trial.

The behavioral and psychological consequences associated with pediatric chronic illness are widespread (Farnik et al., 2010; Klinnert, 2009; Wiedebusch et al., 2010). Chronically, ill children often display increased behavioral and psychological problems as a result of their condition (Hysing, Sivertsen, Stormark, Elgen, & Lundervold, 2009; Louis-Jacques & Samples, 2011; Reynolds & Helgeson, 2011). Caregivers of these children report lower quality of life, greater personal health concerns (Brehaut et al., 2009; Farnik et al., 2010; Murphy, Christian, Caplin, & Young, 2007), limit their activities, and have increased depression, marital issues, and family problems (Brehaut et al., 2009; Murphy et al., 2007).

Based on the intensity of EGID symptoms and treatments, we expect similar challenges to be present in this population. Adult EGID patients report challenges in managing their illness that adversely impact health-related quality of life (Taft, Kern, Keefer, Burstein, & Hirano, 2011; Taft, Kern, Kwiatek, et al., 2011). A recent pediatric study found that both parents and children have multiple disease-specific concerns about managing an EGID (Franciosi et al., 2011). These concerns differed from general measures of quality of life, highlighting the need to investigate the unique experiences of children with EGIDs and their parents.

To date, no study has evaluated the role of caregiver stress (CS) in children with EGIDs. Understanding this phenomenon in these patients is important since poor caregiver health and distress has a direct impact on the child, including more hospitalizations (Kelly & Hewson, 2000), more functional disability (Streisand, Swift, Wickmark, Chen, & Holmes, 2005), and possibly more behavioral problems (Hilliard, Monaghan, Cogen, & Streisand, 2011). As CS is often associated with increased psychological distress (Hauenstein, 1990; Yee & Schulz, 2000) and may be mediated by levels of perceived self-efficacy (Keefe et al., 2003; Zeiss, Gallagher-Thompson, Lovett, Rose, & McKibbin, 1999), it is important to assess these factors when understanding CS in this population. The main goals of this study are to: (a) characterize CS, psychological distress and self-efficacy in parents of children with EGIDs; (b) characterize behavioral difficulties in children with EGIDs; and (c) evaluate the relationships between CS, psychological distress, self-efficacy, and child behavior.

Patients and Methods
Participant Recruitment

Caregivers aged 18–70 years with a child between the ages of 0 and 17 years diagnosed with an EGID were recruited via two patient advocacy groups: (a) the American Partnership for Eosinophilic Disorders website (http://www.apfed.org) parent support group listing and (b) The Campaign Urging Research for Eosinophilic Disease Foundation. Support group administrators were emailed with study information to disseminate to group members. Parents of either gender who were responsible for caring for the child with EGID met inclusion criteria outlined in the recruitment email. Nineteen support groups located across the United States received the initial inquiry. Of these, twelve (63%) responded and agreed to share the study information with group members, two email addresses were invalid, and 5 did not respond to the initial contact. This study was approved by the institutional review board of Northwestern University.

Demographic and Clinical Backgrounds

A total of 192 caregivers consented and 163 completed study measures (Completion rate = 85%). Demographic and clinical data (Table I) were normally distributed with the exception of parental education. Thirty-one children (19%) were under the age of 3 years. Most children in this sample used EGID medications, with 54% using a proton pump inhibitor (e.g. omeprazole), 45% oral or inhaled steroids, 27% Montelukast, and 25% an acid reducer. Dietary therapies were common, with more than half

Table I. Sample Demographic & Clinical Variables

Variable	N = 163
Parent demographics	
Female	98%
Mother to child	98%
Age (years; mean ± SD)	38.5 ± 7.0
No. of children with EGID	
1	83%
2	15%
3 or more	2%
Caucasian	94%
Non-Hispanic	98%
Married/cohabitating	90%
Education (years)[a]	16.0
Family Income	
$10 K–$40 K	23%
$41 K–$85 K	36%
>$85 K	41%
Urban/suburban dweller	83%
Child demographics	
Male	72%
Age	7.7 ± 5.1
Grade in School	
PreK or Earlier	45%
1–6	31%
7–12	24%
>9 Missed School Days	37%
Child clinical variables	
EGID Dx (years)	6.1 ± 4.0
>12 months to Dx	50%
Have EGID Symptoms Every Day	45%
Recent Flare Severity (out of 10)	6.0 ± 2.6
No. of food sensitivities	12.1 ± 8.0
Current remission	28%
No. of medications	
1–3	64%
4–9	20%
>4 Procedures (past year)	27%
>4 MD appointments (past year)	85%
Dietary treatments (last 30 days)	
Elimination diet	58%
Elemental diet	22%
Elemental formula diet	51%
Food reintroduction trial	35%
Feeding tube use (last 30 days)	23%

[a]Nonnormal distribution presented as median.

using one in the past 30 days, and 23% utilizing a feeding tube within this timeframe.

Measures

All participants completed online questionnaires. Caregivers self-reported all information about themselves and one child with EGID. Cookies were used to prevent participants from completing the survey more than once, with Internet protocol address logging and review to identify duplicate entries for removal.

Caregiver Demographic Information
Gender, relationship to child, ethnicity, race, age, marital status, education, family income, and town population.

Child Information
Gender, age, school grade, number of years with EGID, months from symptom presentation to receive diagnosis, number of food sensitivities, all EGID symptom frequency in a given week, remission status, most recent flare severity (scale of 1 "most mild" to 10 "most severe"), current medications, and dietary therapies including a general question about the child being on a restricted diet for EGID in the last 30 days. Number of missed school days, doctor visits, procedures, and emergency room visits in the past year were collected.

CS
Caregivers completed the Pediatric Inventory for Parents (PIP), a 42-item self-report measure of frequency of and difficulty with various caregiver-specific stressors over the last 7 days. These are categorized by Communication, Emotional Functioning, Medical Care, and Role Function (Streisand, Braniecki, Tercyak, & Kazak, 2001). The PIP yields four subscale scores, a total frequency score, and total difficulty score with higher scores indicating greater CS. The PIP demonstrates excellent reliability (α from .80 to .96) and validity across several illness groups and is considered a "well-established" measure by evidence-based assessment standards (Alderfer et al., 2008). The PIP demonstrated excellent internal consistency in this sample (Cronbach's α: Frequency = 0.95, Difficulty = 0.95).

Caregiver Psychological Distress
The Brief Symptom Inventory-18 (BSI-18) measured caregivers' psychological distress, yielding a global severity index and three symptom scales: depression, anxiety, and somatization (Derogatis & Melisaratos, 1983). Higher scores indicate more distress. The BSI-18 demonstrates good reliability (Cronbach's α for global severity = 0.89; somatization = 0.74; depression = 0.84; anxiety = 0.89) and validity. For the current sample, Cronbach's α values for the global scale (0.92) and each subscale ($S = 0.82$, $D = 0.86$, $A = 0.86$) were good. Established clinical cutoff scores for significant pathology are ≥ 13 for women and ≥ 10 for men on all subscales (Derogatis, 2000).

Caregiver Self-Efficacy

The General Self-Efficacy Scale (GSES) measured caregivers' belief in their ability to cope with a variety of difficult life demands (i.e. perceived self-efficacy). Ten items are answered via a 4-point Likert scale. The GSES is available in 30 languages and is a widely used unidimensional measure of general perceived self-efficacy. The GSES consistently demonstrates excellent reliability (α from .76 to .90) and validity (Schwarzer, 1995) across multiple cultures (Scholz, Dona, Sud, & Schwarzer, 2002). Reliability statistics for the current sample were consistent with previously reported data (Cronbach's $\alpha = 0.89$). Normative data are available for a US sample of 1,594 adults.

Child Behavioral Difficulties

The Strengths and Difficulties Questionnaire (SDQ) (Goodman, 1997) measured behavioral attributes of the child with EGID as perceived by the participant caregiver. The SDQ is a 25-item measure with five subscales: Emotional Symptoms, Conduct Problems, Hyperactivity/Inattention, Peer Relationship Problems, and Prosocial Behavior. There are three age-specific versions to the SDQ (3–4, 5–10, and 11–17 years). Normative data for the SDQ are available by age and country. The SDQ demonstrates acceptable reliability (subscale α from .51 to .76) and validity. In the current sample, Cronbach α scores for each subscale were adequate (Emotional = 0.69, Conduct = 0.60, Hyperactive = 0.84, Peer = 0.60, Prosocial = 0.68).

Data Analysis

Raw scores were exported from the online system and entered into the Statistical Package for the Social Sciences v19 (IBM-SPSS, Chicago IL, USA) for analysis. Data were sufficiently powered ($\geq .80$) for all analyses). Preliminary tests for normal distribution, outliers, and missing data were conducted. Independent measures t-tests and one-way ANOVA with Tukey's HSD post hoc testing evaluated differences between demographic groups on dependent variables. To ensure that parents of children under 3 years had sufficient experience with caring for a child with EGID, we divided the sample (0–2 years vs. 3 or more years of age) and compared the mean results for the PIP, BSI-18, and GSES via independent samples t-tests. No significant differences for outcome measures were found between the two age categories; thus all parents were included in analyses using these scales. We removed those children under the age of 3 years from analyses using the SDQ, since it is only validated for children aged 3 years and older. Pearson's correlations and stepwise multiple regressions evaluated the relationships between CS and psychological distress, self-efficacy, and child behavior.

Results

Parental CS, Psychological Distress, and Self-Efficacy

Mothers reported CS related to caring for a child with an EGID. Unmarried parents reported greater frequency of, $t(154) = -3.10$, $p = .002$), and difficulty with, $t(148) = -2.98$, $p = .003$, 95% CIs (-47.9 to -10.5) and (-44.4 to -9.0] CS. Those from households with lower income reported greater difficulty with CS, $F(8,148) = 2.43$, $p = .02$. Significant differences for CS were not found for parent age and education level. Increased CS was associated with higher psychological distress and lower self-efficacy (Table II). Several caregivers reported psychological distress above BSI-18 clinical cutoff scores, including approximately 25% reporting significant depression and somatization and 50% reporting significant anxiety. Caregivers had similar levels of perceived self-efficacy as U.S. normative controls.

Child Behavior

Children with an EGID were rated as having greater emotional difficulties (borderline or abnormal range) than US normative controls (Table III). Females demonstrated more emotional difficulties than males (Mean ± SD; 5.4 ± 2.6 vs. 4.4 ± 2.5), $t(136) = -2.02$, $p = .046$, 95% CI (-2.0 to -0.02), as did children not in remission (5.1 ± 2.4 vs. 3.7 ± 2.7), $t(136) = 3.02$, $p = .003$, 95% CI (0.48 to 2.3). Children aged 11 years and older rated poorer for peer problems while children under the age of 8 years exhibited more and hyperactivity/inattention. All age groups fell within the "Normal" range for conduct problems and prosocial behavior, although significantly lower than peers. Behavior ratings correlated with several child demographic and clinical variables (Table IV) including the number of procedures the child has had, time since the EGID diagnosis, and symptom severity.

Predictors of CS

Next, we analyzed the relationships between parent and child variables and CS frequency and difficulty via Pearson's correlations. Those with statistical significance at or below .05 were entered into a series of stepwise hierarchical regression models. Model 1 evaluated the relative contributions of parent and child variables to the frequency of CS; Model 2 repeated this regression with difficulty with CS as the criterion (Table V). For each model, Step 1 included the significantly correlated parent demographic

Table II. Means, Standard Deviations and Intercorrelations for CS, Psychological Distress, and Self-Efficacy Scores

Variable	M (SD)	Norm†	1	2	3	4
1. CS (PIP) Frequency—Total[e]	133.0 (32.2)	N/A	–	.69**	.57**	−.27**
Communication[a]	18.6 (4.8)					
Emotional function[b]	54.8 (12.5)					
Medical care[c]	26.1 (9.1)					
Role function[d]	34.6 (8.8)					
2. CS (PIP) Difficulty—Total[e]	135.4 (31.0)	N/A		–	.61**	−.26**
Communication[a]	17.1 (5.1)					
Emotional function[b]	55.3 (12.3)					
Medical care[c]	28.2 (8.0)					
Role function[d]	34.8 (8.9)					
3. Psychological distress (BSI-18)—Total[h]	34.0 (13.0)	≥ 13.0			–	−.24**
Depression[f]	11.1 (5.1)	28%				
Anxiety[g]	13.2 (5.6)	46%				
Somatization[g]	9.8 (4.3)	20%				
4. Perceived Self-Efficacy (GSES)[i]	31.1 (4.8)	29.5 ± 5.1				–

Note. Maximum possible score: [a]30, [b]80, [c]45, [d]55, [e]210, [f]25, [g]30, [h]85, [i]40.
†BSI-18: 1,122 (517 female) US adults. Established clinical cutoff score of 13.0 for female respondents on each subscale. GSES: 1,594 (49.1% female) US adults. PIP: normative data not currently available.
*P ≤ .05, **P ≤ .01.

variable (marital status), psychological distress, and self-efficacy; Step 2 included significantly correlated child demographic and clinical variables (recent flare severity, feeding tube use, number of medications, elemental formula use, elemental diet use); Step 3 included significantly correlated child behavior variables.

Parental psychological distress, child EGID flare severity, and child emotional difficulties remained significant predictors of both frequency and difficulty with CS. Psychological distress demonstrated the greatest predictive weight, accounting for 38% of the variance in frequency, and 44% of the variance in difficulty. Using a feeding tube as treatment for the EGID predicted frequency but not difficulty with CS, and parental self-efficacy showed a negative predictive relationship with frequency of CS.

Discussion

The EGIDs are emerging chronic conditions with an increasing prevalence in the past decade, garnering much needed attention to optimize their diagnosis and medical management. Only within the last year has focus shifted to include the psychosocial impact EGIDs may have. Our findings demonstrate a multifaceted relationship between the clinical presentation of the EGID, its treatment, CS, and child behavior. Mothers in the current sample appear to be experiencing significant CS and burden associated with these illnesses, warranting further inquiry in this area.

Certain demographic traits make caregivers more susceptible to CS, such as the child's gender (Holden, Chmielewski, Nelson, Kager, & Foltz, 1997), parent's age (Canning, Harris, & Kelleher, 1996), and socioeconomic status (Canning et al., 1996; Holden et al., 1997). We found lower family income and not being married were associated with increased CS. This may be due to costs often associated with EGID treatments, such as purchasing allergen-free foods or shopping at specialty stores (Taft, Kern, Keefer, et al., 2011), or increased costs from formulas, medications, or insurance copayments for multiple contacts with the medical system. Since our sample was mothers of children with EGIDs, CS may be associated with balancing work, home, and childcare responsibilities.

A modest percentage of caregivers had significant levels of psychological distress and decreased perceived self-efficacy, both associated with greater CS. These findings are similar to those identified among parents of children with Type 1 diabetes (Streisand et al., 2005). Parents of children with an EGID may benefit from interventions targeting comorbid depression or anxiety which may be impacting their ability to cope effectively with CS. Treatments should also seek to improve parental self-efficacy, especially as it relates to managing their child's EGID.

We also sought to evaluate parent-rated behavior in children with EGIDs. The greatest difference found when compared to same-age peers was for emotional difficulties across all age groups. Younger children were rated higher

Table III. SDQ Scores of Children With EGID Versus 9,878 Normative Controls[a] (United States) by Age Group

SDQ Scale	Age group	U.S. norms[b]	EGID children[c]	P	95% CI	EGID class
Emotional difficulties	4–7	1.5 ± 1.7	4.1 ± 2.5	All	−2.9 to −2.3	Borderline
	8–10	1.5 ± 1.9	4.9 ± 2.8	<.00001	−1.2 to 0.4	Abnormal
	11–14	1.7 ± 2.0	5.3 ± 1.9		−3.9 to −3.3	Abnormal
	15–17	1.5 ± 1.8	5.4 ± 2.6		−4.2 to −3.6	Abnormal
Conduct problems	4–7	1.4 ± 1.6	2.3 ± 1.9	<.00001	−1.2 to −0.6	Normal
	8–10	1.3 ± 1.7	2.2 ± 1.3	<.01	−1.2 to −0.6	Normal
	11–14	1.4 ± 1.8	2.6 ± 2.0	<.001	−1.5 to −0.9	Normal
	15–17	1.2 ± 1.5	1.9 ± 1.4	<.03	−0.9 to −0.5	Normal
Hyperactivity inattention	4–7	3.2 ± 2.5	6.0 ± 3.0	All	−3.2 to −2.4	Borderline
	8–10	2.9 ± 2.6	5.4 ± 2.9	<.00001	−2.9 to −2.1	Normal
	11–14	2.7 ± 2.6	4.8 ± 3.0		−2.5 to −1.7	Normal
	15–17	2.3 ± 2.2	4.0 ± 3.2		−2.1 to −1.3	Normal
Peer problems	4–7	1.3 ± 1.5	2.2 ± 1.9	<.00001	−1.1 to −0.7	Normal
	8–10	1.5 ± 1.6	2.2 ± 1.5	<.03	−1.0 to −0.5	Normal
	11–14	1.4 ± 1.6	2.7 ± 2.1	<.00001	−1.6 to −1.0	Borderline
	15–17	1.4 ± 1.5	2.9 ± 2.0	<.0001	−1.7 to −1.3	Borderline
Prosocial behavior	4–7	8.4 ± 1.9	7.4 ± 1.8	<.0002	5.4 to 7.6	Normal
	8–10	8.8 ± 1.7	7.7 ± 1.6	<.001	0.8 to 1.4	Normal
	11–14	8.7 ± 1.8	7.7 ± 1.6	<.0004	0.7 to 1.3	Normal
	15–17	8.7 ± 1.6	7.5 ± 1.8	<.0003	0.9 to 1.5	Normal

[a]U.S. normative controls. Data obtained from the National Health Interview Survey (NHIS) conducted by the Centers for Disease Control in 2001. A total of 91% of reporters were parents.
[b]Sample size for normative age groups: 4–7, $n=2779$; 8–10, $n=2064$; 11–14, $n=2770$; 15–17, $n=2265$.
[c]Sample size for experimental age groups: 4–7, $n=58$; 8–10, $n=27$; 11–14, $n=28$; 15–17, $n=25$.

Table IV. Correlations between Child Demographic and Clinical Characteristics and Behavioral Ratings

Child variable	ED	HI	PP	CP	PB
Age	.26**	−.27**	.08	−.11	.19*
Years with EGID	.16*	−.09	−.06	−.07	.22**
No. of food allergies	−.02	.22**	.04	.08	−.15
Recent Flare Severity	.19*	.11	.18*	.14	−.02
No. of procedures past year	.02	.09	−.10	.19*	−.19*
No. of MD visits past year	.26**	.06	.09	.10	−.23**

Note. ED = emotional difficulties; HI = hyperactivity inattention; PP = peer problems; CD = conduct problems; PS = prosocial behavior.
*$P \leq .05$, **$P \leq .01$.

for hyperactivity-inattention, while older children demonstrated greater peer problems. While within the normal range, children with EGID demonstrated lower prosocial behavior and greater peer rejection than their peers. Parents may perceive their child is different from peers and thus attempt to protect their child by limiting social interactions. Alternatively, parents may see their child as being left out or avoidant of social events due to food restrictions that may make socializing challenging (Franciosi et al., 2011). Children with EGIDs may be susceptible to peer rejection due to being judged based on their illness status (Alderfer, Wiebe, & Hartmann, 2001), with children with more severe EGID symptoms or intrusive treatments experiencing greater peer rejection (Alderfer, Wiebe, & Hartmann, 2002). Cumulatively, these factors could lead to decreased social behavior in these children. Psychosocial interventions with these children should consider age-specific issues, whereas addressing overall emotional difficulties that are likely to be present.

Congruent with other pediatric illnesses such as cerebral palsy (Sipal, Schuengel, Voorman, Van Eck, & Becher, 2010), asthma, abdominal pain, and headaches (Feldman, Ortega, Koinis-Mitchell, Kuo, & Canino,

Table V. Stepwise Multivariate Analyses of Parental and Child Predictors of CS

Predictor variables	CS–frequency				CS–difficulty			
	r	R^2 Adj	ΔR^2	β	r	R^2 Adj	ΔR^2	β
Parent variables (Step 1)								
Global BSI-18	.58**	.36	.37	.60	.61**	.43	.43	.66
Self-efficacy	−.29**	.38	.02	−.15	−.26**			
Unmarried	.24**	.39	.02	.14	.24**			
Disease variables (Step 2)								
Recent Flare Severity	.26**	.45	.03	.15	.26**	.44	.01	.11
Feeding tube use	.21*	.43	.04	.19	.15			
No. of medications	.18*				.10			
Elemental formula	.18*				.15			
Elemental diet	.17*				.15			
Child behavior (Step 3)								
Emotional difficulty	.26**	.46	.01	.12	.25*	.46	.01	.10
Conduct problems	.16				.18*			
Hyperactivity	.09				.07			
Peer problems	.14				.14			
Prosocial behavior	−.16				−.13			

Betas reported are from the step at which the variable was entered into the equation.
*$P < .05$, **$P < .01$.

2010), CS is related to child behavior in this population. Children with EGIDs exhibiting greater emotional difficulties and conduct problems have parents who report greater CS. Conversely, children rated higher in prosocial behavior have parents with lower CS levels. Based solely on parent ratings, we cannot conclude children with EGID actually have greater behavioral problems or if parent CS and psychological distress influence perceptions of their child's behavior (Hilliard et al., 2011). Further inquiry into this relationship is warranted.

There are some limitations to this study to consider when interpreting its results. This study utilized a cross-sectional, nonexperimental design, and relied on self-report data from a single informant. Future studies utilizing prospective or longitudinal designs with input from multiple people in contact with the child would provide more in depth explanations of the preliminary relationships we have identified. We recruited caregivers from regional support group members with 100% online participation. It is possible these caregivers are more distressed or utilize coping strategies that differ from parents who do not use support groups. Parents seek support groups when their child exhibits more severe behavioral problems (Mandell & Salzer, 2007) or to gain information about their child's condition and available services (Koroloff & Friesen, 1991). Since EGIDs are emerging conditions, parents who join support groups may have less access to information about their child's condition, which could exacerbate CS levels. To improve generalizability of study findings, participants should be recruited via other sources such as outpatient pediatric general practice and pediatric gastroenterology clinics.

The study sample is essentially Caucasian mothers of children with an EGID, with the majority having a college education and all having Internet access thereby reflecting a sample likely from a higher socioeconomic status. Caution should be taken in applying these results to fathers and caregivers of other racial or ethnic backgrounds or those with less educational attainment. We did not differentiate between EGID diagnoses so we are unable to evaluate any potential differences by disease location. Current epidemiological data on EGIDs are evolving and vary by diagnosis, with eosinophilic esophagitis (EoE) being more prevalent in Caucasian males but eosinophilic gastroenteritis (a much rarer condition than EoE) being evenly distributed by gender and ethnicity; our sample paralleled EoE epidemiology data.

As the medical management of EGIDs evolves, it is important to acknowledge the role CS, psychological distress, or child behavior problems may have in outcomes, especially in refractory cases. Future research should seek to replicate these findings in more diverse samples and investigate interventions that may mitigate CS in EGIDs. Interventions should aim to alleviate parent CS and psychological distress via empirically supported methods (e.g., CBT, family systems therapy). Psychological treatment should also take into account the child's EGID symptom severity and treatment regimens. Specifically, parents of children using a feeding tube, on a greater number of medications, or being treated with an elemental diet may be at the highest risk for CS. Health care providers should be mindful of the effects of EGID treatments on both caregivers and the child and take care to engage the primary caregiver in the diagnostic and treatment processes.

Funding

This study was funded by a grant from the National Institutes of Health, USA (NIDDK U01 DK0077738 to Laurie Keefer).

Conflicts of interest: None declared.

References

Alderfer, M. A., Fiese, B. H., Gold, J. I., Cutuli, J. J., Holmbeck, G. N., Goldbeck, L., ... Patterson, J. (2008). Evidence-based assessment in pediatric psychology: Family measures. *Journal of Pediatric Psychology, 33*(9), 1046–1061.

Alderfer, M. A., Wiebe, D. J., & Hartmann, D. P. (2001). Social behaviour and illness information interact to influence the peer acceptance of children with chronic illness. *British Journal of Health Psychology, 6*(Pt 3), 243–255.

Alderfer, M. A., Wiebe, D. J., & Hartmann, D. P. (2002). Predictors of the peer acceptance of children with diabetes: Social behavior and disease severity. [Empirical Study]. *Journal of Clinical Psychology in Medical Settings, 9*(2), 121–130.

Assa'ad, A. (2009). Eosinophilic gastrointestinal disorders. *Allergy Asthma Proc, 30*(1), 17–22.

Assa'ad, A. H., Putnam, P. E., Collins, M. H., Akers, R. M., Jameson, S. C., Kirby, C. L., ... Rothenberg, M. E. (2007). Pediatric patients with esophagitis: An 8-year follow-up. *Journal of Allergy and Clinical Immunology, 119*(3), 731–738.

Brehaut, J. C., Kohen, D. E., Garner, R. E., Miller, A. R., Lach, L. M., Klassen, A. F., & Rosenbaum, P. L. (2009). Health among caregivers of children with health problems: Findings from a Canadian population-based study. *American Journal of Public Health, 99*(7), 1254–1262.

Canning, R. D., Harris, E. S., & Kelleher, K. J. (1996). Factors predicting distress among caregivers to children with chronic medical conditions. *Journal of Pediatric Psychology, 21*(5), 735–749.

Derogatis, L. R. (2000). *BSI-18: Administration, Scoring and Procedures Manual*. Minneapolis, MN: National Computer Systems.

Derogatis, L. R., & Melisaratos, N. (1983). The Brief Symptom Inventory: An introductory report. *Psychological Medicine, 13*(3), 595–605.

Eroglu, Y., Lu, H., Terry, A., Tendler, J., Knopes, B., Corless, C., ... Zhang, Z. (2009). Pediatric eosinophilic esophagitis: Single-center experience in northwestern USA. *Pediatrics International, 51*(5), 612–616.

Farnik, M., Brozek, G., Pierzchala, W., Zejda, J. E., Skrzypek, M., & Walczak, L. (2010). Development, evaluation and validation of a new instrument for measurement quality of life in the parents of children with chronic disease. *Health and Quality of Life Outcomes, 8*, 151.

Feldman, J. M., Ortega, A. N., Koinis-Mitchell, D., Kuo, A. A., & Canino, G. (2010). Child and family psychiatric and psychological factors associated with child physical health problems: Results from the Boricua youth study. *The Journal of Nervous and Mental Disease, 198*(4), 272–279.

Franciosi, J. P. (Producer). (2009, August 1, 2011). The Epidemiology of Eosinophilic Esophagitis. *Eosinophilic Gastrointestinal Disorders*. [Presentation].

Franciosi, J. P., Hommel, K. A., Debrosse, C. W., Greenberg, A. B., Greenler, A. J., Abonia, J. P., ... Varni, J. W. (2011). Quality of life in paediatric eosinophilic oesophagitis: What is important to patients? *Child: Care, Health and Development*, Advance online publication. doi:10.1111/j.1365-2214.2011.01265.x.

Franciosi, J. P., Tam, V., Liacouras, C. A., & Spergel, J. M. (2009). A case-control study of sociodemographic and geographic characteristics of 335 children with eosinophilic esophagitis. *Clinical Gastroenterology and Hepatology, 7*(4), 415–419.

Goodman, R. (1997). The strengths and difficulties questionnaire: A research note. *Journal of Child Psychology and Psychiatry, 38*(5), 581–586.

Hauenstein, E. J. (1990). The experience of distress in parents of chronically ill children: Potential or likely outcome? *Journal of Clinical Child Psychology, 19*(4), 356–364.

Hilliard, M. E., Monaghan, M., Cogen, F. R., & Streisand, R. (2011). Parent stress and child behaviour among young children with type 1 diabetes. *Child: Care, Health and Development, 37*(2), 224–232.

Holden, E. W., Chmielewski, D., Nelson, C. C., Kager, V. A., & Foltz, L. (1997). Controlling for general and disease-specific effects in child and family adjustment to chronic childhood illness. *Journal of Pediatric Psychology, 22*(1), 15–27.

Hysing, M., Sivertsen, B., Stormark, K. M., Elgen, I., & Lundervold, A. J. (2009). Sleep in children with chronic illness, and the relation to emotional and behavioral problems–a population-based study. *Journal of Pediatric Psychology, 34*(6), 665–670.

Keefe, F. J., Ahles, T. A., Porter, L. S., Sutton, L. M., McBride, C. M., Pope, M. S., ... Baucom, D. H. (2003). The self-efficacy of family caregivers for helping cancer patients manage pain at end-of-life. *Pain, 103*(1–2), 157–162.

Kelly, A. F., & Hewson, P. H. (2000). Factors associated with recurrent hospitalization in chronically ill children and adolescents. *Journal of Paediatrics and Child Health, 36*(1), 13–18.

Klinnert, M. D. (2009). Psychological impact of eosinophilic esophagitis on children and families. *Immunology And Allergy Clinics of North America, 29*(1), 99–107.

Koroloff, N. M., & Friesen, B. J. (1991). Support groups for parents of children with emotional disorders: A comparison of members and non-members. *Community Mental Health Journal, 27*(4), 265–279.

Liacouras, C. A. (2003). Eosinophilic esophagitis in children and adults. *Journal of Pediatric Gastroenterology and Nutrition, 37*(Suppl 1), S23–S28.

Liacouras, C. A., Furuta, G. T., Hirano, I., Atkins, D., Attwood, S. E., Bonis, P. A., ... Aceves, S. S. (2011). Eosinophilic esophagitis: Updated consensus recommendations for children and adults. *Journal of Allergy and Clinical Immunology, 128*(1), 3–20.

Louis-Jacques, J., & Samples, C. (2011). Caring for teens with chronic illness: Risky business? *Current Opinion in Pediatrics, 23*(4), 367–372.

Mandell, D. S., & Salzer, M. S. (2007). Who joins support groups among parents of children with autism? *Autism, 11*(2), 111–122.

Murphy, N. A., Christian, B., Caplin, D. A., & Young, P. C. (2007). The health of caregivers for children with disabilities: Caregiver perspectives. *Child: Care, Health and Development, 33*(2), 180–187.

Noel, R. J., Putnam, P. E., & Rothenberg, M. E. (2004). Eosinophilic esophagitis. *The New England Journal of Medicine, 351*(9), 940–941.

Oh, H. E., & Chetty, R. (2008). Eosinophilic gastroenteritis: A review. *Journal of Gastroenterology, 43*(10), 741–750.

Pratt, C. A., Demain, J. G., & Rathkopf, M. M. (2008). Food allergy and eosinophilic gastrointestinal disorders: Guiding our diagnosis and treatment. *Current Problems in Pediatric and Adolescent Health Care, 38*(6), 170–188.

Reynolds, K. A., & Helgeson, V. S. (2011). Children with diabetes compared to peers: Depressed? Distressed?: A meta-analytic review. *Annals of Behavioral Medicine, 42*(1), 29–41.

Scholz, U., Dona, B. G., Sud, S., & Schwarzer, R. (2002). Is general self-efficacy a universal construct? Psychometric findings from 25 countries. *European Journal of Psychological Assessment, 18*(3), 242–251.

Schwarzer, R., & Jerusalemm, M. (1995). Generalized Self-Efficacy Scale.

Sipal, R. F., Schuengel, C., Voorman, J. M., Van Eck, M., & Becher, J. G. (2010). Course of behaviour problems of children with cerebral palsy: The role of parental stress and support. *Child: Care, Health and Development, 36*(1), 74–84.

Spergel, J. M., Brown-Whitehorn, T. F., Beausoleil, J. L., Franciosi, J., Shuker, M., Verma, R., & Liacouras, C. A. (2009). 14 years of eosinophilic esophagitis: Clinical features and prognosis. *Journal of Pediatric Gastroenterology and Nutrition, 48*(1), 30–36.

Streisand, R., Braniecki, S., Tercyak, K. P., & Kazak, A. E. (2001). Childhood illness-related parenting stress: The pediatric inventory for parents. *Journal of Pediatric Psychology, 26*(3), 155–162.

Streisand, R., Swift, E., Wickmark, T., Chen, R., & Holmes, C. S. (2005). Pediatric parenting stress among parents of children with type 1 diabetes: The role of self-efficacy, responsibility, and fear. *Journal of Pediatric Psychology, 30*(6), 513–521.

Taft, T. H., Kern, E., Keefer, L., Burstein, D., & Hirano, I. (2011). Qualitative assessment of patient-reported outcomes in adults with eosinophilic esophagitis. *Journal of Clinical Gastroenterology, 45*(9), 769–774.

Taft, T. H., Kern, E., Kwiatek, M. A., Hirano, I., Gonsalves, N., & Keefer, L. (2011). The adult eosinophilic oesophagitis quality of life questionnaire: A new measure of health-related quality of life. *Alimentary Pharmacology & Therapeutics, 34*(7), 790–798.

Verheijden, N. A., & Ennecker-Jans, S. A. (2010). A rare cause of abdominal pain: Eosinophilic gastroenteritis. *Netherlands Journal of Medicine, 68*(11), 367–369.

Wiedebusch, S., Konrad, M., Foppe, H., Reichwald-Klugger, E., Schaefer, F., Schreiber, V., & Muthny, F. A. (2010). Health-related quality of life, psychosocial strains, and coping in parents of children with chronic renal failure. *Pediatr Nephrol, 25*(8), 1477–1485.

Yee, J. L., & Schulz, R. (2000). Gender differences in psychiatric morbidity among family caregivers: A review and analysis. *The Gerontologist, 40*(2), 147–164.

Zeiss, A., Gallagher-Thompson, D., Lovett, S., Rose, J., & McKibbin, C. (1999). Self-efficacy as a mediator of caregiver coping: Development and testing of an assessment model. [Empirical Study]. *Journal of Clinical Geropsychology, 5*(3), 221–230.

Treatment Adherence in Pediatric Eosinophilic Gastrointestinal Disorders

Kevin A. Hommel,[1,2,3,4] PhD, James P. Franciosi,[1,2,5] MD, MS, MSCE, Elizabeth A. Hente,[1,3,4] BA, Annette Ahrens,[1,6] BA, and Marc E. Rothenberg,[1,2,6] MD, PhD

[1]Cincinnati Children's Hospital Medical Center, [2]University of Cincinnati College of Medicine, [3]Center for the Promotion of Treatment Adherence and Self-Management, [4]Division of Behavioral Medicine and Clinical Psychology, [5]Division of Gastroenterology, Hepatology, and Nutrition, and [6]Division of Allergy and Immunology

All correspondence concerning this article should be addressed to Kevin A. Hommel, PhD, Center for the Promotion of Treatment Adherence and Self-Management, Division of Behavioral Medicine and Clinical Psychology, MLC-7039, Cincinnati Children's Hospital Medical Center, 3333 Burnet Avenue, Cincinnati, OH, 45229, USA. E-mail: kevin.hommel@cchmc.org

Received April 25, 2011; revisions received August 25, 2011; accepted September 27, 2011

Objective Examine treatment adherence rates in pediatric eosinophilic gastrointestinal disorders (EGID). **Methods** Participants were children aged 2.5–18 years with eosinophilic esophagitis or eosinophilic gastroenteritis (EGE) and their caregivers. A multimethod, multi-informant assessment including parent report and electronic monitoring was utilized, with a 90% cut point for nonadherence. **Results** Medication nonadherence prevalence was 30%. Adherence frequency was 91% ± 14% (0–100%) per parent report and 100% ± 69% (0–194%) per electronic monitors. Tube-feeding adherence was 99% ± 3%. Food allergen exposures were less than 1 per 2 weeks, with 33% nonadherence prevalence. Patients with EGE and toddlers with both conditions demonstrated poorer medication adherence (p's < .05). Caregivers reported higher number of missed medication doses than food exposures (p < .05). **Conclusions** The prevalence and range of nonadherence demonstrates that subsets of these patients are nonadherent. Adherence to treatment in EGID is complex and multifaceted, with nonadherence varying across treatments.

Key words adherence; compliance; eosinophil; gastrointestinal.

Introduction

Pediatric eosinophilic gastrointestinal disorders (EGID) are a group of chronic gastrointestinal tract inflammatory conditions that often require long-term medication and severe dietary restrictions of allergic foods. An endoscopic procedure is needed to take biopsies of the mucosa in the GI tract to establish the specific diagnosis. Two of the more common EGID conditions are eosinophilic esophagitis (EoE) and eosinophilic gastroenteritis (EGE). While EoE is characterized by elevated levels of eosinophils [i.e., 15 eosinophils/hpf (peak value) is considered a minimum threshold for a diagnosis of EoE] (Liacouras et al., 2011) and inflammation in the esophagus, EGE inflammation and eosinophil concentration is located primarily in the stomach and/or small intestine. In general, a diagnosis of EGE is based on above normal levels (DeBrosse, Case, Putnam, Collins, & Rothenberg, 2006) of eosinophils and their location in the GI tract. Patients with EoE experience symptoms including dysphagia, pain, food impaction, gastroesophageal reflux disease (GERD), and vomiting; patients with EGE may experience symptoms of pain, vomiting, and diarrhea. While there is no published practice guidelines for treatment of these disorders, an updated consensus recommendations for treatment has recently been published (Liacouras, et al., 2011). Therapies for these conditions include, but are not limited to, oral medication in pill form, swallowed steroid therapies (e.g., swallowed fluticasone using a metered dose inhaler designed for asthma treatment) to topically coat the affected GI mucosal surfaces to reduce inflammation and dietary food antigen elimination diets to address underlying food allergies as the principal etiology for these conditions. As the prevalence of pediatric EGID continues to increase (Liacouras, et al., 2011), management of these conditions represents an important concern for pediatric healthcare professionals. Treatment regimens for EGID are often complex, demanding, and require organization, cooperation, and planning by both patients and their parents. These treatments are further complicated by potential side effects of medications, ease with which prohibited foods can be obtained, patient versus parent responsibility for treatments, and the financial and social costs. Yet, to date there have been no published studies examining adherence in children with EGID.

Nonadherence to prescribed treatment regimens is a common issue across pediatric chronic illness populations, with nonadherence prevalence estimates of 50% in children (Rapoff, 2010) and 75% (Logan, Zelikovsky, Labay, & Spergel, 2003) to 88% (Hommel, Davis, & Baldassano, 2009) in adolescents. Although there are no known studies of nonadherence in EGID, data from inflammatory bowel disease (IBD) and asthma, which are managed via oral medication, and celiac disease, which is managed via dietary restriction therapies, offer insight into the potential adherence problems that patients with EGID may experience. In pediatric asthma, nonadherence in children is common. Walders and colleagues (Walders, Kopel, Koinis-Mitchell, & McQuaid, 2005) reported a 54% rate of nonadherence to daily medication. Nonadherence to inhaled corticosteroids in children and adolescents has been documented at 51% (McQuaid, Walders, Kopel, Fritz, & Klinnert, 2005) and 48% (McQuaid, Kopel, Klein, & Fritz, 2003). In addition, Bauman and colleagues (Bauman et al., 2002) reported that 45% of young children with asthma either did not have a prescription filled or was given more than or less than what was prescribed. Nonadherence rates in pediatric IBD and celiac disease range from 16% (Ooi, Bohane, Lee, Naidoo, & Day, 2007) to 62% (Mackner & Crandall, 2005) in IBD for medication nonadherence and from 5% (Rashid et al., 2005) to 70% (Westman, Ambler, Royle, Peat, & Chan, 1999) in celiac disease (Hommel, Mackner, Denson, & Crandall, 2008) for gluten-free diet nonadherence. Using both patient- and parent-report interview assessments of medication nonadherence in adolescents with IBD, Mackner and Crandall (2005) found nonadherence (defined as <100% of medication consumed) rates of 57–62% according to adolescent and parent reports, respectively. Our research, using both subjective (i.e., self-report) and objective (i.e., pill counts) assessment methods, has documented nonadherence prevalence rates of 64–88% depending on medication type and nonadherence frequency rates of 38–49% in adolescents with IBD (Hommel et al., 2009). Thus, there is empirical evidence that nonadherence is prevalent and frequent in two gastrointestinal conditions that involve treatments similar to those that patients with EGID are prescribed. Documenting rates of nonadherence in patients with EGID will address a potentially significant aspect of clinical care that may have substantial impact on health outcomes (e.g., uncontrolled GI tract inflammation, esophageal food impaction, development of an esophageal stricture, poor growth, pain, worsening symptoms, etc.).

Examination of disease management issues, particularly nonadherence, therefore, represents a significant need in the pediatric EGID population. Accordingly, the present study was designed to determine the prevalence and frequency of treatment nonadherence, including medication, tube feeding, and dietary restrictions, in a cohort of children with EGID using multi-informant parent-report (i.e., maternal and paternal reporting) assessment of adherence (as well as objective electronic monitoring in a subsample). Using this approach, we conceptualized nonadherence on a continuum by examining frequencies, but also acknowledged, via examination of prevalence, the clinical importance of distinguishing adherent versus nonadherent patients. We hypothesized that a substantial proportion of patients would demonstrate nonadherence and that nonadherent behavior would be evident across treatment types (i.e., oral medication, tube feedings, and dietary restriction therapies).

Methods
Participants

This study was performed with the approval of the Cincinnati Children's Hospital Medical Center (CCHMC) Institutional Review Board. Patients with EGID were recruited from local and referral populations at CCHMC and its Cincinnati Center for Eosinophilic Disorders (CCED). Inclusion criteria were (a) patients age 2.5–18 years and (b) primary diagnosis of EGID, including EoE and EGE. Exclusion criteria were (a) diagnosis of severe developmental delay as evidenced by chart review (due to limited comprehension of questionnaires) and (b) diagnosis of a chronic condition other than EGID. Eligible participants that were recruited consisted of (a) new patients seen in the CCED, (b) existing patients followed in the outpatient gastroenterology clinic, or (c) existing patients attending a national educational conference for patients diagnosed with EGID and their families. These patients' medical records were reviewed to ensure that they met inclusion criteria. Of the 116 families contacted, nine declined participation (five questionnaires took too much time, two not interested in research, and two family overwhelmed with clinic visit), one withdrew (did not have enough time to complete questionnaires), one was diagnosed with reflux instead of EGID, one was excluded from analyses due to procedural error, and eight did not return complete data. Therefore, the final sample included 96 patients with EGID and their caregivers.

Study Design and Procedures

We conducted a cross-sectional study of EGID patients and their families who were identified during clinic or endoscopy appointments with the cohort ranging from initial diagnosis to well-established patients. Participants provided informed consent and caregiver and patient age-specific assessments were conducted during one visit. Assessments were conducted according to appointment type (i.e., clinic appointment, outpatient surgery, or conference meeting) and time available for completion to accommodate patient and family schedules. If the family did not have sufficient time to complete all assessments in person, they were provided with a prepaid, addressed envelope to complete forms at home and return by mail. Study staff conducted follow-up phone calls to collect any outstanding assessments. Patients who were prescribed swallowed corticosteroid therapy via a metered-dose inhaler (MDI) were given MediTrack Doser electronic monitor devices to monitor three months of medication adherence. Electronic monitors were mailed to study staff after completion of each 30-day period, and data were transferred to a database for analysis.

Measures

Caregivers completed a demographic form providing data on caregiver ages, education, marital status, employment status, and household income.

EGID Treatment Adherence Questionnaire

The Treatment Adherence Questionnaire (TAQ) was developed specifically for the study to assess the unique adherence factors involved in treatment of EGID. It is a 12-item parent report questionnaire that measures patient adherence to both medication and dietary restriction regimens. Factors assessed include medication adherence, timing of missed medications, adherence to dietary restriction recommendations (defined as refraining from consuming unwanted food allergen exposures such as eating a food that unknowingly contained an allergenic ingredient), tube-feeding adherence, and responsibility for completing treatments. Single-item measurement is used to assess each of these factors. Example questions include:

- Children and adolescents often have difficulty taking medications and doing tube feedings. They may forget, have activities that conflict with the treatment, or just decide not to take a dose of medication or do a tube-feeding treatment. There may be other reasons too. All of these reasons are completely understandable.
- Please tell us the number of medication doses your child/adolescent has missed in the past two weeks: _____.
- Please tell us the number of tube feeding treatments your child/adolescent has missed in the past two weeks: _____.

MediTrack Dosers

MediTrack Doser electronic devices were attached to the top of a patient's MDI and recorded the number of compressions exhausted from the MDI. The Doser device consists of an LCD screen that attaches to the top of the MDI and displays the number of compressions daily, as well as the number of inhalations remaining in the canister. Dosers record a maximum of 30-days of data. Patients were provided three Dosers to track three months of adherence. Thirteen patients were prescribed swallowed corticosteroid therapy via a MDI at the time of consent. Data were available for 12 patients as one did not use the electronic monitor as requested. Similar to other electronic monitors, Dosers have the potential to fail to record inhalations or may record additional compressions of the MDI that were not inhaled.

Data Analyses

Raw data were entered into a secure database and data quality analysis was performed. All data analyses were conducted in PASW 18.0. Parent-reported adherence data were available for all prescribed medications; Doser electronic data were also available for a subsample of patients prescribed swallowed fluticasone. Descriptive statistics were calculated for demographic information, parent-report adherence data, and electronic monitor adherence data. Data were compared using independent samples t-tests and paired samples t-tests. A multivariate analysis of variance was also conducted to examine differences in adherence based on age, categorized as toddler (ages 2–4 years; $N=26$), young child (ages 5–7 years; $N=25$), child (ages 8–12 years; $N=28$), and adolescent (ages 13–18 years; $N=17$). These categories are consistent with prior studies in pediatric populations (Varni, Seid, & Kurtin, 2001). All tests were considered significant at the $p<.05$ level. Dosers record for 30 days then automatically overwrite (i.e., return to Day 1 to re-record) days until data are recorded. To control for this overwriting, Doser data were truncated, with the first 5 days of each month deleted. This provided a more conservative approach to data interpretation. The cut point for nonadherence was set at 90% across adherence behaviors assessed (e.g., medication, diet, etc.). This value is slightly higher than commonly seen in adherence research. Although an 80% cut point is often used, it is strictly arbitrary and not disease- or treatment specific or tied to clinical outcome. Additionally, 90% was used in this study because of the potentially significant consequences of nonadherence (e.g., uncontrolled GI tract inflammation, esophageal food impaction, anaphylaxis, development of an esophageal stricture, poor growth, and pain) in EGID compared to other chronic disease groups which have less immediate and/or severe outcomes associated with nonadherence.

Results

Patient Demographics

Family demographic and patient disease parameters for this study included patient age, gender, ethnicity, diagnosis, primary and secondary caregiver age, relation to patient, marital status, employment status, education level, and annual family income. Descriptive data for these variables are shown in Table I.

Medication Adherence by Parental Report and Electronic Monitor Data

Mean medication adherence frequency per maternal report ($N=85$) was $91\%\pm14\%$; paternal report ($N=42$) was $95\%\pm6\%$. Thirty percent of the sample was nonadherent per maternal report and 15% per paternal report. Importantly, the range of medication nonadherence was 0–100% for maternal report and 79–100% for paternal report, demonstrating substantial variability in medication adherence in this sample. A paired samples t-test was conducted to examine differential ratings by parents and revealed nonsignificant differences between maternal and paternal ratings ($p>.05$). Independent samples t-test revealed a significant difference between EoE ($N=82$) and EGE ($N=14$) patients on maternal report of medication adherence ($t=-2.28$, $p<.05$), with EGE patients demonstrating poorer adherence (Figure 1). Additionally,

Table I. *Demographic and Disease-Related Descriptive Data*

N	96
Patient age (years)	8.31 ± 4.33; range = 2.05–18.37
Patient gender (% male)	77.1
Ethnicity (%)	
Caucasian	84.4
African American	2.1
Hispanic	2.1
Asian	2.1
Biracial	8.3
Other	1.0
Primary caregiver relation to patient (%)	
Biological Mothers	95.8
Biological Father	4.2
Primary caregiver age	39.70 ± 5.82; range = 27.36–55.23
Primary caregiver marital status (percent married)	89.6
Primary caregiver education level (percent with at least some college education)	71.9
Primary caregiver employment status (%)	
Employed part time	27.1
Employed full time	32.3
Secondary caregiver relation to patient (%)	
Biological father	82.3
Biological mother	4.2
Stepfather	3.1
Grandmother	2.1
Secondary caregiver age	42.11 ± 6.84; range = 28.31–69.25
Secondary caregiver marital status (percent married)	95.5
Secondary caregiver education level (percent with at least some college education)	66.7
Secondary caregiver employment status (%)	
Employed part time	1.1
Employed full time	93.2
EGID Diagnosis (%)	
Eosinophilic esophagitis	85.4
Eosinophilic gastroenteritis	14.6
Annual family income (%)	
$0–$25,000	2.1
$25,001–$50,000	9.4
$50,001–$75,000	12.5
$75,001–$100,000	19.8
$100,001–$125,000	18.8 (median)
$125,001–$150,000	11.5
$150,001–$175,000	4.2
$175,001–$200,000	2.1
Over $200,000	16.7

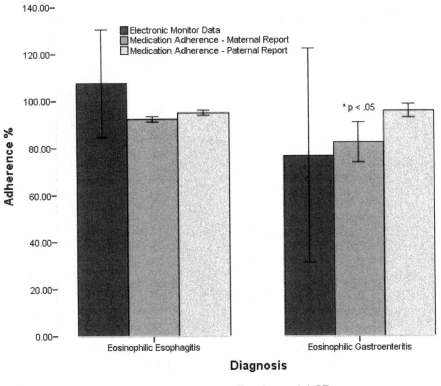

Figure 1. Medication adherence frequency for patients by diagnosis. Asterisks indicate EoE and EGE patients significantly different at $p<.05$ for medication adherence–maternal ratings.

a significant difference was observed between age groups based on paternal report of medication adherence ($F = 3.64$, $p < .05$), with toddlers with both conditions demonstrating poorer adherence than young children (Figure 2).

Analysis of the Doser electronic monitor data ($N = 12$) revealed $100\% \pm 69\%$ adherence; however, this also revealed a substantial range of 0–194%, with approximately one-half of those patients overdosing. Thus, nonadherence was bidirectional with swallowed fluticasone resulting in both underdosing and overdosing (Figure 3).

Tube Feeding Adherence by Parental Report

Twelve patients were prescribed tube-feeding treatment. Adherence to this treatment was $99\% \pm 3\%$ per maternal report and $98\% \pm 4\%$ per paternal report. Thus, maternal and paternal ratings were congruent for tube-feeding adherence. The range of adherence was 91–100%, with 75% of mothers and 67% of fathers reporting 100% adherence (Figure 3). Differential ratings by parents were examined using a paired samples t-test, which revealed nonsignificant differences between maternal ($N = 12$) and paternal ($N = 5$) ratings ($p > .05$).

Dietary Adherence by Parental Report

Food allergen exposures were calculated as whole numbers because there was no denominator. That is, because dietary restriction represents an absence of a behavior, there is no prescribed number of behavioral events by which to divide. Mean maternal ($N = 71$) and paternal ($N = 43$) reports of unwanted food allergen exposures portrayed similar rates with 0.87 and 0.40 exposures over the previous two weeks, respectively. Thirty-three percent and 14% of the patients reported at least one exposure during the previous 2 weeks per maternal and paternal report, respectively (Figure 4). There was also general consistency in report of accidental food allergen exposures, with mothers reporting 0.26 and fathers reporting 0.37 accidental food allergen exposures over the previous two weeks. A paired samples t-test revealed nonsignificant differences between maternal and paternal ratings ($p > .05$). Number of food allergen exposures did not differ significantly based on diagnosis of anaphylaxis ($p > .05$).

The number of missed medication doses was also compared to food allergen exposures to determine if differences in adherence behavior existed based on type of treatment. Both maternal and paternal reports of missed

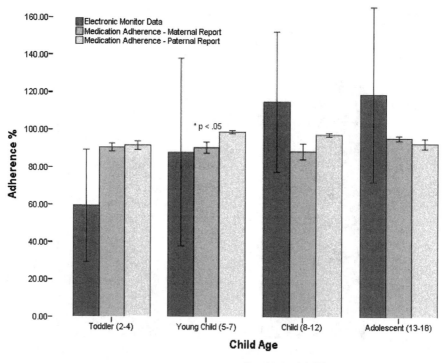

Figure 2. Medication adherence frequency for patients by age. Asterisks indicate toddlers and young children significantly different at $p < .05$ for medication adherence–paternal ratings.

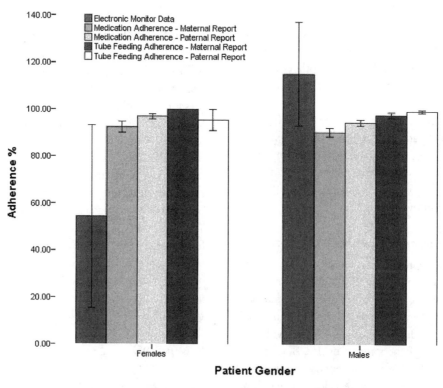

Figure 3. Medication and tube-feeding adherence frequency for patients by gender.

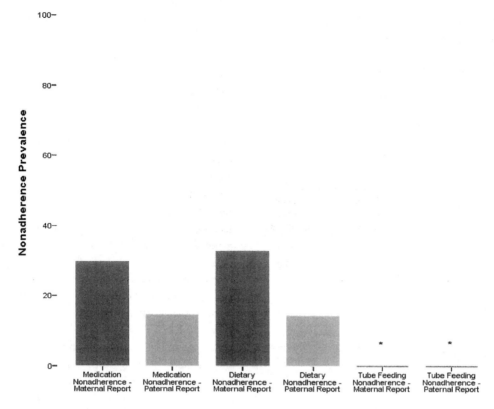

Figure 4. Nonadherence prevalence by treatment type. Asterisks indicate tube-feeding nonadherence prevalence = 0.

medication doses were compared to food allergen exposures via paired samples t-tests. Missed medication doses per maternal report ($N=68$) (2.38 ± 3.25) were significantly higher than mean food allergen exposures (0.88 ± 1.93), $t=-3.47$, $p<.01$. Similarly, per paternal report ($N=37$), missed medication doses (1.24 ± 1.52) were significantly higher than mean food allergen exposures (0.46 ± 1.19), $t=2.47$, $p<.05$.

Medication Organization and Allocation of Treatment Responsibility

Medications were most frequently kept in the household kitchen cupboard or on the kitchen counter, per maternal (69%) and paternal (57%) report. Only 17% of mothers and 18% of fathers reported using a pill box to organize their child's medications, although this may reflect prescription rates of medication in pill form for treatment of EGID. No maternal or paternal reporters indicated keeping medications in parent's bedroom. Findings regarding allocation of treatment responsibility are detailed in Table II. There was good agreement between mothers and fathers regarding mothers' level of treatment responsibility across treatment-related tasks; however, fathers rated their level of responsibility slightly higher than mothers rated fathers' responsibility.

Discussion

This study is the first to examine nonadherence in children diagnosed with an EGID. The findings indicate that there is a 30% nonadherence prevalence rate for medication therapy based on parental report, with a nonadherence frequency range of 0–100% and a range of 0–194% based on electronic monitor data. In contrast, tube-feeding adherence was remarkably high (99%) with little variability. Dietary adherence data revealed that on average, patients were exposed to less than one food allergen that they were supposed to be avoiding in the previous two weeks; however, there was a 33% prevalence of dietary nonadherence (i.e., primary caregivers reporting at least one exposure in previous 2 weeks). Significant differences in medication adherence were found for patient diagnosis, with EGE patients demonstrating poorer adherence. Toddlers demonstrated poorer medication adherence than young children. Missed medication doses were significantly higher than number of food allergen exposures per both maternal and paternal report.

A substantial proportion of the patients in this sample demonstrated nonadherence to medication and dietary recommendations. This, combined with the observed range of medication nonadherence, demonstrates that subsets of these patients have particular difficulty adhering to

Table II. *Allocation of Treatment Responsibility per Parent Report*

Who is in charge of making sure your child's medications have been taken?	Maternal report n = 90 (%)	Paternal report n = 51 (%)
Mother	92.2	96.1
Father	60.0	82.4
Child/Adolescent	18.9	13.7
Grandmother	6.7	5.9
Grandfather	2.2	3.9
Older sibling of patient	–	2.0
Not applicable	2.2	–
Who is in charge of making sure your child's dietary recommendations are followed?	**Maternal report n = 90 (%)**	**Paternal report n = 51 (%)**
Mother	93.3	94.0
Father	68.9	78.0
Child/Adolescent	14.4	12.0
Grandmother	10.0	6.0
Grandfather	6.7	2.0
Not applicable	5.6	4.0
Who is in charge of making sure your child's tube feeding treatments have been completed?	**Maternal report n = 12 (%)**	**Paternal report n = 12 (%)**
Mother	100	100
Father	91.7	100
Child/Adolescent	33.3	–
Grandmother	16.7	–
Older sibling	8.3	20.0
Not applicable	–	–
Who is in charge of getting your child's medicine?	**Maternal report n = 90 (%)**	**Paternal report n = 51 (%)**
Mother	97.8	94.1
Father	45.6	68.6
Child/Adolescent	3.3	5.9
Grandmother	4.4	2.0
Not applicable	2.2	–

treatment regimens. Moreover, there was objective evidence of both underdosing and overdosing with swallowed corticosteroid therapy, indicating bidirectional nonadherence. While adherence to dietary recommendations was better than medication regimens, patients were still being exposed to food allergens and only a small proportion of those exposures were accidental. Thus, dietary adherence may also be problematic; however, objective assessment of dietary patterns is warranted to further articulate issues concerning adherence to this treatment approach. In contrast, EGID patients are able to adhere to tube-feeding treatments well, with very little variability. EGE patients may have more difficulty adhering to medication than EoE patients, which may suggest a difference in perception of symptom relief between patient diagnostic groups. Medication adherence in toddlers may be more challenging than other age groups, which might represent behavioral challenges to getting toddlers to take medications. Also the comparison of missed medication doses and dietary adherence suggests that medication adherence may be more difficult for families. The majority of participants reported effective organizational strategies for managing their treatments and mothers were uniformly rated as being primarily responsible for making sure medications were taken and refilled, dietary recommendations were followed, and tube feedings were completed. These findings regarding organizational factors and treatment responsibility have important clinical implications. For example, attention to improving organizational strategies may not result in considerable improvement in adherence. However, given that disease management in this population is primarily done by mothers, focusing on transition of responsibility at a developmentally appropriate time in the patients' lives should help with long-term management into adulthood. In addition, the findings of this study suggest that clinicians should focus most of their self-management support on medication and dietary adherence compared to tube-feeding adherence as the latter does not appear to be problematic based on these initial results. Assessing difficulties in adhering to medication and diet regularly, assessing barriers, and developing action plans for overcoming these barriers may be particularly helpful. Further, providing families with toddler-age patients with specific behavior management strategies (e.g., reward contingencies, differential attention, and positive reinforcement for desired behaviors) that may impact medication adherence would likely be quite beneficial. Collectively, the findings of this initial investigation suggest that adherence to treatment in EGID is complex and multifaceted, with patients level of nonadherence varying across treatments.

The examination of multiple types of adherence, which cover the most common treatments for EGID, allowed identification of nonadherence frequency across a range of treatments. Sampling from both local and referral populations as well as conference attendees provided a potentially broader pool from which patients were sampled. Inclusion of objective electronic monitor assessment for medication adherence provided the opportunity to supplement parent-report data and to observe bidirectional nonadherence that would not otherwise have been revealed. Notably, pediatric behavioral science has historically neglected examination of paternal data and there is an increasing emphasis on the inclusion of fathers in observational and treatment research (Phares, Lopez, Fields, Kamboukos, & Duhig, 2005).

Our use of both maternal and paternal informants for adherence data allowed for evaluation of discrepancies in reporting of adherence rates. However, these findings must also be interpreted within the context of a few limitations, including the use of parent-report adherence assessment data. While subjective assessment is particularly common in exploratory investigations of adherence in novel populations like this, self- and parent-report adherence data generally represents overestimations of adherence (Rapoff, 2010). Thus, our observed parent-report adherence rates may be generous estimates of adherence and should be substantiated via future research utilizing objective methods. In addition, given the small N and consequent cell sizes for tube feeding and electronic monitor adherence as well as the small number of EGE patients in the study, generalization of these findings is not yet warranted until replication with a larger sample can be conducted. This sample also comprised primarily male patients who were Caucasian and came from middle-to-upper socioeconomic backgrounds, with parents who were mostly married, educated, and employed. Future research on adherence in this population should focus on diversifying the samples to the extent possible. Finally, the cross-sectional nature of the study precluded examination of trajectories of adherence over time. This will be necessary to determine behavioral patterns that require intervention to improve disease management skills.

Future research should focus on longitudinal assessment of adherence using a multimethod approach comprising objective and subjective (e.g., dietary interview data, 24-hr random recall of diet, patient self-report, etc.) methods. This will enable predictive modeling via examination of trajectories of adherence and related clinical outcomes as well as identification of optimal timing for intervention (e.g., when adherence is likely to decrease). This research should also focus on the relationship between adherence and disease outcomes such as symptom severity, healthcare utilization, etc., which will aid in identifying the most accurate cut point for identification of nonadherent patients for whom intervention will be most needed. Subsequently, development and testing of behavioral intervention models to improve adherence and self-management, taking into account issues such as barriers to adherence and psychosocial functioning, will be critical to assuring the efficacy of treatment regimens and health outcomes in this population.

Funding

Food Allergy Project, the Buckeye Foundation and the Campaign Urging Research for Eosinophilic Disease (CURED) Foundation (partial); Center for the Promotion of Treatment Adherence and Self-Management at Cincinnati Children's Hospital Medical Center (partial).

Conflict of Interest statement: Marc E. Rothenberg MD, PhD, has proprietary interest in reslizumab, a drug being developed by Cephalon. All other authors, none declared.

References

Bauman, L. J., Wright, E., Leickly, F. E., Crain, E., Kruszon-Moran, D., Wade, S. L., & Visness, C. M. (2002). Relationship of adherence to pediatric asthma morbidity among inner-city children. *Pediatrics, 110*(1 Pt 1), e6.

DeBrosse, C. W., Case, J. W., Putnam, P. E., Collins, M. H., & Rothenberg, M. E. (2006). Quantity and distribution of eosinophils in the gastrointestinal tract of children. *Pediatric and Developmental Pathology, 9*(3), 210–218.

Hommel, K. A., Davis, C. M., & Baldassano, R. N. (2009). Objective versus subjective assessment of oral medication adherence in pediatric inflammatory bowel disease. *Inflammatory Bowel Disease, 15*(4), 589–593.

Hommel, K. A., Mackner, L. M., Denson, L. A., & Crandall, W. V. (2008). Treatment regimen adherence in pediatric gastroenterology. *Journal of Pediatric Gastroenterology and Nutrition, 47*(5), 526–543.

Liacouras, C. A., Furuta, G. T., Hirano, I., Atkins, D., Attwood, S. E., Bonis, P. A., ... Aceves, S. S. (2011). Eosinophilic esophagitis: Updated consensus recommendations for children and adults. *Journal of Allergy and Clinical Immunology, 128*(1), 3–20.e26.

Logan, D., Zelikovsky, N., Labay, L., & Spergel, J. (2003). The Illness Management Survey: Identifying adolescents' perceptions of barriers to adherence. *Journal of Pediatric Psychology, 28*(6), 383–392.

Mackner, L. M., & Crandall, W. V. (2005). Oral medication adherence in pediatric inflammatory bowel disease. *Inflammatory Bowel Diseases, 11*(11), 1006–1012.

McQuaid, E. L., Kopel, S. J., Klein, R. B., & Fritz, G. K. (2003). Medication adherence in pediatric asthma: Reasoning, responsibility, and behavior. *Journal of Pediatric Psychology, 28*(5), 323–333.

McQuaid, E. L., Walders, N., Kopel, S. J., Fritz, G. K., & Klinnert, M. D. (2005). Pediatric asthma management in the family context: The family asthma management system scale. *Journal of Pediatric Psychology, 30*(6), 492–502.

Ooi, C. Y., Bohane, T. D., Lee, D., Naidoo, D., & Day, A. S. (2007). Thiopurine metabolite monitoring in paediatric inflammatory bowel disease. *Alimentary Pharmacology and Therapeutics, 25*(8), 941–947.

Phares, V., Lopez, E., Fields, S., Kamboukos, D., & Duhig, A. M. (2005). Are fathers involved in pediatric psychology research and treatment? *Journal of Pediatric Psychology, 30*(8), 631–643.

Rapoff, M. A. (2010). *Adherence to Pediatric Medical Regimens* (2nd ed.). New York: Springer.

Rashid, M., Cranney, A., Zarkadas, M., Graham, I. D., Switzer, C., Case, S., ... Butzner, J. D. (2005). Celiac disease: Evaluation of the diagnosis and dietary compliance in Canadian children. *Pediatrics, 116*(6), e754–759.

Varni, J. W., Seid, M., & Kurtin, P. S. (2001). PedsQL 4.0: Reliability and validity of the Pediatric Quality of Life Inventory version 4.0 generic core scales in healthy and patient populations. *Medical Care, 39*(8), 800–812.

Walders, N., Kopel, S. J., Koinis-Mitchell, D., & McQuaid, E. L. (2005). Patterns of quick-relief and long-term controller medication use in pediatric asthma. *Journal of Pediatrics, 146*(2), 177–182.

Westman, E., Ambler, G. R., Royle, M., Peat, J., & Chan, A. (1999). Children with coeliac disease and insulin dependent diabetes mellitus–growth, diabetes control and dietary intake. *Journal of Pediatric Endocrinology and Metabolism, 12*(3), 433–442.

Commentary: Psychological and Behavioral Challenges for Families of Children with Eosinophilic Gastrointestinal Disorders

Mary D. Klinnert, PhD
National Jewish Health

All correspondence concerning this article should be addressed to Mary D. Klinnert, PhD, National Jewish Health, 1400 Jackson Street, Denver, CO, 80206, USA. E-mail: klinnertm@njhealth.org

Received March 12, 2012; revisions received March 17, 2012; accepted March 18, 2012

The current issue of the *Journal of Pediatric Psychology* includes two papers about children and adolescents with eosinophilic gastrointestinal diseases, or EGIDs. Each paper addresses key behavioral and psychological aspects of pediatric EGIDs. The first paper, by Taft and colleagues, characterizes caregiver stress in the parents of children with EGIDs and describes the relationships between the caregivers' pediatric illness stress experiences and their own psychological functioning, as well as their children's behavioral adjustment (Taft, Ballou, & Keefer, 2012). The second paper, by Hommel and colleagues, examines treatment adherence rates for children with EGIDs and their families (Hommel, Franciosi, Hente, Ahrens, & Rothenberg, 2011). Together, the papers provide an initial look at this recently recognized disease in terms of the challenges posed for the caregivers of the children with EGIDs, and to some extent for the children themselves, as they strive to cope with the illnesses and follow the recommended treatments aimed at disease management. The goal here is to underscore the importance of certain aspects of the initial findings from the papers and to further describe disease characteristics and related impacts that must be considered in future research regarding behavioral and psychological aspects of pediatric EGIDs.

The paper by Taft and colleagues focuses on caregiver stress that is experienced by mothers of children with EGIDs, mostly with eosinophilic esophagitis (EoE). In comparison with parent stress levels measured with the same instrument in other studies of pediatric illness (e.g., Hilliard, Monaghan, Cogen, & Streisand, 2010), stress levels for caregivers in this study were extraordinarily high. Demographic correlates of the high caregiver stress levels, low socioeconomic status and single parenting, may reflect reduced resources and support for meeting medical care demands for these children. Caregiver stress was also associated with disease variables including symptoms and disease management burden. In the Taft study, symptom burden was measured using mothers' ratings of "recent flare severity." For EoE, the maternal response to a "recent flare" not only includes an assessment of severity of the child's symptoms, but also an attempt to determine how the symptom might be associated with a particular food exposure. This determination is especially challenging because most eosinophilic inflammation results from non-immunoglobulin E (IgE)-mediated allergic processes, with delayed responses that evolve over hours and days following food allergen exposure (Atkins, Kramer, Capocelli, Lovell, & Furuta, 2009), clouding the identification of culprit foods. Many children with EoE also have IgE-mediated food allergies, with symptoms that occur immediately after ingestion and have potential for life threatening anaphylaxis. Distinguishing between IgE-mediated and non-IgE-mediated food allergies may be critical for understanding caregiver anxiety and children's distress regarding dietary restrictions and accidental food exposure.

Certain qualitative aspects of EGID symptoms also can be associated with heightened caregiver stress. For EoE, the most commonly diagnosed of the EGIDs, presenting symptoms vary according to patient age. For example, feeding dysfunction is the most common primary presenting symptom for very young children (Mukkada et al., 2010). Epidemiological studies have shown that as many as a third of children diagnosed with EoE are less than 3–5 years of age, so studies of pediatric patients that encompass the entire age range from 0 to 18 years likely include a substantial proportion of young children with feeding problems. Having a young child with food refusal or vomiting, often resulting in poor weight gain or failure to thrive, elicits high anxiety, and is extraordinarily distressing for parents. Abdominal pain is the most common presenting symptom for older children; the ambiguity of this complaint, often lacking validating external evidence (unlike the typical fever rule for school attendance for healthy children), presents another type of management challenge for mothers. It is not surprising that the Taft study showed clinically significant levels of anxiety for 46% and of depression for 28% of the maternal caregivers, considering the dilemmas raised by the occurrence of symptom flares for children with EoE.

Besides symptom assessment and response, central features of disease management for pediatric EGIDs involve adherence with treatment recommendations. As emphasized in both the Taft and Hommel papers, current EGID treatments are complex, intensive, and demanding, and require significant parental monitoring. Hommel and colleagues assessed treatment adherence midst this complexity, enlisting fathers as well as mothers as informants. The investigators found 30% of families were nonadherent, that is, did not meet criteria for dispensing medication, enforcing dietary restrictions, or providing tube feedings. In addition to presenting this clinically important information, these investigators characterized families in terms of the allocation of treatment responsibility for medical or dietary treatments. Although fathers consistently reported taking more responsibility than their wives said they did, overall most fathers apparently played a significant role in most aspects of providing treatment. Children and adolescents had only small proportions of responsibility allocated to them. Overall, the data suggested that children with EGIDs play a relatively small role in managing their disease, fathers have a substantial role, but mothers bear the primary responsibility. This pattern is consistent with the extremely high maternal-caregiver stress levels reported in the Taft study.

In addition to treatment adherence and symptom assessment, parent-caregivers face other multifaceted challenges. Many of the concerns and burdens for parents of children with EoE are similar to those that occur among other pediatric chronic conditions, for example, communicating with medical personnel or helping children endure diagnostic procedures. However, parents of children with EoE have multiple illness-specific concerns as well. The majority of pediatric patients with EoE have concurrent allergic diseases including atopic dermatitis, allergic rhinitis, asthma, and/or IgE-mediated food allergies (Straumann et al., 2012), compounding the disease burden for children and the management burden for caregivers. Because a primary treatment approach for EoE involves dietary restrictions, parents have concerns about the adequacy of the quantity, nutritional value, and palatability of their children's nutritional intake, and how best to manage the dietary restrictions of the child with EoE within the larger family context. Finally, the fact that EGIDs has been recognized only recently may itself contribute to parents' high illness-related stress levels. The medical community is still learning about EGIDs and evaluating optimal treatment approaches and, as a result, families may receive differing medical recommendations. Also, important members of children's social networks, such as school personnel and extended family, often have no knowledge of EoE or eosinophilic gastroenteritis, and they require education about the disease above and beyond the collaborative planning with alternate caregivers that is typically required of parents of children with chronic illness. Thus, recent recognition of these illnesses may be a unique factor contributing to extraordinarily high levels of maternal-caregivers' illness-related stress for pediatric EGIDs.

The two papers discussed here have made important inroads into an initial understanding of behavioral and psychosocial issues related to pediatric EoE. Together, the papers provide complementary views of current disease management for these children. Treatment regimens are complex and non-adherence is prevalent, yet treatment demands are among the many emotional burdens and responsibilities that underlie extremely high maternal-caregiver stress levels. Caregivers reported increased emotional and social problems for their children, although the extent to which these concerns reflect parental bias related to their own stress is unknown. Regardless, further research is urgently needed to better understand the specific demands and challenges associated with high levels of caregiver stress and psychological distress among parents of children with EGIDs. Research is also needed to define the impact of disease specific factors on children's emotional and social development, to determine ways for children to participate in their disease management, and to explore optimal strategies for coping with the challenges they face. With a better understanding of specific challenges encountered by the children with EoE and by their parents, it will be possible to develop interventions focused on helping children and their families cope with the immense challenges posed by these diseases.

Conflict of interest: None declared.

References

Atkins, D., Kramer, R., Capocelli, K., Lovell, M., & Furuta, G. T. (2009). Eosinophilic esophagitis: The newest esophageal inflammatory disease. *Nature Reviews Gastroenterology & Hepatology, 6*, 267–278.

Hilliard, M., Monaghan, M., Cogen, F., & Streisand, R. (2010). Parent stress and child behaviour among young children with type 1 diabetes. *Child: Care, Health and Development, 37,* 224–232.

Hommel, K., Franciosi, J., Hente, E., Ahrens, A., & Rothenberg, M. (2011). Treatment adherence in pediatric eosinophilic gastrointestinal disorders. *Journal of Pediatric Psychology.* Advance online publication. doi:10.1093/jpepsy/jsr090

Mukkada, V., Haas, A., Creskoff Maune, N., Capocelli, K., Henry, M., Gilman, N., ... Atkins, D. (2010). Feeding dysfunction in children with eosinophilic gastrointestinal diseases. *Pediatrics, 126*(3), e1–e7.

Straumann, A., Aceves, S., Blanchard, C., Collins, M., Furuta, G., Hirano, I., ... Simon, H. U. (2012). Pediatric and adult eosinophilic esophagitis: Similarities and differences. *Allergy, 67,* 477–490.

Taft, T., Ballou, S., & Keefer, L. (2012). Preliminary evaluation of maternal-caregiver stress in pediatric eosinophilic disorders. *Journal of Pediatric Psychology.* Advance online publication. doi:10.1093/jpepsy/jsr118

Concurrent and Longitudinal Bidirectional Relationships Between Toddlers' Chronic Pain and Mental Health: The Generation R Study

Noor J. Wolff,[1,2] PhD, Anne-Sophie E. Darlington,[1] PhD, Joke A. M. Hunfeld,[1] PhD, Vincent W. V. Jaddoe,[2,3,4] MD, PhD, Albert Hofman,[3] MD, PhD, Hein Raat,[5] MD, PhD, Frank C. Verhulst,[6] MD, PhD, Jan Passchier,[1,7] PhD, and Henning Tiemeier,[3,6] MD, PhD

[1]Department of Medical Psychology and Psychotherapy, Erasmus University Medical Center, [2]The Generation R Study Group, Erasmus University Medical Center, [3]Department of Epidemiology, Erasmus University Medical Center, [4]Department of Pediatrics, Erasmus University Medical Center, [5]Department of Public Health, Erasmus University Medical Center, [6]Department of Child and Adolescent Psychiatry/Psychology, Erasmus University Medical Center, and [7]Department of Clinical Psychology, VU University

All correspondence concerning this article should be addressed to Henning Tiemeier, MD, PhD, Erasmus University Medical Center, Department of Child and Adolescent Psychiatry, PO Box 2060, 3000 CB, Rotterdam, The Netherlands. E-mail: h.tiemeier@erasmusmc.nl

Received June 16, 2011; revisions received December 15, 2011; accepted December 21, 2011

Objective The aim was to investigate the concurrent and longitudinal associations of chronic pain with behavioral and emotional problems in toddlers, as it is not known which comes first in life. **Methods** The study was embedded in the Generation R Study, a prospective population-based cohort study. Parents of 3,751 toddlers completed questionnaires of their child's health and development. Behavioral and emotional problems were measured at 1.5 and 3 years, chronic pain was measured at 2 and 3 years. **Results** There were concurrent associations between chronic pain and internalizing problems, e.g. anxiety/depression symptoms. However, chronic pain did not precede the development of new behavioral and emotional problems. Also, behavioral and emotional problems did not precede new-onset chronic pain, except for somatic symptoms, which increased the likelihood of chronic pain. **Conclusions** Chronic pain was associated with concurrent internalizing problems. Somatic complaints were not only concurrently related to pain but also predicted new-onset pain.

Key words behavioral and emotional problems; children; chronic pain; toddlers.

Introduction

Child chronic pain, consisting of both pain from diagnosed diseases and medically unexplained pain, is often accompanied by psychological problems, such as anxiety and depression (e.g., Campo et al., 2004; Mulvaney, Lambert, Garber, & Walker, 2006). Most previous studies found an association of pain with the presence of elevated psychological symptoms of depression and anxiety (e.g., Campo, Comer, Jansen-Mcwilliams, Gardner, & Kelleher, 2002; El-Metwally, Halder, Thompson, Macfarlane, & Jones, 2007; El-Metwally, Salminen, Auvinen, Kautiainen, & Mikkelsson, 2006; Larsson & Sund, 2005, 2007; Mulvaney et al., 2006). However, child chronic pain has also been related to anxiety disorders and depressive disorders (e.g. DSM-IV diagnoses in Dufton, Dunn, & Compas, 2009; Feldman, Ortega, Koinis-Mitchell, Kuo, & Canino, 2010, and DSM-III-R diagnoses in Egger, Angold, & Costello, 1998; Egger, Costello, Erkanli, & Angold, 1999). Some studies found chronic pain to be also related to other psychological problems, such as concentration difficulties (Aromaa, Rautava, Helenius, & Sillanpaa, 1998), lower perceived self-worth (Mulvaney et al., 2006), somatic complaints (Dufton et al., 2009; Larsson & Sund, 2007; Walker, Garber, Van Slyke, & Greene, 1995), conduct disorder (Egger et al., 1998), and oppositional defiant disorder and attention-deficit hyperactivity disorder, but only in boys (Egger et al., 1999).

The biopsychosocial approach to chronic pain states that biological changes, psychological status, and the sociocultural context all need to be considered in order to gain a complete understanding of a person's perception and response to pain and illness (Gatchel, Peng, Peters, Fuchs, & Turk, 2007). However, research evidence can only be integrated if knowledge on the separate aspects is accumulating. As this is not yet the case in research of young children's pain, this study focuses on the psychological factors only. According to the biopsychosocial model, the psychological factors can both influence and be influenced by pain experience. However, it is not yet known whether there is only a short-term interrelatedness, such as when depressive or anxiety symptoms reflect the immediate stress caused by chronic pain, or whether one (or each) problem can also be a longitudinal cause of the other. Evidence for the short-term interrelatedness of child chronic pain and psychological problems comes from studies using cross-sectional designs (e.g., El-Metwally et al., 2006; Walker, Garber, & Greene, 1993). Some longitudinal studies yielded evidence for psychosocial problems preceding new onset of child chronic pain (Egger et al., 1998, 1999; El-Metwally et al., 2007; Jones, Silman, & Macfarlane, 2003; Jones, Watson, Silman, Symmons, & Macfarlane, 2003; Stanford, Chambers, Biesanz, & Chen, 2008) or persistence of chronic pain (Larsson & Sund, 2005, 2007; Mulvaney et al., 2006). Interestingly, other studies found evidence for the reverse causal path. Studies of adolescents with chronic pain showed both internalizing problems at 1-year follow-up (Walker et al., 1995) and psychiatric disorders in adulthood (Hotopf, Carr, Mayou, Wadsworth, & Wessely, 1998). However, in the 1-year follow-up study, adolescents also had chronic pain at follow-up (Walker et al., 1995), it is thus still unclear whether there is an actual longitudinal effect. We found no studies that investigated both directions of effects simultaneously. Moreover, it is still unknown what the relation is between chronic pain and psychological problems in very young children. Almost all of the studies investigating chronic pain and psychological problems used samples aged 8 years and older. Only three studies set their minimum age of inclusion at 4, 5, or 6 years (Campo et al., 2002; Feldman et al., 2010; Mulvaney et al., 2006), yet numbers of children in these young age categories were low. By focusing on the first few years of life, it may be possible to better disentangle the factors associated with the onset of chronic pain in children and to find out whether there is only short-term interrelatedness with psychological problems or whether there are longitudinal effects.

Thus, the aim of this study was to investigate the concurrent and longitudinal relations between chronic pain and psychological problems in toddlers. We hypothesized that chronic pain was associated with concurrent depressive and anxiety symptoms, but we also explored relations with other behavioral and emotional problems. Furthermore, we studied the longitudinal relations in both directions, to be able to answer the question of 'what comes first'.

The toddlers' chronic pain was defined as pain existing recurrently or continuously for more than 3 months, consistent with the definition recommended by the IASP (Merskey & Bogduk, 1994) and PedIMMPACT (McGrath et al., 2008) and used in previous (prevalence) research of chronic pain in toddlers (Perquin et al., 2000).

Methods
Design
The current investigation was conducted within the Generation R Study, a population-based cohort study from fetal life onwards in Rotterdam, The Netherlands. The Generation R Study, designed to investigate determinants of health, development, and growth, has been described previously in detail (Jaddoe et al., 2010). The Medical Ethical Committee of the Erasmus Medical Center, Rotterdam, approved of the study.

Several previously published articles are based on data from the Generation R Study and investigate various determinants of emotional and behavioral problems. However, no article has related child emotional and behavioral problems or any other child variable to chronic pain in children.

Participants
All pregnant women living in Rotterdam with expected dates of delivery between April 2002 and January 2006 were invited to participate. Midwives and obstetricians informed eligible mothers about the study. The research staff then contacted these mothers to provide additional information and obtain written informed consent. Fathers were contacted via the mothers and if they wanted to participate, they received and completed a consent form as well. A total of 7,295 families gave consent for postnatal follow-up and 4,450 completed the first measurements of child behavioral and emotional problems, at 1.5 years, and chronic pain, at 2 years. At the follow-up measurement wave at 3 years, 3,751 of these parents again completed questions concerning chronic pain and behavioral and emotional problems (follow-up rate 84% of 4,450). At this measurement

wave, 49.3% were boys. The mean age of the children was 36.5 months ($SD = 1.2$ months), that of mothers was 35.2 years, and that of fathers was 37.6 years. The national origin of the children was 69.9% Dutch, 9.3% other Western, such as European or American, and 19.6% other non-Western, such as Moroccan, Turkish, or Surinamese.

Child Behavioral and Emotional Problems

Child mental health was assessed using the Dutch version of the Child Behavior Checklist for toddlers (CBCL/1.5–5 years; Achenbach & Rescorla, 2000), at 1.5 and 3 years. The CBCL/1.5–5 is a 99-item questionnaire designed to obtain ratings of behavioral and emotional problems by parents of 1.5- to 5-year-old children. It contains seven syndrome scales: emotionally reactive, anxious-depressed, somatic complaints, withdrawn, sleep problems, attention problems, and aggressive behavior. Parents are asked to rate the occurrence of their child's behavior within the past 2 months on a scale from 0 (not true) to 2 (often true). Scores for each subscale were summed, thus scores were continuous. The somatic complaints subscale contains four items on "pain without medical cause". We excluded these four items from the subscale, because they overlapped with items of the chronic pain measure. Good reliability and validity are reported for the English and Dutch CBCL/1.5–5 years (Achenbach & Rescorla, 2000; Tick, Ende, Koot, & Verhulst, 2007). At 1.5 years, the questionnaire was completed mostly by mothers (97% of the 4,450 parents) and rarely by fathers (3%). At 3 years, mothers and fathers each reported on their child's behavioral and emotional problems (i.e., two ratings per child). A total of 3,751 mothers and 3,055 fathers completed that questionnaire.

Child Chronic Pain

Child chronic pain was measured with the Pain List (Perquin et al., 2000), at 2 and 3 years. The Pain List contains items regarding the experience of pain in the last 3 months and several items regarding characteristics of pain, such as the location, frequency, intensity, duration, and interference (i.e., disruption of daily activities). Other items covered the parent's idea about the cause of the child's pain and whether a cause had been identified by a physician. The questions on intensity and interference were Visual Analogue Scales (VAS) ranging from 0 to 100. Most other items were categorical. The questions on cause and diagnosis were open-ended questions. At 2 years, the questionnaire was completed mostly by mothers (96% of the 4,450 parents) and rarely by fathers (4%). At 3 years, mothers and fathers each reported on their child's pain (i.e., two ratings per child). A total of 3,724 mothers and 3,063 fathers completed that questionnaire; data of at least one parent were available for a total of 3,751 children.

Pediatric chronic pain was coded as being present when parents indicated that their child experienced recurrent or continuous pain for more than 3 months. Everyday pain due to teething or resulting from play, such as falling or bumping into objects or other people, was excluded as 'chronic pain', because it is a normal occurrence in children that age (Fearon, McGrath, & Achat, 1996; Von Baeyer, Baskerville, & McGrath, 1998). Moreover, everyday pain does not lead to higher likelihood of absence from preschool or frequent health care use. To exclude everyday pain, one of the authors (N.W.) reviewed the answers to the open-ended question about the parent's idea of the cause of the pain, in the subsample of children with pain for more than 3 months. This question was completed by 1,191 parents (27%) at 2 years, 622 mothers (17%) at 3 years, and 417 fathers (14%) at 3 years. Many parents did not answer this question because they were instructed to skip the question if they had indicated on the first question that their child did not have pain in the last 3 months. Mentioned causes that fell into the categories "teething," "normal for this age," "bumping/falling during play," "infection/virus/influenza" were coded as everyday pain. All other answers to the question about the parents' idea of the cause of the pain (e.g., recurrent otitis media, laryngitis, constipation, rheumatism, growing pains, intestinal disease, eczema, fracture, or stress/anxiety) were coded as "not everyday pain." We also coded 'not everyday pain' if parents answered that they had no idea of the cause of the pain or if parents did not complete this question.

For each measurement moment, we defined a dichotomous chronic pain variable based on the 3 months criterion. Then, we recoded all children with everyday pain as not having chronic pain. At 3 years, the new-onset chronic pain variable was defined as chronic pain that was not present at the 2 years measurement but that had developed at the 3 years measurement.

Covariates

The following covariates were assessed: child sex, age, ethnicity, gestational duration, birth weight, medical history during the first 2 years of life (multiple visits to the general practitioner, visit to the medical specialist, hospitalization, chronic health condition diagnosed by a physician), parental education, parental age, parity, parental chronic pain, and parental mental health (BSI at child's age 3 years). These variables were obtained from questionnaires and from the midwife and hospital records. Parental education was categorized as no or primary (elementary school or less), secondary (high school, lower vocational training), or high (higher vocational training and university). The child's ethnicity was classified by the countries of birth of the parents, according to the standard classification criteria of Statistics Netherlands (2004).

Data Analyses

To calculate the new-onset chronic pain variable at 3 years, we used follow-up information by the parent who was the informant at 2 years; in 99% of cases the same informant could be used. The 2-year-old chronic pain was mostly mother reported (96%). Thus, the variable new-onset chronic pain was also mostly mother reported. We therefore chose to use mother-reports of the behavioral and emotional problems as well. Data on father-reported chronic pain at 3 years and on father-reported mental health at 3 years was available, so we were able to repeat the respective analyses using father-reported data to test consistency. Results of father-reported data were largely similar to results based on mother-reported data. If results changed meaningfully, these are reported in the results section.

In all analyses, the children with new-onset chronic pain were compared to the children without chronic pain. That is, the children with persistent pain (presence of chronic pain at 2 and 3 years) were excluded from the analyses.

To describe the sample, we ran analyses of covariates with the dependent variable chronic pain. Furthermore, we calculated ranges, means and standard deviations of the emotional and behavioral problems for the chronic pain group and the non chronic pain group. Next, we conducted unadjusted t-test analyses to provide some insight in the crude relations of chronic pain with emotional and behavioral problems. We tested the homogeneity of variance assumption using Levene's test for equality of variances, but the assumption was not violated.

Before running the actual regression analyses, we tested which covariates confounded the associations. Covariates were selected based on their effect in any of the core analyses (i.e., longitudinal and concurrent) using the CBCL internalizing and externalizing syndrome scales and chronic pain. We calculated the unadjusted effect estimate of the relation between determinant and outcome and compared it to the effect estimate of determinant and outcome after adding a covariate to the analysis, by calculating the percentage of change in effect estimate. This was repeated for all covariates separately. Covariates leading to more than 5% change in effect estimate were entered in a stepwise analysis in descending order of percentage of change. Covariates that changed effect estimates more than 5% in one or more stepwise analyses were kept as confounders in all final models. Consequently, we adjusted for the following confounders: child sex and ethnicity, and each parents' anxiety.

We used linear regression analyses to investigate the concurrent associations of new-onset chronic pain at 3 years with behavioral and emotional problems at 3 years and the almost concurrent associations of chronic pain at 2 years with behavioral and emotional problems at 1.5 years. Chronic pain was set as independent variable and the behavioral and emotional problems were set as dependent variables, because there is more evidence in the literature that pain leads to psychological problems than the reverse direction. The linear regression assumptions of normality, linearity and homoscedasticity were tested and were not violated.

Likewise, linear regression analyses were used to examine the longitudinal association between chronic pain and the behavioral and emotional problems. To this aim, we related chronic pain at 2 years to behavioral and emotional problems at 3 years. To control for the effect of pre-existence of the behavioral and emotional problem, we adjusted for these problems at 1.5 years. The linear regression assumptions of normality, linearity, and homoscedasticity were tested and were not violated.

The longitudinal relation between behavioral and emotional problems and chronic pain was examined with logistic regression analyses. To this aim, we investigated the association of behavioral and emotional problems at 1.5 years with new-onset chronic pain at 3 years. To control the analyses for pre-existing pain, new-onset pain was defined as chronic pain that was present at 3 years but not at 2 years.

All of the analyses mentioned above were conducted with each of the different CBCL syndrome scales. All analyses were conducted in SPSS version 17.

Results

Child Characteristics

Of the 3,751 children, 49 (1.3%) had chronic pain at 2 years. At 3 years, the chronic pain prevalence was 2.3% ($n = 87$) according to mothers (3,724 reports available) and 2.4% ($n = 73$) according to fathers (3,063 reports available). In 23 cases both parents reported chronic pain at 3 years, so there were in total 137 children of whom one or both parents reported child chronic pain. Only seven children had chronic pain that persisted from 2 to 3 years; these children were excluded from further analyses. Thus, the sample for analyses consisted of 3,744 children.

To determine whether there was new-onset chronic pain at 3 years, we used the report of the parent that also reported at 2 years, which was mostly the mother, as described above. There were 78 children (2.1%) with new-onset chronic pain at 3 years. As can be seen in Table I, slightly more girls than boys had new-onset chronic pain, but the difference between sexes was not significant. Children with new-onset chronic pain were more likely to have had contact with a medical specialist than children without chronic pain ($\chi^2_{(1)} = 5.7$, $p = .02$). They also were more likely to have anxious fathers ($t_{(66)} = 2.3$, $p = .02$). Of the children with new-onset chronic pain, five children had previously diagnosed chronic health conditions (data not shown in table). One of them had hypophosphatemic rickets, which may cause pain in the bones, two children had asthma and two children had eczema.

Table II presents the means and standard deviations of the behavioral and emotional problems for the chronic pain group and for the group without chronic pain; it also provides the observed range of scores and the means of the Dutch norm group. Furthermore, the t-test statistics of the mean difference between the groups are presented; these are unadjusted associations.

Nonresponse Analyses

Nonresponse analyses showed that families who did not complete the questionnaire at 3 years had a higher percentage of children of non-Western origin (38.4% vs. 19.8% of the completers), χ^2 (2, $n = 4,319) = 106.0$, $p < .001$. These families had 1.6 years younger mothers ($t = -7.7$, $p < .001$) and 1.1 years younger fathers ($t = -3.8$, $p < .001$) and their children had higher scores on all behavioral and emotional problems at 1.5 years (sumscore difference 0.35, $t = 3.8$, $p < .001$ for being emotionally reactive; sumscore difference 0.40, $t = 5.7$, $p < .001$ for

Table I. *Child and Parent Characteristics (n = 3,744)*

Characteristic	No chronic pain ($n = 3,666$) M (SD) or %	New-onset chronic pain[a] ($n = 78$) M (SD) or %	t (df) or χ^2 (df)	p
Child sex (% boy)	49.5%	39.7%	2.9 (1)	.09
Child age in months	36.5 (1.2)	36.6 (1.5)	0.6 (3742)	.54
Gestational duration in weeks	39.9 (1.7)	39.9 (1.5)	0.4 (3741)	.71
Birth weight in kilograms	3.451 (0.565)	3.456 (0.573)	0.1 (3738)	.93
Child ethnicity			3.3 (2)	.20
Dutch	70.6%	77.9%		
Non-Dutch, Western[b]	9.4%	10.4%		
Non-Dutch, non-Western[b]	20.0%	11.7%		
Contacted general practitioner (% four times or more)[c]	41.0%	48.0%	1.5 (1)	.22
Contacted medical specialist (% twice or more)[c]	25.2%	37.3%	5.7 (1)	.02
Hospitalized (% once or more)[c]	16.5%	18.7%	0.3 (1)	.61
Maternal age in years	35.3 (4.4)	34.2 (4.7)	−2.1 (3742)	.04
Paternal age in years	37.6 (5.0)	37.1 (4.6)	−0.7 (3742)	.47
Maternal educational level			0.4 (2)	.81
No or primary	4.0%	2.6%		
Secondary	34.4%	33.8%		
High	61.6%	63.6%		
Paternal educational level			0.1 (2)	.96
No or primary	3.8%	3.6%		
Secondary	33.9%	32.1%		
High	62.4%	64.3%		
Parity (% of children firstborn)	59.3%	69.3%	3.1 (1)	.08
Maternal anxiety (at age child 3 years)	0.18 (0.31)	0.24 (0.36)	1.5 (79)	.13
Paternal anxiety (at age child 3 years)	0.15 (0.26)	0.26 (0.39)	2.3 (66)	.02

Note. Children with and without new-onset chronic pain were compared on the listed characteristics using t-tests and χ^2-tests.
[a]New-onset chronic pain at age 3 was defined as pain lasting longer than 3 months, presenting after the measurement of pain at 2 years.
[b]Non-Dutch Western ethnicities include European and American origin, non-Western ethnicities include all other countries of origin, such as Morocco, Turkey, or Surinam.
[c]Assessments of the infant's medical history spanned the period of 0–2 years of age.

Table II. Child Behavioral and Emotional Problems

Behavioral and emotional problems	Observed range in n = 3,744	No chronic pain (n = 3,666) M (SD)	New-onset chronic pain[a] (n = 78) M (SD)	t (df)	p	M in Dutch norm group[b]
At 1.5 years						
Emotionally reactive	0–13	1.60 (1.79)	1.79 (2.09)	0.9 (3,734)	.35	2.15
Anxious-depressed	0–15	1.08 (1.34)	1.16 (1.29)	0.5 (3,742)	.59	1.95
Somatic complaints	0–12	1.42 (1.50)	1.87 (1.86)	2.1 (79)	.036	1.86
Somatic complaints excluding pain items	0–9	1.18 (1.20)	1.50 (1.38)	2.0 (79)	.045	n/a
Withdrawn	0–11	0.68 (1.08)	0.80 (1.22)	0.9 (3,740)	.37	1.19
Sleep problems	0–12	1.85 (2.19)	2.26 (2.18)	1.6 (3,742)	.10	2.41
Attention problems	0–10	2.09 (1.75)	2.39 (1.99)	1.4 (80)	.18	2.41
Aggressive behavior	0–33	8.30 (5.32)	9.52 (5.82)	2.0 (3,740)	.046	10.84
At 3 years						
Emotionally reactive	0–13	1.54 (1.73)	1.88 (1.99)	1.7 (3,738)	.09	2.15
Anxious-depressed	0–11	0.91 (1.39)	1.40 (1.69)	3.1 (3,742)	.002	1.95
Somatic complaints	0–11	1.48 (1.59)	3.43 (2.20)	7.7 (79)	<.001	1.86
Somatic complaints excluding pain items	0–8	1.19 (1.23)	1.97 (1.41)	5.5 (3,737)	<.001	n/a
Withdrawn	0–12	0.84 (1.23)	1.19 (1.40)	2.5 (3,739)	.014	1.19
Sleep problems	0–14	1.83 (2.06)	2.93 (2.60)	3.7 (79)	<.001	2.41
Attention problems	0–9	1.37 (1.55)	1.37 (1.57)	−0.0 (3,740)	.97	2.41
Aggressive behavior	0–33	6.85 (5.09)	8.40 (5.43)	2.7 (3,739)	.008	10.84

Note. Children with and without new-onset chronic pain were compared on the listed characteristics using unadjusted t-tests.
[a]New-onset chronic pain at age 3 years was defined as pain lasting longer than 3 months, presenting after the measurement of pain at 2 years.
[b]Means of the Dutch norm group of 2- and 3-year-old children in 2003, taken from the study by Tick, Ende, Koot, and Verhulst (2007).

being anxious/depressed; sumscore difference 0.24, $t = 3.2$, $p = .001$ for somatic complaints; sumscore difference 0.27, $t = 4.4$, $p < .001$ for being withdrawn; sumscore difference 0.53, $t = 5.1$, $p < .001$ for sleep problems; sumscore difference 0.22, $t = 2.8$, $p = .005$ for attention problems; and sumscore difference 0.65, $t = 2.8$, $p = .004$ for aggressive behavior).

Pain Characteristics of Children with Chronic Pain

The most common pain locations at 2 years were the ear (39%) and abdomen (29%). About 45% ($n = 22$) of children had pain occurring once a week or more frequently. The mean pain intensity was 41 on a scale of 0 to 100 ($SD = 26$). Many children had some difficulties with their daily activities ($M = 28$ on a scale of 0 to 100, $SD = 28$), but only 5 (11%) of children were incapable of doing anything on one or more days because of the pain.

For the new-onset chronic pain at 3 years, the most common pain locations were the abdomen (55%) and arms/legs (22%). About 56% ($n = 44$) of children had pain occurring once a week or more frequently. The mean pain intensity was 35 on a scale of 0 to 100 ($SD = 24$). Many children had some difficulties with their daily activities ($M = 22$ on a scale of 0 to 100, $SD = 22$), but only 9 (13%) of children were incapable of doing anything on one or more days because of the pain.

Concurrent Relations Between Chronic Pain and Mental Health

Table III shows the concurrent associations of the new-onset chronic pain at 3 years (mostly mother-reported) with mother-reported behavioral and emotional problems at 3 years. Children with new-onset chronic pain had more anxious-depressed symptoms, had more somatic complaints other than pain, were more withdrawn, had more sleep problems, and showed more aggressive behavior. After Bonferroni corrections using threshold $p = .007$ (i.e., .05/7), the associations with anxious-depressed symptoms, somatic complaints excluding pain, and sleep problems remained significant. For children with chronic pain, the means of these three problems were increased by 0.45, 0.73, and 1.0 units respectively (Table III; B-values are mean differences).

The data on father-reported chronic pain and father-reported behavioral and emotional problems showed that, in comparison to mother-reported data, chronic pain was not related to anxious-depressed behavior and aggressive behavior. Otherwise, associations for father-reported data on pain and behavioral and emotional problems had a similar pattern to associations for mother-reported data.

Table III. Models of the Association of Chronic Pain at 2 and 3 Years with Behavioral and Emotional Problems at 3 Years

Predictor	Emotionally Reactive			Anxious-depressed			Somatic Complaints Excluding Pain[c]			Withdrawn			Sleep Problems			Attention Problems			Aggressive Behavior		
	B (95% CI)	ΔR^2	Total R^2	B (95% CI)	ΔR^2	Total R^2	B (95% CI)	ΔR^2	Total R^2	B (95% CI)	ΔR^2	Total R^2	B (95% CI)	ΔR^2	Total R^2	B (95% CI)	ΔR^2	Total R^2	B (95% CI)	ΔR^2	Total R^2
Longitudinal predictor: Chronic pain at 2 years[a]	−0.044 (−0.502 to 0.413)	<.001	.251	−0.026 (−0.399 to 0.346)	<.001	.237	−0.127 (−0.475 to 0.222)	<.001	.150	−0.129 (−0.467 to 0.209)	<.001	.188	−0.186 (−0.754 to 0.383)	<.001	.193	−0.258 (−0.665 to 0.149)	<.001	.253	−1.194 (−2.475 to 0.086)#	.001	.321
Concurrent predictor: New-onset chronic pain at 3 years[b]	0.230 (−0.147 to 0.606)	<.001	.087	0.447 (0.150 to 0.745)**	.002	.105	0.736 (0.465 to 1.006)***	.007	.063	0.318 (0.050 to 0.586)*	.001	.075	1.033 (0.582 to 1.485)***	.005	.070	−0.064 (−0.404 to 0.275)	<.001	.051	1.311 (0.213 to 2.409)*	.001	.085

[a]This row in the table presents results of seven longitudinal linear regression models (seven columns) in which chronic pain at 2 years was entered as predictor and each of the seven behavioral or emotional problems at 3 years as outcome variable. All linear regression models were adjusted for ethnicity, gender, maternal, and paternal anxiety measured at 3 years, and the respective behavioral or emotional problem at 1.5 years. B-values represent unstandardized regression coefficients from linear regression analyses, which can be interpreted as the mean differences between the pain and no pain groups.
[b]This row in the table presents results of seven concurrent linear regression models (seven columns) in which chronic pain at 3 years was entered as predictor and each of the seven behavioral or emotional problems at 3 years as outcome variable. All linear regression models were adjusted for ethnicity, gender, and maternal and paternal anxiety measured at 3 years. New-onset chronic pain at age 3 was defined as pain lasting longer than 3 months, presenting after the measurement of pain at 2 years. B-values represent unstandardized regression coefficients from linear regression analyses, which can be interpreted as the mean differences between the pain and no pain groups.
[c]Pain items were excluded in the somatic complaints scale because of overlap with the pain measure. When pain items were included, the results were: B = −0.054, 95% CI = −0.512 to 0.405, p = ns, ΔR^2 = <.001, total R^2 = .146; and B = 1.867, 95% CI = 1.518 to 2.217, p = <.001, ΔR^2 = .027, total R^2 = .084, respectively.
#p < .10; *p < .05; **p < .01; ***p < .001.

When analyzing the (almost) concurrent relations between chronic pain at 2 years and behavioral and emotional problems at 1.5 years, the children with chronic pain had a .542 increased score of other, nonpain somatic complaints (p = .003, ΔR^2 = .002, total R^2 = .040). There was also a trend of children with chronic pain to have more anxiety/depression symptoms (mean difference = 0.359, p = 0.07, ΔR^2 = .001, total R^2 = .099). Other associations were not significant.

Longitudinal Associations of Chronic Pain With Mental Health

Table III presents the associations of chronic pain with the CBCL syndrome scales. Chronic pain at 2 years did not longitudinally increase any behavioral or emotional problem at age 3 years.

Longitudinal Associations of Mental Health With Chronic Pain

Table IV presents the odds ratios (ORs) for new-onset chronic pain. Children who showed more somatic complaints at 1.5 years, were more likely to develop chronic pain by age 3, even after pain items were excluded from the somatic complaints measure (OR = 1.26 per SD increase in somatic complaints excluding pain items). No other CBCL syndrome scales were associated with new-onset chronic pain at 3 years.

Discussion

We presented data on a large sample of toddlers taken from the general population. We showed that most behavioral and emotional problems in 1.5-year-old toddlers did not increase the risk of new-onset chronic pain during follow-up at age 3 years. However, if children had somatic complaints at 1.5 years, they were more likely to develop chronic pain at 3 years. Chronic pain in toddlers did not increase the risk of newly developed behavioral and emotional problems. Thus, only one significant longitudinal relation was found if baseline pain and mental health problems are accounted for. However, we observed concurrent relations of chronic pain and somatic complaints at both ages. If children had chronic pain at 3 years, they not only had more somatic complaints, but were also more likely to have other concurrent internalizing problems, such as symptoms of anxiety and depression, and sleep problems.

First of all, we will discuss the developmental period in which we performed our research. The term longitudinal was used in this study to make clear that the follow-up associations were different from the concurrent

Table IV. *Model of the Association of Behavioral and Emotional Problems at 1.5 Years with New-Onset Chronic Pain at 3 Years*

Predictor	New-onset chronic pain 3 years[a]		
	OR (95% CI)	ΔR²	Total R²
Behavioral and emotional problems 1.5 years			
Emotionally reactive (per SD)	1.06 (0.84–1.34)	<.001	.025
Anxious-depressed (per SD)	1.05 (0.83–1.33)	<.001	.025
Somatic complaints excluding pain[b] (per SD)	1.27 (1.02–1.58)*	.006	.031
Withdrawn (per SD)	1.11 (0.88–1.41)	.001	.026
Sleep problems (per SD)	1.20 (0.97–1.50)#	.003	.028
Attention problems (per SD)	1.15 (0.93–1.43)	.002	.027
Aggressive behavior (per SD)	1.21 (0.97–1.51)#	.004	.029

[a]This table presents results of seven longitudinal logistic regression models in which each of the seven behavioral or emotional problems at 1.5 years was entered as predictor and new-onset chronic pain at 3 years as outcome variable. All logistic regression models were adjusted for ethnicity and gender of the child and for maternal and paternal anxiety measured at 3 years. The outcome measure new-onset chronic pain at age 3 years was defined as pain lasting longer than 3 months, presenting after the measurement of pain at 2 years. Behavioral and emotional problems were not adjusted for each other. The Nagelkerke R^2 and Nagelkerke R^2 change of each model are presented.
[b]Pain items were excluded in the somatic complaints scale because of overlap with the outcome measure. When pain items were included, the result was: OR (95% CI) = 1.30 (1.06–1.60), $p = .01$, $\Delta R^2 = .008$, total $R^2 = .033$.
#$p < .10$; *$p < .05$.

associations that were tested. "Longitudinal" as it is used here should be interpreted as "1-year follow-up." Our results may not be automatically generalizable to older children or longer follow-up periods. Toddlerhood is a very specific part of childhood; children develop rapidly and their verbal skills increase dramatically. Psychologically, periods of sleep disruption, moodiness, being withdrawn, and aggressiveness are expected and transient. Still, differences between children of the same age might be very informative. Another challenge is that at 2 years, parent report of children's problems may still have its difficulties as parents mostly need to rely on behavior observations, whereas at 3 years, most parents can base their answers on both child behavior and child verbal reports, which probably increases the reliability of parental questionnaire reports. Due to the rapid development of toddlers and because there was virtually no knowledge about pain in very young children, we chose to examine toddlers and use a relatively short follow-up period. Short follow-up periods are often chosen, because of the rapid developmental transitions of toddlers.

It is interesting that somatic complaints at 1.5 years increased the likelihood of new-onset chronic pain at 3 years. Concurrent relations between chronic pain and somatic complaints were also evident. Other studies also found consistent longitudinal and concurrent relations between pain and other somatic symptoms (Dufton et al., 2009; Jones, Silman et al., 2003; Jones, Watson et al., 2003; Larsson & Sund, 2007; Walker et al., 1995). Previous research has also noted that somatic symptoms frequently become chronic and can even lead to the development of somatization disorder later in life (Rocha, Prkachin, Beaumont, Hardy, & Zumbo, 2003). Although we included both children with medically explained pain and with medically unexplained pain, we speculate that this association is driven by a subgroup of children with a developing tendency to somatize.

Our result that other behavioral and emotional problems were not longitudinally associated with chronic pain differs from the results of three studies investigating the relation of mental health and pain in adolescents while also adjusting for baseline pain (El-Metwally et al., 2007; Jones, Silman et al., 2003; Jones, Watson et al., 2003). All three studies found that the total score of psychosocial difficulties as measured with the Strengths and Difficulties Questionnaire and especially the subscale conduct problems predicted new-onset pain in 11- to 14-year-olds, although one study only found this result in boys (El-Metwally et al., 2007). Given that these three studies involve older children, probably the longitudinal association between psychological problems and chronic pain becomes apparent only later in life. This discrepancy suggests that toddlers with behavioral and emotional problems do not have an increased risk of developing chronic pain within a short-term follow-up, except if they have somatic complaints. Moreover, young children with chronic pain do not have an increased risk of developing new behavioral and emotional problems within a short-term follow-up. In sum, there is no evidence for short-term longitudinal effects, in both directions, between chronic pain and behavioral and emotional problems in the preschool ages, except for somatic complaints. More research is necessary to discover the relations between pain and mental health between the ages of 3 and 11 years.

There were clear associations between chronic pain and concurrent internalizing problems. The increases in internalizing problems if children had chronic pain were moderate; however, explained variance was low. The clinical relevance for a single child may thus not be very high, but the differences are consistent and may well be important on a group level. To explain these associations, the traditional long-term cause—consequence approach will not be useful. Rather, the associations should be seen as short-term interrelatedness, with several possible explanations. First, if a child experiences pain, then sleep problems and more anxious behavior may be a direct consequence. If the pain stops, then so do the internalizing problems. Second, very young children often express stress and emotions as physical symptoms because they lack the cognitive and verbal skills to identify and express stress verbally. A third explanation is the diathesis-stress model of chronic pain (Dersh, Polatin, & Gatchel, 2002; Merikangas & Stevens, 1997). According to this model, there are pre-existing, semi-dormant characteristics in some individuals before the onset of pain that are activated by the stress of having (to cope with) chronic pain (Dersh et al., 2002). This model can also be used to explain why we found no longitudinal relations of pain and mental health: the onset of chronic pain and the onset of internalizing problems are directly linked and thus immediate.

With regards to the prevalence rate in our study, the data show that 1.3% of 2-year-old children and 2.3% of 3-year-old children experienced chronic pain. This is lower than prevalence estimates reported in other population samples, for example the 12% in 0- to 3-year-old children in the seminal study by Perquin et al. (2000). Their very high prevalence estimate has not been replicated. However, the differences may be well be related to the context in which the questions were asked. Respondents read the instructions and incorporate the context in which the questions are asked to interpret what they should report (Passchier, Hunfeld, Jelicic, & Verhage, 1993; Schwarz, 1999). The questions on child chronic pain in the present study were embedded in a large questionnaire booklet including a wide variety of questions on normal development and health. This approach is unlikely to bias parent reports of their child's pain, leading to a more valid prevalence estimate. Furthermore, we excluded everyday pains, whereas Perquin et al. (2000) did not report excluding such pains that are prevalent in the preschool ages but do not constitute a genuine chronic pain.

Although population-based, a limitation to this study is that we had a selective sample, as children with non-Western origin and with more psychological problems were more likely to be lost to follow-up. Another limitation is that both chronic pain and behavioral and emotional problems were reported by two parents, but not by other nonfamily informants. Moreover, we defined chronic pain as pain existing for more than 3 months. Although it is a commonly used definition, it does not attempt to differentiate between children with medically explained pain and those with unexplained pain or pain caused by emotional distress. Furthermore, some parents may have misinterpreted the questionnaire introduction as they reported everyday pains, which were present for more than 3 months. Thus, we used the question about the parents' idea of the cause of the pain to exclude everyday pains from the chronic pain group. However, 17 parents indicated that they did not know the cause of their child's pain and 6 parents did not complete the question on cause of the pain. In these cases, we assumed that the reported chronic pain was not everyday pain. However, some misclassification may have occurred. To prevent possible misclassification, future research should include a question specifically asking whether the reported pain is everyday pain or the questionnaire introduction should state very explicitly that the questionnaire is not about everyday pains. A further limitation is that the mean pain intensity and influence on daily functioning were quite low. This suggests that the chronic pain in our sample may have been less severe than the pain seen in clinical settings, implying that results should be generalized cautiously to children with chronic pain presenting to medical care. Furthermore, reporter bias may not be ruled out completely, as certain parents' observations of their child may be influenced by their own health problems or demographics. Although analyses were adjusted for parental anxiety and the associations were not confounded by parental chronic pain, depression, age, or education, residual confounding might still exist.

Future studies should investigate the age range of 3- to 11-year-olds to find out at which age a longitudinal relation between psychosocial characteristics and chronic pain becomes apparent. Also, we have shown that there are many concurrent associations between chronic pain and internalizing problems. Future research should investigate in which children the pain is accompanied by internalizing problems and how this affects daily functioning.

We conclude that within the short and rapidly changing period of toddlerhood, somatic complaints are longitudinally and concurrently related to chronic pain. Other behavioral and emotional problems are not longitudinally related to new-onset chronic pain. Also, chronic pain does not precede the development of behavioral and emotional problems. But if chronic pain is present, the toddler is likely to also suffer from internalizing problems including anxiety/depression, sleep problems and nonpain somatic complaints. This suggests that many children are vulnerable to suffering from multiple health problems simultaneously. This comorbidity can possibly impact on daily functioning. A clinical implication is that children presenting with chronic pain complaints to primary health care should be screened for concurrent mental health symptoms, and vice versa. If appropriate, children may be referred for treatment of these secondary symptoms. Also, children with pain and other somatic symptoms may be developing a tendency to somatize. Health care professionals should be aware that an early stage of somatization may exist in toddlers.

Acknowledgments

The Generation R Study is conducted by the Erasmus Medical Center, Rotterdam in close collaboration with the Erasmus University Rotterdam, the Municipal Health Service Rotterdam area, the Rotterdam Homecare Foundation and the Stichting Trombosedienst & Artsenlaboratorium Rijnmond (STAR), Rotterdam. The authors wish to thank the parents and children that participate in the Generation R Study.

Funding

The study described in this article was supported by the Netherlands Organization for Health Research and Development (ZonMw; grant numbers 11.000.0004, 10.000.1003); the Foundation Erasmus Pain Fighting Fund (Stichting Erasmus Fonds Pijnbestrijding); the Innovation Fund for Health Care Insurers (Innovatiefonds Zorgverzekeraars; grant number 928); and a VIDI grant to H. Tiemeier from the Netherlands Organization for Scientific Research (NWO; grant number 017.106.370). The Generation R Study is made possible by financial support from the Erasmus Medical Center, Rotterdam, the Erasmus University Rotterdam, and the Netherlands Organization for Health Research and Development (ZonMw).

Conflicts of interest: Prof. Verhulst is a contributing author of the Achenbach System of Empirically Based Assessment, from which he receives remuneration. The other authors have no conflicts of interest.

References

Achenbach, T. M., & Rescorla, L. A. (2000). *Manual for the ASEBA preschool forms and profiles*. Burlington: University of Vermont, Research Center for Children, Youth, and Families.

Aromaa, M., Rautava, P., Helenius, H., & Sillanpaa, M. L. (1998). Factors of early life as predictors of headache in children at school entry. *Headache, 38*(1), 23–30.

Campo, J. V., Bridge, J., Ehmann, M., Altman, S., Lucas, A., Birmaher, B., ... Brent, D. A. (2004). Recurrent abdominal pain, anxiety, and depression in primary care. *Pediatrics, 113*(4), 817–824.

Campo, J. V., Comer, D. M., Jansen-Mcwilliams, L., Gardner, W., & Kelleher, K. J. (2002). Recurrent pain, emotional distress, and health service use in childhood. *Journal of Pediatrics, 141*(1), 76–83.

Dersh, J., Polatin, P. B., & Gatchel, R. J. (2002). Chronic pain and psychopathology: Research findings and theoretical considerations. *Psychosomatic Medicine, 64*(5), 773–786.

Dufton, L. M., Dunn, M. J., & Compas, B. E. (2009). Anxiety and somatic complaints in children with recurrent abdominal pain and anxiety disorders. *Journal of Pediatric Psychology, 34*(2), 176–186.

Egger, H. L., Angold, A., & Costello, E. J. (1998). Headaches and psychopathology in children and adolescents. *Journal of the American Academy of Child and Adolescent Psychiatry, 37*(9), 951–958.

Egger, H. L., Costello, E. J., Erkanli, A., & Angold, A. (1999). Somatic complaints and psychopathology in children and adolescents: Stomach aches, musculoskeletal pains, and headaches. *Journal of the American Academy of Child and Adolescent Psychiatry, 38*(7), 852–860.

El-Metwally, A., Halder, S., Thompson, D., Macfarlane, G. J., & Jones, G. T. (2007). Predictors of abdominal pain in schoolchildren: A 4-year population-based prospective study. *Archives of Disease in Childhood, 92*(12), 1094–1098.

El-Metwally, A., Salminen, J. J., Auvinen, A., Kautiainen, H., & Mikkelsson, M. (2006). Risk factors for traumatic and non-traumatic lower limb pain among preadolescents: A population-based study of Finnish schoolchildren. *BMC Musculoskeletal Disorders, 7*, 3.

Fearon, I., McGrath, P. J., & Achat, H. (1996). 'Booboos': the study of everyday pain among young children. *Pain, 68*(1), 55–62.

Feldman, J. M., Ortega, A. N., Koinis-Mitchell, D., Kuo, A. A., & Canino, G. (2010). Child and family psychiatric and psychological factors associated with child physical health problems: Results from the Boricua youth study. *Journal of Nervous and Mental Disease, 198*(4), 272–279.

Gatchel, R. J., Peng, Y. B., Peters, M. L., Fuchs, P. N., & Turk, D. C. (2007). The biopsychosocial approach to chronic pain: Scientific advances and future directions. *Psychological Bulletin, 133*(4), 581–624.

Hotopf, M., Carr, S., Mayou, R., Wadsworth, M., & Wessely, S. (1998). Why do children have chronic abdominal pain, and what happens to them when they grow up? Population based cohort study. *British Medical Journal, 316*(7139), 1196–1200.

Jaddoe, V. W., van Duijn, C. M., van der Heijden, A. J., Mackenbach, J. P., Moll, H. A., Steegers, E. A., ... Hofman, A. (2010). The Generation R Study: Design and cohort update 2010. *European Journal of Epidemiology, 25*(11), 823–841.

Jones, G. T., Silman, A. J., & Macfarlane, G. J. (2003). Predicting the onset of widespread body pain among children. *Arthritis and Rheumatism, 48*(9), 2615–2621.

Jones, G. T., Watson, K. D., Silman, A. J., Symmons, D. P., & Macfarlane, G. J. (2003). Predictors of low back pain in British schoolchildren: A population-based prospective cohort study. *Pediatrics, 111*(4 Pt 1), 822–828.

Larsson, B., & Sund, A. M. (2005). One-year incidence, course, and outcome predictors of frequent headaches among early adolescents. *Headache, 45*(6), 684–691.

Larsson, B., & Sund, A. M. (2007). Emotional/behavioural, social correlates and one-year predictors of frequent pains among early adolescents: Influences of pain characteristics. *European Journal of Pain, 11*(1), 57–65.

McGrath, P. J., Walco, G. A., Turk, D. C., Dworkin, R. H., Brown, M. T., Davidson, K., & Zeltzer, L. (2008). Core outcome domains and measures for pediatric acute and chronic/recurrent pain clinical trials: PedIMMPACT recommendations. *Journal of Pain, 9*(9), 771–783.

Merikangas, K. R., & Stevens, D. E. (1997). Comorbidity of migraine and psychiatric disorders. *Neurologic Clinics, 15*(1), 115–123.

Merskey, H., & Bogduk, N. (1994). *Classification of chronic pain: Descriptions of chronic pain syndromes and definitions of pain terms* (2nd ed.). Seattle: IASP Press.

Mulvaney, S., Lambert, E. W., Garber, J., & Walker, L. S. (2006). Trajectories of symptoms and impairment for pediatric patients with functional abdominal pain: A 5-year longitudinal study. *Journal of the American Academy of Child and Adolescent Psychiatry, 45*(6), 737–744.

Passchier, J., Hunfeld, J. A. M., Jelicic, M., & Verhage, F. (1993). Suggestibility and headache reports in schoolchildren: A problem in epidemiology. *Headache, 33*(2), 73–75.

Perquin, C. W., Hazebroek-Kampschreur, A. A., Hunfeld, J. A., Bohnen, A. M., van Suijlekom-Smit, L. W., Passchier, J., & van der Wouden, J. C. (2000). Pain in children and adolescents: A common experience. *Pain, 87*(1), 51–58.

Rocha, E. M., Prkachin, K. M., Beaumont, S. L., Hardy, C. L., & Zumbo, B. D. (2003). Pain reactivity and somatization in kindergarten-age children. *Journal of Pediatric Psychology, 28*(1), 47–57.

Schwarz, N. (1999). Self-reports. How the questions shape the answers. *American Psychologist, 54*(2), 93–105.

Stanford, E. A., Chambers, C. T., Biesanz, J. C., & Chen, E. (2008). The frequency, trajectories and predictors of adolescent recurrent pain: A population-based approach. *Pain, 138*(1), 11–21.

Statistics Netherlands. (2004). *Allochtonen in Nederland [Immigrants in the Netherlands]*. Statistics Netherlands: Voorburg.

Tick, N. T., Ende, J. v. d., Koot, H. M., & Verhulst, F. C. (2007). Fourteen-year changes in emotional and behavioral problems of very young Dutch children. *Journal of the American Academy of Child and Adolescent Psychiatry, 46*(10), 1333–1340.

Von Baeyer, C. L., Baskerville, S., & McGrath, P. J. (1998). Everyday pain in three- to five-year-old children in day care. *Pain Research Management, 3*(2), 111–116.

Walker, L. S., Garber, J., & Greene, J. W. (1993). Psychosocial correlates of recurrent childhood pain: A comparison of pediatric patients with recurrent abdominal pain, organic illness, and psychiatric disorders. *Journal of Abnormal Psychology, 102*(2), 248–258.

Walker, L. S., Garber, J., Van Slyke, D. A., & Greene, J. W. (1995). Long-term health outcomes in patients with recurrent abdominal pain. *Journal of Pediatric Psychology, 20*(2), 233–245.

Multimethod Assessment of Children's Distress During Noninvasive Outpatient Medical Procedures: Child and Parent Attitudes and Factors

Christina M. Rodriguez,[1] PhD, Vanessa Clough,[2] MS, Anjali S. Gowda,[1] BS, and Meagan C. Tucker,[1] MA

[1]Department of Psychology, University of North Carolina, Greensboro and [2]Department of Psychology, University of Otago

All correspondence concerning this article should be addressed to Christina M. Rodriguez, PhD, Department of Psychology, University of North Carolina, Greensboro, P.O. Box 26170, Greensboro, NC, 27402-6170, USA. E-mail: c_rodriguez@uncg.edu

Received August 13, 2011; revisions received January 16, 2011; accepted January 17, 2011

The present study assessed behavioral distress during noninvasive outpatient procedures in children ages 4–10 years using a multimethod approach. Factors hypothesized to exacerbate children's distress included parents' and children's attitudes toward healthcare, children's knowledge of medical settings, and parental anxiety. A total of 53 parent–child dyads were recruited from outpatient clinics, with procedural distress assessed via child report, parent report, and direct observation. Some differences emerged depending on the method used to gauge distress. Children's healthcare attitudes and knowledge were associated with observed and child-reported distress, but parent's personal anxiety was associated only with their own perceptions of children's procedural distress. Parents' attitudes toward healthcare were associated with their anxiety but not with children's behavioral distress or healthcare attitudes. Findings are discussed in terms of more consistent findings regarding children's healthcare knowledge and attitudes versus the potential need for additional research on more divergent findings regarding parents' anxiety and healthcare attitudes.

Key words attitudes toward healthcare; behavioral distress; children's knowledge; multimethod; outpatient medical patients; parent–child relations.

Although medical procedures can be daunting for many, children are often more disturbed and threatened by medical situations because of the separation from caregivers and the novelty of the situation. Children's adverse reactions to medical situations have long been recognized (Prugh, Staub, Sands, Kirschbaum, & Lenihan, 1953), although efforts have continued over the intervening decades to identify factors that mitigate or exacerbate children's procedure-related distress (e.g., Mahoney, Ayers, & Seddon, 2010). Such reactions include short-term sequelae to hospitalization and surgery, such as depression, sleep disturbance, and aggression (Yap, 1988), but distress is also observed during outpatient procedures (Bachanas & Roberts, 1995). In operationalizing distress in this study, because of our multi-informant approach, behavioral manifestations of distress (e.g., crying, verbalized distress, solicitations for comfort) reportable across sources were emphasized rather than inferring children's mood states.

Distress and anxiety in children undergoing invasive or painful medical procedures may be predictable (e.g., McMurtry, Chambers, McGrath, & Asp, 2010), but distress behavior and anxiety can actually amplify the perception of pain (McGrath, 1994). Moreover, the experience of pain can complicate our ability to disentangle the child's reaction to a pediatric situation independent of their affective or behavioral response to the pain or invasiveness involved in a given medical procedure. Even without physically invasive or painful processes during medical procedures, children can become distressed because of misgivings about the equipment/setting or because of memories of pain from earlier upsetting pediatric experiences (von Baeyer, Marche, Rocha, & Salmon, 2004). Yet compared to the volume of literature on distress during painful and/or invasive medical procedures, surprisingly little research has explored children's distress during noninvasive procedures, which are common occurrences in the lives of most children.

Although research is limited, one study observed children demonstrated both behavioral and physiological distress even when the procedure was not invasive or painful, which can interfere with the smooth delivery of needed medical intervention (Tyc, Klosky, Kronenberg, & Armendi, 2002). In noninvasive medical procedures without pain, like X-ray examinations, young children can still experience procedural distress that can interfere with diagnostic and treatment processes and outcomes (Bradford, 1990). Interventions have been developed that would be appropriate to children undergoing noninvasive pediatric procedures (Klosky et al., 2004; Stevenson et al., 1990). Nonetheless, despite the modest number of studies confirming that behavioral distress occurs during noninvasive pediatric contexts, research has not adequately identified factors that potentially exacerbate behavioral distress during procedures that do not induce pain. The current study thus explicitly investigated variables that may be associated with children's behavioral distress during nonpainful outpatient medical procedures that would not be confounded by a reaction to pain that could arise from a physically invasive medical process.

Children possess a number of individual characteristics that may relate to their distress behavior but children's behavior is also influenced by their parents. The classic notion of emotional contagion suggests that one's emotional distress may be transmitted to another (Escalona, 1953; Hatfield, Cacioppo, & Rapson, 1994). Essentially, emotion contagion theory is congruent with basic social learning theory (Bandura, 1969), which proposes behavior can be learned through modeling. Parents can thus model behavior, including emotional distress and communicate beliefs to their children, which in the pediatric context would include parents modeling and/or conveying their distress and beliefs about the pediatric visit to their children.

Beginning with child-level background characteristics, several factors have been associated with increased distress behaviors. For example, younger children are generally more likely to demonstrate a wider variety and greater intensity of distress than older children during medical procedures (Bachanas & Roberts, 1995; Blount, Landolf-Fritsche, Powers, & Sturges, 1991; Jay, Ozolins, Elliott, & Caldwell, 1983; Tyc et al., 2002). In addition, girls may be more likely than boys to demonstrate distress.

For example, females display higher levels of distress during painful procedures, such as bone marrow aspirations (Blount et al., 1991; Katz, Kellerman, & Siegel, 1980) and during hospitalization (Saylor, Pallmeyer, Finch, & Eason, 1987), although such gender differences with girls are not systematically observed (e.g., Rodriguez & Boggs, 1994), particularly in younger children (Goodenough et al., 1999).

Apart from demographic characteristics, child-level factors pertaining to their pediatric history are also relevant to child distress. For example, one major intervention approach to minimize children's pediatric distress involves providing information regarding the medical procedures (Jaaniste, Hayes, & von Baeyer, 2007), predicated on the belief that preparatory information reduces distress (Palermo, Drotar, & Tripi, 1999). Higher anxiety is often observed among children with the least familiarity with medical procedures and instruments (e.g., Claar, Walker, & Smith, 2002). A child's prior experience with medical settings and procedures is also likely to influence their attitudes toward those same settings and procedures. But relatively little is known about children's attitudes toward healthcare as it relates to their distress, even in the literature on invasive medical procedures. Children with more negative, unfavorable attitudes toward healthcare, as well as their mothers' negative attitudes toward healthcare, evidenced greater distress during annual well-child outpatient visits that included a blood test (Bachanas & Roberts, 1995). Such unfavorable attitudes reflect a general dislike of healthcare entities and the belief that they are ineffective and should be avoided (e.g., Bush & Holmbeck, 1987).

Consistent with social learning theory, attitudes toward health reflect shared family-level cognitions about illness (Gochman, 1997), supported by studies showing children often adopt the health beliefs and habits of their parents (e.g., Bush & Iannotti, 1988). Children's attitudes about healthcare are associated with their mothers' attitudes, with modest effect sizes using variants of the same measure given to the child and parent (Bachanas & Roberts, 1995; Hackworth & McMahon, 1991). Thus, a parent may hold negative, unfavorable attitudes toward healthcare professionals and medical settings which can sway a child's developing attitudes such that children mirror parents' attitudes, which in turn could affect children's behavioral distress.

Emotional contagion theory also suggests parents' reactions to the medical situation can influence their children's distress during a procedure. Parents can theoretically facilitate their children's coping during painful procedures (Bustos, Jaaniste, Salmon, & Champion, 2008), but some parental attempts to help their child cope are actually associated with greater distress (Cohen, Bernard, Greco, & McClellan, 2002). Indeed, parents' own distress behavior is associated with their children's greater distress (Mahoney et al., 2010) perhaps because parents expect their child to become distressed, which is then reflected in children's anticipatory distress even in noninvasive procedures (Tyc et al., 2002). Parents may experience anxiety before their child's procedure that is communicated to the child (Prins, 1994). Thus, parent-level anxiety and attitudes are theoretically connected via social learning to children's beliefs and distress.

A critical research design issue pertains to integrating various perspectives. Researchers advocate including a range of methods, highlighting the limits of single source and monomethod approaches (Holmbeck, Li, Schurman, Friedman, & Coakley, 2002). Assessment with children, parents, and observational measures is optimal (e.g., McClellan et al., 2009), wherein rating scales and direct observation are clearly useful (e.g., Blount & Loiselle, 2009). Parents are often relied upon because of their familiarity with the child's distress behaviors. Yet distress also reflects a subjective experience, rendering children's perspectives invaluable. Although child self-report may be complicated by doubts arising from the respondent's age, researchers have meaningfully included the report of children as young as three (e.g., Blount et al., 1992).

Consequently, the purpose of the present study was to conduct a multi-informant, multimethod assessment of young children's behavioral distress (parent reported, child reported, and direct observation), targeting nonpainful, noninvasive medical procedures, a relatively under-studied segment of the pediatric psychology literature. Among the factors of primary interest were parents' and children's health-related attitudes, which have also not been well studied, particularly as they relate to distress during noninvasive procedures. Based on social learning theory, negative parental attitudes toward healthcare were hypothesized to be mirrored by children's negative attitudes that would be associated with their procedure-related behavioral distress. Parental anxiety was similarly anticipated to relate to children's procedural distress.

The study targeted children as young as four; thus we incorporated self-report strategies appropriate for young children. For example, existing self-reports of children's healthcare attitudes pose questions assuming children are familiar with the medical aspects (or ask a child to estimate what they believe their attitude could be when unfamiliar; Bush & Holmbeck, 1987), which would be more complicated and abstract for young children. We were also interested in the role of children's knowledge of pediatric equipment and settings as it relates to their healthcare attitudes and distress. Thus, we designed a measure to obtain attitudes for aspects of healthcare with which they were familiar. We hypothesized children with less knowledge of and poorer attitudes toward healthcare would display elevated distress behavior. Since parental factors were theorized to affect children's distress, we examined whether children's knowledge of and attitudes toward healthcare would predict parent reported, child reported, and observer reported behavioral distress beyond what might be attributed to parental anxiety and healthcare attitudes.

Method
Participants

Participants were 53 children between 4 and 10 years old ($M = 7.08$ years, $SD = 1.95$ years) who presented at outpatient medical clinics at Dunedin Public Hospital, located in Dunedin, New Zealand with a catchment area of the wider Otago region. Of these children, 32 were male and 21 were female. Parents (81% mothers) reported on their child's race/ethnicity, with 85% indicating European descent. The majority (88.7%) of children were living in two-parent homes with a modal annual family income between NZ$30–45,000 (average national family income was NZ$46,100). Children were being seen for outpatient services for one of four noninvasive medical procedures: electroencephalogram (EEG, $n = 13$); electrocardiogram (ECG, $n = 7$); chest X-ray (X-ray, $n = 3$); or ear/nose/throat examination (ENT, $n = 22$). According to parent report, the majority of the children (54.7%) had previous outpatient hospital visits, nearly half had experienced an overnight stay (45.3%), and only a third (34%) had never experienced that day's procedure before, suggesting this was a relatively medically 'experienced' sample of children.

Measures
Parent Report
The *Behavioral Upset in Medical Patients-Revised* Hospital scale (BUMP Hospital; Rodriguez & Boggs, 1994; Saylor et al., 1987) assesses a child's behavioral distress in a hospital setting. Caretakers report on 28 items using a 5-point Likert scale, where higher scores are indicative of greater distress. For example, parents indicated their extent of agreement with the item, "Clinging, needs lots of reassurance". The reliability and concurrent validity of the BUMP Hospital have been investigated with an inpatient sample, with internal consistency at .87 (Rodriguez & Boggs, 1994). For the current study, two items were removed as not applicable to a nonhospitalized sample (items inquiring about sleep). In the current study, this 26-item version

of the BUMP-R Hospital maintained high reliability, with Cronbach's α at .90.

The *Attitudes towards Doctors and Medicine Questionnaire* (ADMQ; Marteau, 1990) is a 19-item measure of an adult's attitudes toward the medical profession, including opinions regarding the effectiveness of medicine and doctors to promote health versus their reluctance or skepticism. Parents responded on a 6-point Likert scale, with high scores reflecting more *positive* attitudes. Internal consistency has been previously reported as ranging from .61 to .76 as well as retest reliabilities ranging from .61 to .81 with support for concurrent validity (Marteau, 1990). In the current sample, parental ADMQ scores evidenced adequate internal consistency ($\alpha = .79$).

The *State-Trait Anxiety Inventory* (STAI; Spielberger, 1983) State anxiety scale is a widely used measure of self-reported anxiety in adults. Parents completed the STAI State anxiety scale to determine their situationally specific anxiety immediately prior to the child's procedure. These 20 items are rated on a 4-point Likert scale, wherein higher scores suggest greater anxiety. Scores are scaled to *T*-scores with a mean of 50. Considerable psychometric evidence supports the reliability and validity of the STAI, with a high median α of .92 (Spielberger, 1983).

Child Report

The *Behavioral Upset in Medical Patients-Child Self-Report Version* (Child-BUMP; Rodriguez & Boggs, 1998) is a 27-item pictorial scale of items adapted from the BUMP Hospital scale above. All items are phrased in language understandable for children ages 4 and above. Modeled after the format of the Harter self-competence scales (Harter & Pike, 1983), the Child-BUMP presents items in a two-step process. Children are asked to select one of two line drawings depicting the child's behavior that best describes them; for example, "This girl cried a little" versus "This girl cried a lot". Each item is followed by two choices regarding the frequency (e.g., "always" versus "sometimes"). Thus, each item yields a score from 1 to 4, with higher scores suggesting greater behavioral distress. The picture in each item of most distress is counterbalanced, presented alternately either left or right on the page. Male and female versions are identical except for the sex of the child depicted in the drawing, with half of the items shaded to represent a non-White population. Since the Child-BUMP was initially designed for a hospitalized sample (Rodriguez & Boggs, 1998), two items were dropped (equivalent to the two sleep items dropped from the BUMP Hospital noted above). Internal consistency was reported for the 27 items of the Child-BUMP at .76, with modest correlations supporting concurrent validity with parent report of distress (Rodriguez & Boggs, 1998). In the current sample, the 25 remaining Child-BUMP items demonstrated modest internal consistency ($\alpha = .69$). An examination of the item characteristics indicated two of the items ("this girl says she's sad" and "this girl doesn't talk about things that bug her") did not contribute well to the total score. Dropping these two items considerably improved the reliability, bringing Cronbach's α to .80. Thus, given the enhanced reliability of this abbreviated 23-item version, this Child-BUMP total score is used in our analysis. To examine whether the Child-BUMP evidences stability, we also orally administered the Child-BUMP to a separate sample of 40 comparison children between ages 4 and 10 years (recruited from a preschool and elementary school) on two occasions (1 month apart, $M = 30.5$ days, $SD = 3.1$) regarding their perception of their distress when they are sick. For the 23-item Child-BUMP used in this analysis, the retest correlation was high, at .80.

The *Children's Medical Opinions Survey* (C-MOS) was designed for this study to assess children's attitudes toward healthcare. Children are presented nine photos in three categories: health professionals (doctor, nurse); health setting (hospital, examination room); instruments/procedures (stethoscope, medicine, injection, blood pressure cuff, and the instrument/procedure they just had). Photos were of the actual items in the hospital units in this study, chosen by the participating medical clinics as the most frequently used that would be familiar to children in the age range. While looking at the photo, the child is asked if they recognize the item (Yes/No); this preliminary step established if the child had knowledge of the item, with total scores from 0 to 9 on C-MOS Knowledge across photos. Only if the child reported recognition of the item were they then asked two attitude questions in the two-step model described above for the Child-BUMP. For example, for a stethoscope, in the first attitude question in the first step, children are asked if the item would help them feel good or bad, followed by a second step about the intensity of that attitude (e.g., "a lot" vs. "a little" good/bad). This question was designed to assess their perception of effectiveness (comparable to the ADMQ concept). The second attitude question asked if they liked the item, again in two steps; the second step indicated intensity, evaluating whether they felt positively/negatively toward the object/medical professional. Two independent developmental psychologists specializing in children's language development were consulted and items were modified until both experts considered the language appropriate for children ages 4 years and above. Summary scores were then generated summing across items for a C-MOS Judgment score for "good/bad" attitudes, averaged to be proportional to the total number of items with which they were familiar (i.e., they would not be asked their opinion regarding an item if they reported no recognition of the item). Similarly, C-MOS Favorable scores are the average of all "like" ratings, proportional to recognized items. Ultimately, each attitude item yields a 4-point score ranging from 1 to 4, with an equivalent range for the summary scores given that they are based on averages, with higher scores indicating more favorable attitudes.

In our sample, C-MOS Knowledge internal consistency was modest, at .64; although not optimal, knowledge is not likely to reflect high consistency in this age group because familiarity with one item would not ensure familiarity with another. Attitude scores demonstrated high reliability, with C-MOS Judgment scores at $\alpha = .86$ and C-MOS Favorable scores at $\alpha = .87$. Based on the independent sample of 40 schoolchildren described above in the Child-BUMP, the C-MOS was also administered twice, 1 month apart. Stability for C-MOS Knowledge was .50, which is acceptable given that knowledge would likely increase over time, particularly as children likely inquired about items they were unfamiliar with after the first session. For attitude scores, C-MOS Judgment scores demonstrated good stability at .64 and C-MOS Favorable at .88.

Observation

The *Observation Scale of Behavioral Distress-Revised* (OSBD; Jay & Elliot, 1986) is designed for direct observational ratings, originally for children undergoing bone marrow aspirations and lumbar punctures. The coding system has been applied to other procedures (e.g., Powers, Blount, Bachanas, Cotter, & Swan, 1993). Using eight operationally defined behavioral signs of anxiety/behavioral distress, coders track whether the child exhibits information seeking, crying, screaming, restraint by others, verbal resistance, eliciting emotional support, verbal pain, and flailing. Each category is weighted according to intensity of the behavior (e.g., screaming and flailing are weighted higher than verbal resistance). The OSBD was coded in continuous 15-s intervals, tallying occurrence of each behavior; interval codes included behavior exhibited during procedure preparation (first eight 15-s intervals), during the procedure (ten 15-s intervals), and completion of the procedure (first eight 15-s intervals). For all but the EEG, this allowed for the entire procedure to be recorded; for EEG, which was longer, three phases were targeted for three procedure-related events (lying on the bed to begin EEG for four intervals, blowing on a windmill for three intervals, flashing lights for three intervals). Weighted mean interval scores within each phase contributed to the Total OSBD Distress score across phases. Prior studies support the psychometrics of the OSBD, with concurrent validity with other ratings of distress and good inter-rater reliability, with a correlation coefficient of .99 (Jay et al., 1983). In this study, 19 tapes were coded independently by another rater (36% of tapes), resulting in an inter-rater correlation of .95 for the weighted scores, an overall rate of agreement of 98.5% and Cohen's κ of .66 on unweighted tallies across phases. Nearly half the sample evidenced some behavioral distress, with ~1% of any tallies involving a pain code.

Procedures

Approval for this study was obtained by the university Institutional Review Board and informed consent acquired. Parents of a child in the age range scheduled for an outpatient clinic visit received letters describing the study with their appointment reminder or were approached during their visit if unscheduled. Those parents expressing interest in participating at the time of their appointment were enrolled in the study (approximately 34 parents declined primarily due to time constraints). The parent completed the STAI on their own anxiety immediately before the scheduled procedure, while the researcher set up the videocamera in the procedure room. The parent was always present during the child's procedure. Immediately after the procedure, the videocamera was stopped and the parent and child were taken to a quiet area of the clinic, where the parent completed demographic information, the ADMQ on their own attitudes and the BUMP-R Hospital on how their child behaved during the procedure. Meanwhile, the researcher privately interviewed the child, orally administering the C-MOS and Child-BUMP.

Results

Potential Covariates

T-tests or correlations were initially performed to determine whether measures differed relative to background characteristics to evaluate the need for covariates. No significant differences in outcome variables were identified for parent age and education or child gender (all $p > .05$). There were no clear differences across different medical procedures (all *F*-tests, $p > .05$) with the exception of those receiving an EEG demonstrating somewhat more knowledge than those receiving the other procedures [$F(3, 45) = 2.91\ p \leq .05$]. Greater family income was associated only with favorable parental attitudes on the ADMQ ($r = .32$, $p \leq .05$). As can be seen in Table I, child age was associated with several measures and, of the questions assessing prior pediatric experience, the number of prior hospital outpatient visits demonstrated some association with

Table I. Mean, Standard Deviations, and Correlations between Measures by Source

	M (SD)	Range	1	2	3	4	5	6	7	8	9
Parent Report											
1. STAI	46.94 (10.19)	34–89	–								
2. ADMQ	74.96 (9.73)	52–99	−.28*								
3. BUMP Hospital	48.09 (13.76)	29–97	.37*	−.12							
Observational											
4. OSBD	1.56 (3.66)	0–20	.08	.12	**.30***						
Child Report											
5. Child-BUMP	42.96 (7.87)	29–64	−.04	−.06	**.29***	**.10**					
6. CMOS Knowledge	8.08 (1.32)	4–9	−.06	.28*	−.10	−.38*	−.28*				
7. CMOS Judgment	3.19 (.48)	2.00–4	.02	−.13	−.30*	−.40**	−.42**	−.02			
8. CMOS Favorable	3.10 (.56)	1.67–4	−.10	.11	−.14	−.29*	−.46***	.31*	.46***		
Covariates											
9. Age	7.08 (1.95)	4–10	−.08	.05	−.39**	−.43***	−.11	.36	.11	−.01	
10. No. of Hospital outpatient	Median 3–5	0–16+	.03	−.01	.25	−.15	.10	.04	−.02	.28*	.14

Note. Bolded values are intercorrelations between outcome measures. STAI = State-Trait Anxiety Inventory; ADMQ = Attitude towards Doctors and Medicine Questionnaire; BUMP = Behavioral Upset in Medical Patients-Revised Hospital; Child-BUMP = Child Self-Report of Behavioral Upset in Medical Patients; CMOS = Children's Medical Opinions Survey, Knowledge, Favorable, and Good/Bad Judgment scales; OSBD = Observation Scale of Behavioral Distress-Revised.
*$p \leq .05$; **$p \leq .01$; ***$p \leq .001$.

measures. Given this pattern, age and number of prior outpatient visits were considered potential covariates predicting children's distress in the multivariate analyses.

Bivariate Associations

For parental reports of children's distress, an examination of the correlations (Table I) indicated greater parental anxiety related to their report of child distress. Parent report of child distress was also correlated with child reported and observed distress. However, BUMP Hospital scores were unrelated to parents' attitudes toward healthcare or children's CMOS Knowledge scores, but significantly correlated with children's judgment scores about doctors and medicine as good for them. Children's self-reported distress was significantly associated with their attitude scores but unrelated to either observed distress or parents' anxiety or attitudes toward healthcare. Finally, direct observation of distress was significantly correlated with children's CMOS scores such that children with greater knowledge and more positive attitudes evidenced less distress. Observed distress was unrelated to parental anxiety or parental healthcare attitudes.

Of potential interest, parents' higher anxiety was associated with their more negative personal healthcare attitudes but not with children's knowledge or attitudes. Parents with more negative personal attitudes had children who had less knowledge of pediatric settings. Children with greater knowledge on the CMOS did evidence more favorable attitudes toward healthcare.

Multivariate Analyses

Three independent hierarchical multiple regression analyses were performed to predict children's behavioral distress, with BUMP Hospital, OSBD, and Child-BUMP total scores as dependent variables. Hierarchical multiple regression techniques were performed wherein potential covariates were first entered (e.g., child age, number prior outpatient visits) followed by theorized parental factors in a second block (STAI and ADMQ scores), with a final block of child-level variables (CMOS Knowledge, Judgment, and Favorable scores) to determine if these explained variance beyond the parent factors.

Initially predicting OSBD scores, with covariates, parent, and child factors entered as described above, $R^2 = .37$, $F(7, 45) = 3.75$, $p \leq .01$. But examination of those variables contributing significant unique variance in observed distress scores ultimately retained only age as a covariate, with CMOS Knowledge and Judgment scores in the child block. In other words, parent factors in the second step did not contribute significant unique variance to OSBD scores, and when entering the two attitude scores simultaneously, the analyses favored retaining CMOS Judgment scores (i.e., the child's evaluation of the effectiveness of healthcare over their opinions on favorability). Note that the CMOS Knowledge score was marginally significant but did appear to be accounting for variance and was thus retained in final model in the interests of completeness. Thus, the final, most parsimonious regression predicting OSBD scores resulted in an $R^2 = .33$, $F(3, 49) = 7.91$, $p \leq .001$ (see Table II for final regression results).

Table II. *Final Hierarchical Multiple Regression Equation Results for Child Distress*

Observed Distress (OSBD Total) Results	β	t	Δr²
Block 1			.19
Child Age	−.31	−2.48*	
No. of hospital outpatient visits			
Block 2			.14
CMOS knowledge	−.23	−1.89ᵃ	
CMOS judgment	−.32	−2.66**	

$R = .57$, $F(3, 49) = 7.91***$
$R^2 = .33$ (Adj $R^2 = .29$)

Child-reported Distress (Child BUMP) results	β	t
CMOS judgment	−.26	−1.91#
CMOS favorable	−.34	−2.47*

$R = .51$, $F(2, 50) = 8.87***$
$R^2 = .26$ (Adj $R^2 = .23$)

Parent-reported distress (BUMP Hospital) results	β	t	Δr²
Block 1			.25
Child age	−.41	−3.53***	
No. of hospital outpatient visits	.30	2.59**	
Block 2			.11
STAI State Anxiety	.33	2.88**	

$R = .60$, $F(3, 49) = 9.16***$
$R^2 = .36$ (Adj $R^2 = .32$)

Note. Tables include Beta weights, incremental or change in r^2 (Δr^2), multiple correlation coefficient (R), squared multiple correlation coefficient (R^2), and adjusted squared multiple correlation (adj R^2). BUMP = Behavioral Upset in Medical Patients-Revised Hospital; Child-BUMP = Child Self-Report of Behavioral Upset in Medical Patients; CMOS = Children's Medical Opinions Survey, Knowledge, Favorable, and Good/Bad Judgment scales; OSBD = Observation Scale of Behavioral Distress-Revised.

#$p = .06$; *$p \leq .05$; **$p \leq .01$; ***$p \leq .001$.

In the regression analyzing Child-BUMP scores as the outcome, with covariates, parent and child factors entered as described above, $R^2 = .34$, $F(7, 45) = 3.39$, $p \leq .01$. However, none of the covariates or parent factors contributed significant unique variance in child-reported distress. In the child block, both attitude scores contributed (CMOS Judgment marginally), thus appearing that negative attitudes on both dimensions were associated with child reported distress, with a final regression predicting Child-BUMP scores of $R^2 = .26$, $F(2, 50) = 8.87$, $p \leq .001$ (see Table II for final regression results).

Finally, in predicting parent-reported BUMP Hospital scores, the full initial regression yielded an $R^2 = .42$, $F(7, 45) = 4.62$, $p \leq .001$. Both covariates were retained but now none of the child-level factors explained significant variance in the parent-reported BUMP Hospital scores beyond parental state anxiety. Thus, the final model retained the covariates and STAI Anxiety scores (but not ADMQ), for a final regression predicting BUMP Hospital scores of $R^2 = .36$, $F(3, 49) = 9.16$, $p \leq .001$ (see Table II).

Discussion

The current study adopted a multi-informant approach to assess behavioral distress in children undergoing noninvasive outpatient medical procedures. Of primary interest was the relation between parents' health-related attitudes and children's health-related attitudes and knowledge as associated with children's distress, assessed by child-report, parent-report, and direct observation. Guided by social learning theory, we hypothesized parental factors, such as anxiety and healthcare attitudes, would relate to children's healthcare attitudes and knowledge that would in turn relate to their behavioral distress. Overall, findings suggest relatively modest consensus across reporters regarding children's behavioral distress during the procedure. Thus, variables of interest were not uniformly related to children's distress. For example, although children's healthcare attitudes were associated with observed and child-reported distress, only parental anxiety predicted parent-reported distress. Consequently, factors that appear to impact children's procedure-related distress may depend on who provides the evaluation of distress.

Based on child report and observation, greater knowledge about medical procedures was related to less child distress, consistent with earlier findings (Claar et al., 2002). Multivariate analyses predicting observed distress particularly suggested greater knowledge was associated with less behavioral distress. Such results support that familiarity and preparatory information surrounding the medical setting can significantly reduce a child's experienced distress (Palermo et al., 1999). What is also interesting is that parents who held more favorable healthcare attitudes themselves also had children with greater knowledge of healthcare, suggesting that the parent's attitudes may relate to their decision to provide better preparation for their children.

Somewhat consistently across source, children's positive attitudes toward healthcare were generally related to children's behavioral distress. Although the limited previous research has implied an association, we did not observe the previously reported overlap between parent and child healthcare attitudes (e.g., Bachanas & Roberts, 1995). In contrast to that study, the present study did not use a variation of the same measure across reporters, wherein the latter would magnify their findings and possibly account for our different findings. Although one may argue that children may have reported more positive attitudes toward health after the procedure because they had not reacted with distress to the recently completed procedure, the significant bivariate associations of children's judgment of efficacy with observed distress and parent-reported distress suggest that children with more positive attitudes about healthcare may indeed evidence less procedural distress. In fact, children's judgment of the effectiveness of healthcare was retained not only in predicting child-reported distress but when predicting observed distress.

But parents' attitudes toward healthcare were not associated with children's distress according to any of the sources. This result is again inconsistent with the study suggesting parents' healthcare attitudes (using the variant measure approach) predicted observed distress during well-child visits (Bachanas & Roberts, 1995). Although research on parental healthcare attitudes as it relates to children's distress is quite limited, such inconsistency suggests more research is needed to investigate the connection between parents' healthcare attitudes to childrens' developing healthcare attitudes and their subsequent procedural distress.

Parental anxiety was significantly retained only in their report of children's distress, not child reported or observed distress. Comparable to prior suggestions that parental distress influences children's distress (Mahoney et al., 2010), the fact that this was limited to parent report suggests source bias may play a role. Parental anxiety was associated with personal negative healthcare attitudes but not children's attitudes. In sum, parental anxiety appears to have limited influence on children's distress, highlighting the need to consider who is reporting on that child's behavioral distress. Assessing parental catastrophizing or anxiety sensitivity may be useful directions for research as well as obtaining alternative sources of reports for parental anxiety.

Finally, as noted in previous investigations (e.g., Tyc et al. 2002), age was a significant covariate. Younger children appear less knowledgeable, and perhaps this unfamiliarity renders them less adaptive to the novelty of the pediatric setting, thereby increasing their procedural distress. Similarly, given that younger children would be more medically inexperienced, the extent of prior medical experience was associated with children's knowledge and attitudes and parent-reported distress, consistent with prior literature on invasive medical procedures (e.g., Claar et al., 1986). But we did not observe sex differences across any measures. Prior findings on gender differences have been mixed; greater clarity is needed on whether girls are indeed more likely to display distress, which may interact with children's age (Goodenough, et al., 1999).

Although several important factors were included in this study, a few limitations should be noted. First, we conducted multivariate analyses with a small sample to enrich the findings; but for example, the sample was too small to factor analyze the CMOS (Costello & Osborne, 2005). Clearly, further psychometric evaluation of the new and modified measures used in this study is warranted. The participants were also recruited from clinics in New Zealand and were relatively medically experienced; thus, this knowledgeable sample may not generalize to the average child experiencing routine noninvasive medical procedures. Given the sample size, we could not clearly evaluate potential differences in reactions to the variety of protocols intrinsic to diverse noninvasive medical procedures. Future work could provide additional insights to our findings by targeting a larger, less medically knowledgeable, ethnically diverse sample of children from other healthcare systems, explicitly comparing different medical procedures.

One imperative avenue for future research is to further examine children's attitudes about medical settings, which is infrequently studied, perhaps due to concerns surrounding children's age and their ability to effectively report their own attitudes. The current study employed a new pictorial measure designed specifically to assess attitudes proportional to their knowledge. Our findings suggest that children's attitudes regarding how effective and positive they view healthcare indeed may relate to their observed and self-reported distress. Further research on children's healthcare attitudes using developmentally appropriate measures is thus needed. Moreover, the role of parental healthcare attitudes should be examined, specifically whether specific parental attitudes could positively sway children's attitudes and thereby mitigate their distress.

Overall, the current findings underscore the need to obtain multiple reporters as distress appears to reflect the "eye of the beholder". Relying solely on parent report of children's distress, for example, may be affected by parents' personal distress. These results demonstrate children's knowledge and healthcare attitudes may play a role in their behavioral distress in noninvasive procedures. Parents who prepare their children in advance of medical procedures, not simply by providing knowledge but conveying broader healthcare attitudes, could potentially ease their children's distress. The vast majority of pediatric research relies on assessing distress in children undergoing invasive, often painful, medical procedures, although children exhibit distress in noninvasive procedures (Tyc et al., 2002). Some have considered whether there is a distinction between distress and pain response during painful procedures (Blount & Loiselle, 2009). By researching distress in noninvasive procedures, we can uncover more purely psychological aspects of distress elicited by the pediatric context independent of pain response.

Funding

This study was supported by funding from an Otago Research Grant in Dunedin, New Zealand.

Conflicts of interest: None declared.

References

Bachanas, P. J., & Roberts, M.C. (1995). Factors affecting children's attitudes toward health care and responses to stressful medical procedures. *Journal Pediatric Psychology, 20*, 261–275.

Bandura, A. (1969). *Principles of behavior*. New York: Hold, Rinehart, & Winston.

Blount, R. L., Bachanas, P. J., Powers, S. W., Cotter, M., Franklin, A., Chaplin, W., ... Blount, S. D. (1992). Training children to cope and parents to coach them during routine immunizations: Effects on child, parent and staff behaviors. *Behavior Therapy, 23*, 689–705.

Blount, R. L., Corbin, S. M., Sturges, J. W., Wolfe, V. V., Prater, J. M., & James, L. D. (1989). The relationship between adults' behavior and child coping and distress during BMA/LP procedures: A sequential analysis. *Behavior Therapy, 20*, 585–601.

Blount, R. L., Landolf-Fritsche, B., Powers, S. W., & Sturges, J. W. (1991). Differences between high and low coping children and between parent and staff behaviors during painful medical procedures. *Journal of Pediatric Psychology, 16*, 795–809.

Blount, R. L., & Loiselle, K. A. (2009). Behavioural assessment of pediatric pain. *Pain Research & Management, 14*, 47–52.

Bradford, R. (1990). Short communication: The importance of psychosocial factors in understanding child distress during routine X-ray procedures. *Journal of Child Psychology and Psychiatry, 6*, 973–982.

Bush, J. P., & Holmbeck, G. N. (1987). Children's attitudes about health care: Initial development of a questionnaire. *Journal of Pediatric Psychology, 12*, 429–443.

Bush, P. J., & Iannotti, R. J. (1988). Origins and stability of children's health beliefs relative to medicine use. *Social Science & Medicine, 27*, 345–352.

Bustos, T., Jaaniste, T., Salmon, K., & Champion, G. D. (2008). Evaluation of a brief parent intervention teaching coping-promoting behavior for the infant immunization context: A randomized controlled trial. *Behavior Modification, 32*, 450–467.

Claar, R. L., Walker, L. S., & Smith, C. A. (2002). The influence of appraisals in understanding children's experiences with medical procedures. *Journal of Pediatric Psychology, 27*, 553–563.

Cohen, L. L., Bernard, R. S., Greco, L. A., & McClellan, C. B. (2002). A child-focused intervention for coping with procedural pain: Are parent and nurse coaches necessary? *Journal of Pediatric Psychology, 27*, 749–757.

Costello, A. B., & Osborne, J. W. (2005). Best practices in exploratory factor analysis: Four recommendations for getting the most from your analysis. *Practical Assessment, Research & Evaluation, 10*, Retrieved from http://pareonline.net/getvn.asp?v=10&n=7

Escalona, S. (1953). Emotional development in the first year of life. In M. J. E. Senn (Ed.), *Problems of infancy and childhood*. New York: Josiah Macy Jr. Foundation Press.

Gochman, D. S. (1997). *Handbook of health behavior research IV: Relevance for professionals and issues for the future*. New York: Plenum.

Goodenough, B., Thomas, W., Champion, G. D., Perrott, D., Taplin, J. E., von Baeyer, C. L., & Ziegler, J. B. (1999). Unravelling age effects and sex differences in needle pain: Ratings of sensory intensity and unpleasantness of venipuncture pain by children and their parents. *Pain, 80*, 179–190.

Hackworth, S. R., & McMahon, R. J. (1991). Factors mediating children's health care attitudes. *Journal of Pediatric Psychology, 16*, 69–85.

Hatfield, E., Cacioppo, J. T., & Rapson, R. L. (1994). *Emotional contagion*. New York: Cambridge University Press.

Harter, S., & Pike, R. (1984). The pictorial scale of perceived competence and social acceptance for young children. *Child Development, 55*, 1969–1982.

Holmbeck, G. N., Li, S. T., Schurman, J. V., Friedman, D., & Coakley, R. M. (2002). Collecting and managing multisource and multimethod data in studies of pediatric populations. *Journal of Pediatric Psychology, 27*, 5–18.

Jaaniste, T., Hayes, B., & von Baeyer, C. L. (2007). Providing children with information about forthcoming medical procedures: A review and synthesis. *Clinical Psychology: Science and Practice, 14*, 124–143.

Jay, S. M., & Elliott, C. H. (1986). *Manual for the Observation Scale of Behavioral Distress-Revised.* Unpublished manuscript. Los Angeles, CA.

Jay, S. M., Ozolins, M., Elliott, C. H., & Caldwell, S. (1983). Assessment of children's distress during painful medical procedures. *Health Psychology, 2,* 133–147.

Katz, E. R., Kellerman, J., & Siegel, S. E. (1980). Behavioral distress in children with cancer undergoing medical procedures: Developmental considerations. *Journal of Consulting and Clinical Psychology, 48,* 356–365.

Klosky, J. L., Tyc, V. L., Srivastava, D. K., Tong, X., Kronenberg, M., Booker, Z. J., ... Merchant, T. E. (2004). Brief report: Evaluation of an interactive intervention designed to reduce pediatric distress during radiation therapy procedures. *Journal of Pediatric Psychology, 29,* 621–626.

Mahoney, L., Ayers, S., & Seddon, P. (2010). The association between parent's and healthcare professional's behavior and children's coping and distress during venepuncture. *Journal of Pediatric Psychology, 35,* 985–995.

Marteau, T. M. (1990). Attitudes to doctors and medicine: The preliminary development of a new scale. *Psychology & Health, 4,* 351–386.

McClellan, C. B., Schatz, J. C., Mark, T. R. M., McKelvy, A., Puffer, E., Roberts, C. W., & Sweitzer, S. M. (2009). Criterion and convergent validity for four measures of pain in a pediatric sickle cell disease population. *The Clinical Journal of Pain, 25,* 146–152.

McGrath, P. A. (1994). Psychological aspects of pain perception. *Archives of Oral Biology, 39,* S55–S62.

McMurtry, C. M., Chambers, C. T., McGrath, P. J., & Asp, E. (2010). When 'don't worry' communicates fear: Children's perceptions of parental reassurance and distraction during a painful medical procedure. *Pain, 150,* 52–58.

Palermo, T. M., Drotar, D. D., & Tripi, P. A. (1999). Current status of psychosocial intervention research for pediatric outpatient surgery. *Journal of Clinical Psychology in Medical Settings, 6,* 405–426.

Powers, S. W., Blount, R. L., Bachanas, P. J., Cotter, M. C., & Swann, S. C. (1993). Helping preschool leukemia patients and their parent to cope during injections. *Journal of Pediatric Psychology, 18,* 681–695.

Prins, P. J. M. (1994). Anxiety in medical settings. In T. H. Ollendick, N. J. King, & W. Yule (Eds.), *International handbook of phobic and anxiety disorders in children and adolescents* (pp. 267–293). New York: Plenum Press.

Prugh, D. G., Staub, E. M., Sands, H. H., Kirschbaum, R. M., & Lenihan, E. A. (1953). A study of the emotional reactions of children and families to hospitalization and Illness. *American Journal of Orthopsychiatry, 23,* 70–106.

Rodriguez, C. M., & Boggs, S. R. (1994). Behavioral upset in medical patients-revised: Evaluation of a parent report measure of distress for pediatric populations. *Journal of Pediatric Psychology, 19,* 319–324.

Rodriguez, C. M., & Boggs, S. R. (1998). Assessment of behavioral distress and depression in a pediatric population. *Children's Health Care, 27,* 157–170.

Saylor, C. F., Pallmeyer, T. P., Finch, A. J., Eason, L., Trieber, F., & Folger, C. (1987). Predictors of psychological distress in hospitalized pediatric patients. *Journal of the American Academy of Child and Adolescent Psychiatry, 26,* 232–236.

Spielberger, C. D. (1983). *Manual for the State-Trait Anxiety Inventory.* Palo Alto, CA: Consulting Psychologists Press.

Stevenson, J. G., French, J. W., Tenckhoff, L., Maeda, H., Wright, S., & Zamberlin, K. (1990). Video viewing as an alternative to sedation for young subjects who have cardiac ultrasound examinations. *Journal of the American Society of Echocardiography, 3,* 488–490.

Tyc, V. L., Klosky, J.L., Kronenberg, M., de Armendi, A. J., & Merchant, T.E. (2002). Children's distress in anticipation of radiation therapy procedures. *Children's Health Care, 31,* 11–27.

Von Baeyer, C. L., Marche, T. A., Rocha, E. M., & Salmon, K. (2004). Children's memory for pain: Overview and implications for practice. *The Journal of Pain, 5,* 241–249.

Yap, J. N. (1988). The effects of hospitalization and surgery on children: A critical review. *Journal of Applied Developmental Psychology, 9,* 349–358.

The Role of State Anxiety in Children's Memories for Pain

Melanie Noel,[1] MSc, Christine T. Chambers,[1,2] PhD, Patrick J. McGrath,[1,2,3] PhD, Raymond M. Klein,[1] PhD, and Sherry H. Stewart,[1,3,4] PhD

[1]Department of Psychology, [2]Department of Pediatrics, [3]Department of Psychiatry, [4]Department and Community Health and Epidemiology, Dalhousie University

All correspondence concerning this article should be addressed to Melanie Noel, Centre for Pediatric Pain Research, IWK Health Centre, 5850/5980 University Avenue, Halifax, NS, Canada B3K 6R8. E-mail: melanie.noel@dal.ca

Received November 2, 2011; revisions received December 12, 2011; accepted January 18, 2012

Objective To investigate the impact of experimentally manipulated state anxiety and the influence of anxiety-related variables on children's memories for pain. **Methods** A total of 110 children (60 boys) between the ages of 8 and 12 years were randomly assigned to complete a state anxiety induction task or a control task. Following experimental manipulation, children completed a laboratory pain task, pain ratings, and questionnaire measures of anxiety-related variables. 2 weeks later, children provided pain ratings based on their memories of the pain task. **Results** The experimental manipulation effectively induced state anxiety; however, pain memories did not differ between groups. Irrespective of group assignment, children with higher state anxiety had more negative pain memories. State anxiety uniquely predicted children's pain memories over and above other well established factors. Anxiety sensitivity and trait anxiety were significant predictors of recalled pain-related fear. **Conclusions** These data highlight the importance of anxiety in the development of children's memories for pain.

Key words anxiety sensitivity; children; fear; memory; pain; state anxiety; trait anxiety.

Medical procedures including immunizations and venipunctures are a common source of pain in childhood (Public Health Agency of Canada, 2006). In addition to experiencing pain during medical procedures, many children also experience fear before procedures even begin, which can heighten a child's pain perception (Rhudy & Meagher, 2003). The impact of pain and fear can persist long after medical procedures end; the manner in which children remember painful experiences can influence how they cope with and manage future painful procedures (Chen, Zeltzer, Craske, & Katz, 2000). Pain memories are rooted early in life (for reviews see: Ornstein, Manning, & Pelphrey, 1999; von Baeyer, Marche, Rocha, & Salmon, 2004). Children as young as six months of age can form memories of painful procedures that then influence their reactions to future painful procedures (Taddio, Katz, Ilersich, & Koren, 1997; Weisman, Bernstein, & Schechter, 1998).[1] Early pain memories can persist into adulthood and influence the level of fear and avoidance of medical care later in life (Pate, Blount, Cohen, & Smith, 1996). It has been suggested that memories for pain may initiate the development and maintenance of chronic pain syndromes over time (Flor & Birbaumer, 1994; Sun-ok & Carr, 1999). In fact, memories for pain are often a better predictor of future pain experiences than the initial experience of pain itself (Gedney & Logan, 2006).

---

[1] These studies demonstrated that previous painful experiences could cause changes in infants' behavioral reactions to subsequent pain, suggesting that the infants were sensitized to pain. As noted in a review by von Baeyer et al. (2004), it is possible that these infants had learned to anticipate pain cues and formed some form of long-term memory of the pain experience. These types of long-term memories are implicit (unconscious, nonverbal) and differ from explicit memories (conscious, verbal).

Although young children's recall of previous painful experiences can be accurate (Badali, Pillai, Craig, Geisbrecht, & Chambers, 2000; Lander, Hodgins, & Fowler-Kerry, 1992), remembering is an interpretive process and memories are continually being reconstructed, which makes them susceptible to distortion over time (Bruck, Ceci, Francoeur, & Barr, 1995). Negatively distorted memories of painful medical procedures have been linked to greater distress during subsequent procedures (Chen, Zeltzer, Craske, & Katz, 1999). Furthermore, the level of distress that children experience during painful procedures influences the manner in which pain memories are framed. Across a range of medical procedures, children who report higher levels of pain and distress (e.g., trait anxiety, pain intensity, behavioral distress) tend to develop negatively exaggerated pain memories (Chen et al., 2000; Noel, McMurtry, Chambers, & McGrath, 2010; Rocha, Marche, & von Baeyer, 2009); however, this research has primarily been correlational, which has precluded examination of the causal impact of distress on memory.

Theorists have posited that memory biases exist because highly trait anxious individuals selectively encode and/or retrieve threatening information (Eysenck, Derakshan, Santos, & Calvo, 2007), particularly when those individuals experience high levels of state anxiety (i.e., short-term anxiety that arises in threatening situations; Beck & Clarke, 1997). However, research has largely neglected investigating the role of state anxiety in children's memories for pain, perhaps due to previous assertions of a lack of relationship between the two (Lander et al., 1992; Versloot, Veerkamp, & Hoogstraten, 2008), which could have been due to methodological issues (e.g., timing of the measurement of state anxiety, reliance on parent- vs. self- report measures). Moreover, no study to date has directly examined the impact of state anxiety prior to an acute pain experience on children's memories for pain.

In addition to trait and state anxiety, anxiety sensitivity (i.e., the fear of anxiety-related sensations) could also influence children's pain memories. Anxiety sensitivity is a trait-like variable that is thought to heighten one's propensity to experience anxiety which then increases pain perception (Schmidt & Cook, 1999; Stewart & Asmundson, 2006). Indeed, there is evidence of a robust relationship between child anxiety sensitivity and pain-related anticipatory anxiety, which is a strong predictor of children's pain ratings during laboratory pain (Tsao, Lu, Kim, & Zeltzer, 2006). In addition, anxiety sensitivity in adults has been found to be related to memory biases toward threat-related information (McCabe, 1999). Nevertheless, no study has examined the influence of anxiety sensitivity on children's memories for pain, particularly in the context of other important anxiety-related variables.

The current laboratory-based study investigated the impact of experimentally manipulated state anxiety on children's memories for pain. The impetus for inducing state anxiety among children in the present study was to examine the impact of state anxiety on pain memories as well as to ensure sufficient variability in levels of state anxiety among children immediately prior to completing the pain task. Unlike medical procedures, children do not report being anxious prior to completing laboratory pain induction tasks like the cold pressor task (Tsao, Myers, Craske, Bursch, Kim, & Zeltzer, 2004; Wilby, Chambers, & Perrot-Sinal, 2010). As such, induction of state anxiety was also deemed necessary in order to establish a greater degree of ecological validity and to provide a more accurate analog of a clinical medical procedure context. Therefore, in addition to investigating the impact of experimentally induced state anxiety on pain memories, it was also of conceptual interest to examine state anxiety as a continuous variable that varied among children and that might impact the framing of their pain memories. As such, this study also examined the influence of anxiety-related individual difference variables on children's recall of pain using a correlational design. It was hypothesized that children in the state anxiety induction group would have more negative pain memories than children in the control group. Additionally, it was hypothesized that children with higher scores on a variety of anxiety-related questionnaires (state and trait anxiety, anxiety sensitivity) would also have more negative memories of pain.

Method

The data for this article was collected as part of a larger study examining two distinct research questions that are presented in two empirical papers. The present article examined the impact of state anxiety on children's memories for experimental pain, as well as the influence of anxiety-related individual difference variables on their recall. The other article by Noel et al. (in press) examined the influence of children's pain memories on their expectations and experience of a subsequent painful experience, through investigation of changes in children's distress during multiple exposures to the same pain stimulus over time. This other paper utilized data obtained from an additional laboratory visit, which was not included in the present article and is not relevant to the research questions or aims of the present investigation. As a result, the methods reported below contain only those details relevant to the present study and are an abbreviated version of the larger study protocol. All study materials and procedures were approved by the health centre research ethics board (REB).

Participants

Participants were 110 healthy children (60 boys, 50 girls; $M_{age} = 9.45$ years, $SD = 1.35$) and one of their parents/guardians (99 mothers, 1 stepmother, 9 fathers, 1 stepfather; $M_{age} = 40.3$ years; $SD = 5.94$). By parent-report, the majority of participating children and parents were identified as "white" (86.4%; $n = 95$). The educational breakdown of the parents was self-identified as follows: (a) graduate school/professional training ($n = 30$); (b) university graduate ($n = 39$); (c) partial university (i.e., at least 1 year) ($n = 5$); (d) trade school/community college ($n = 25$); (e) high school graduate ($n = 9$); or (f) some high school ($n = 2$). Children in the state anxiety induction group did not differ from children in the control group on any of the demographic variables (e.g., age, sex, ethnicity, parental education).

In order to participate in the study, children had to be between 8 and 12 years of age and accompanied by a parent/guardian. Participants were excluded from the study if they did not speak English as a first language or had developmental delays or significant hearing or vision impairments. Participants were also excluded if children had been diagnosed with an Anxiety Disorder or Attention Deficit Hyperactivity Disorder and/or had chronic illnesses or health-related medical conditions, including: circulation disorders; heart problems; injuries to their arms or hands. In order to ensure that memory for the experimental pain task was not affected by previous scripts of similar pain experiences, children who had previously completed the experimental pain task (the cold pressor task) were excluded. Finally, children were excluded from the study if they experienced pain (such as headaches, stomach aches, ear/throat pain, muscle or joint pain) on a regular basis (i.e., at least once a month for three consecutive months) that was typically of moderate or severe intensity, that interfered with school or social functioning, and/or for which they took medication. Following enrolment, no families withdrew from the study and no adverse events were reported.

Measures

Pain Intensity

Pain intensity was measured using the one-item Faces Pain Scale-Revised (FPS-R; Hicks, von Baeyer, Spafford, van Korlaar, & Goodenough, 2001). The FPS-R consists of six gender-neutral faces depicting "no pain" (neutral face) to "most pain possible" expressions. Children select a face that represents how much pain she/he feels and the faces are scored: 0, 2, 4, 6, 8, and 10. The FPS-R is the most psychometrically sound self-report measure of pain intensity in children between the ages of 4 and 12 years (Stinson, Kavanagh, Yamada, Gill, & Stevens, 2006).

Pain-related Fear

Pain-related fear was measured using the one-item Children's Fear Scale (CFS; McMurtry, Noel, Chambers, & McGrath, 2011), which was adapted from the Faces Anxiety Scale (McKinley, Coote, & Stein-Parbury, 2003). The CFS consists of five faces representing varying degrees of anxiety/fear. Children are instructed to select a face that represents how scared she/he feels and the ordered faces are scored from 0 to 4. The CFS has shown good evidence of test-retest ($rs = .76$, $p < .001$) and inter-rater ($rs = .51$, $p < .001$) reliability as well as construct validity among children (McMurtry et al., 2011).

Anxiety

Visual Analog Scale

Using a 10-cm visual analog scale (VAS) with the anchors "not nervous/anxious" and "most nervous/anxious", children provided self-report ratings (VAS–child) and parents provided proxy ratings (VAS–parent) of children's state anxiety. Possible scores ranged from 0.00 to 10.00 cm. VASs have previously been used to measure child anxiety among children (Chen, Craske, Katz, Schwartz, & Zeltzer, 2000) and parents (Smith, Shah, Goldman, & Taddio, 2007). There is evidence for the validity of a 10-cm VAS to assess perioperative anxiety among children aged 7–16 years. (Bringuier et al, 2009).

State Trait Anxiety Inventory for Children (STAIC; Spielberger, 1973)

Children's state and trait anxiety was measured using the STAIC. The STAIC consists of both state and trait subscales containing 20 items each. The items on the state subscale of the STAIC (STAIC-s) ask children to rate how they feel at a particular moment in time. The tool was designed to measure transitory anxiety states (i.e., subjective and consciously perceived feelings of state anxiety that vary in intensity and that can fluctuate over time), which are typically elevated in stressful situations. The items on the trait subscale of the STAIC (STAIC-t) ask children to rate how they generally feel and measures relatively stable individual differences in the tendency to experience anxiety states and perceive situations as threatening. The STAIC-s has been found to have good internal consistency (Cronbach's $\alpha = .82–.87$) and evidence of construct validity. Similarly, the STAIC-t shows evidence of good internal consistency (Cronbach's $\alpha = .78-.81$) and concurrent validity (Spielberger, 1973). Given the strong psychometric properties of the STAIC-s, this measure was used as the operationalization of state anxiety in all primary analyses.

Anxiety Sensitivity
Anxiety sensitivity was measured using the Childhood Anxiety Sensitivity Index (CASI; Silverman, Fleisig, Rabian, & Peterson, 1991), which consists of 18 items that assess the tendency to interpret anxiety-related bodily sensations as threatening (e.g., "It scares me when I have trouble getting my breath"). The CASI has been found to have adequate test-retest reliability (range = .62–.78 over 2 weeks) and high internal consistency ($\alpha = .87$; Silverman et al., 1991). Although the measure has a moderate correlation with trait anxiety ($r = .55-.69$), the construct explains variance in fear that is unaccounted for by trait anxiety (Weems, Hammond-Laurence, Silverman, & Ginsburg, 1998).

State Anxiety Induction Task
Children assigned to the state anxiety induction group completed a modified version of the Trier Social Stress Task for Children (TSST-C; Buske-Kirschbaum et al., 1997), in which they *anticipated* having to complete the task vs. actually completing it. Like the unmodified task, the modified version used in the current study involved bringing children into a room containing three chairs, a table, three clipboards containing red pens and rating tools, a television, and a video camera on a tripod. Children completing the TSST-C were told that they would be asked to prepare and deliver a speech in front of three judges who were doctors and researchers in the hospital and who had experience judging public speaking competitions with children their age. They were told that the judges would be rating and evaluating their speeches for quality and that they would be videotaped during that time. Children were instructed that they would have 4 min to prepare the speech and 4 min to deliver the speech. Then, they were told that they would be asked to complete a difficult mental arithmetic task by subtracting specific numbers and that every time they provided an incorrect answer, they would be asked to complete the arithmetic task once again from the beginning. Finally, children were told that many children considered the task to be difficult and that the judges would be arriving soon.[2] The TSST-C involves elements (e.g., uncontrollability, unpredictability, threats to the social self) that have been identified as being strong psychological triggers of the HPA axis that regulates the release of cortisol (i.e., the stress hormone; see Dickerson & Kemeny, 2004; Gunnar, Talge, & Herrera, 2009). Several studies have shown that the TSST-C and modifications of the task are successful in provoking heightened self-perceptions of stress and anxiety among children (Buske-Kirschbaum et al., 1997; 2003; Gunnar, Frenn, Wewerka, & Van Ryzin, 2009; Stroud et al., 2009). Moreover, anticipation of completing the TSST vs. actual completion of the task–which was the modified version of the TSST-C used in the present investigation–has been shown to be as effective in eliciting a stress/anxious response (e.g., increased subjective anxiety, perceived stress, heart rate, cortisol) as the actual completion of the task (Hermann, Vogl, & Maras, 2004).

Control Task
Children assigned to the control group were brought into the same room as children in the state anxiety induction group (described above) and were told that they would be asked to watch a nature video from the video series "Planet Earth" that showed different animals and wildlife. They were reassured that the video camera would not be used for them. Children were instructed that they would watch the video for 12 min and were told that many children thought that the videos were interesting.

Cold Pressor Task
The cold pressor task is an ethically acceptable pain induction technique for use with children (Birnie, Noel, Chambers, von Baeyer, & Fernandez, 2011). It involves children submersing their nondominant hand up to their wrist fold into 10°C water for an informed ceiling of 4 min. Children were asked to leave their hand in the water even if it was uncomfortable; however, they were told that they could remove their hand at any time if it became too uncomfortable or painful to leave it in. The cold pressor device was a commercially manufactured plastic cooler filled with water with a temperature that was maintained at $10 \pm 1°C$ (in keeping with published guidelines; von Baeyer, Piira, Chambers, Trapanotto, & Zeltzer, 2005). A plastic screen separated the cooler into two sections and ice cubes were placed in the first section to cool the water. The device measured 43.5-cm long, 23.5-cm wide, and 28.0-cm deep. Children lowered their hand into the water in the second section through a round opening (13 cm in diameter) in the lid of the cooler. A bilge pump circulated the water to prevent local warming around the child's hand.

---

[2] A copy of the experimental and control group scripts used in this study are available from the corresponding author upon request.

Procedure

Participants were recruited using paper and online advertisements distributed in the community surrounding the health centre. Interested parents contacted the research centre by telephone and completed a series of screening questions to determine study eligibility. Following screening, participating families came to the research centre for an initial visit. Parents and children were separated from each other and remained separated for the entire testing session. Parents provided full and informed consent from a separate adjoining room and watched the entire experiment via video monitors. Children provided assent; however, they were not fully informed about the nature of the experimental or control conditions (i.e., that they would not actually be required to fully complete the tasks). They were also not aware about the memory component of the study in order to ensure that their experience and ratings would not be affected by knowledge that their memories for the pain task would later be assessed. Following provision of assent, children completed the VAS–child to assess their baseline level of anxiety. Then, a different research assistant disclosed to the children to which group they had been randomly assigned. This research assistant assumed a serious demeanor whereas the research assistant who obtained assent from children assumed a friendly demeanor. Next, children were led into the experimental room and given instructions for their respective groups. Immediately following administration of the instructions and while anticipating having to complete the experimental or control tasks, children rated their level of state anxiety on the VAS–child and the STAIC-s. After watching their children receive the instructions via video, parents concurrently provided proxy ratings of children's levels of state anxiety on the VAS–parent. Immediately after measures of state anxiety were completed, children were taken into a separate testing room and completed the cold pressor task. Immediately after children removed their hands from the water, they completed measures of pain intensity and pain-related fear using the FPS-R and the CFS. The administration order of these scales was counterbalanced across children. Next, children were brought into a waiting room and the research assistant who obtained assent informed them that they did not have to complete the speech ("the judge could not make it") or watch the video ("the video equipment is not working"). Children then completed measures of trait anxiety and anxiety sensitivity using the STAIC-t and the CASI. The administration order of these scales was counterbalanced across children.

Prior to leaving the laboratory, parents were given a sealed envelope containing copies of the pain intensity and pain-related fear scales, which were individually contained in sealed and numbered envelopes. Parents were asked to refrain from opening the sealed envelope until a researcher called them to conduct the memory interview. They were also asked to minimize discussion about the experiment in the interim between the laboratory visit and subsequent telephone interview. Children were aware that a research assistant would call them in approximately two weeks to ask them questions; however, they were not aware that they would be asked about their memories of the pain experience. Prior to leaving the laboratory, appointments to conduct the telephone interviews were scheduled with parents.

Approximately 2 weeks following the laboratory visit ($M = 14.00$ days, $SD = 1.24$ days, Range $= 9-19$ days), parents were contacted over the telephone to conduct the memory interviews. Telephone interviews for research on children's memory for cold pressor, venipuncture, and postoperative pain have been effectively conducted with children (Badali et al., 2000, Lander et al., 1992; Noel et al., 2010; Zonneveld, McGrath, Reid, & Sorbi, 1997). Previous memory research has used time frames ranging from 1 week to 1 year (e.g., Badali et al., 2000; Chen et al., 2000;). The present study employed a 2-week time frame in an attempt to limit exclusions as a result of intervening pain experiences and attrition. This attempt was successful in that all participants (100%) who participated in the initial laboratory visit completed the telephone interviews. At the beginning of the interview, parents were asked to refrain from influencing their children's responses so as to not bias their recall. The memory assessment followed a similar protocol to that used with children aged 5–10 years in previous research examining children's memory for venipuncture and cold pressor pain (Badali et al., 2000; Noel et al., 2010). During the memory interview, children could not physically point to the faces in front of the researcher as they had done immediately following completion of the CPT. Therefore, to facilitate ease of telephone communication and to avoid introducing a confounding numerical scale, letters of the alphabet were placed in random order under the faces on each of the scales used during the telephone interviews. Children were reinstructed in the use of each rating scale and oriented to the placement of letters under each face. The order of scale presentation was counterbalanced and randomly numbered from 1 to 2 for ease of telephone communication. Children were asked to recall when they completed the CPT and provided pain intensity and pain-related fear ratings based on their memories of the pain task.

Table I. *Descriptive Data for Measures Obtained at Baseline, Immediately Postpain Task, and During Recall for the Total Sample and Each Experimental Condition*

Variables	Total Sample ($N=110$) M (SD) Range	State Anxiety Induction Group ($n=55$) M (SD) Range	Control Group ($n=55$) M (SD) Range
Baseline state anxiety (VAS–child)	3.05 (2.37) 0.00–9.70	3.19 (2.26) 0.00–8.10	2.91 (2.49) 0.00–9.70
State anxiety postmanipulation (VAS–child)	3.46 (2.60) 0.00–10.00	4.56 (2.51) 0.00–10.00	2.36 (2.22)*** 0.00–7.25
State anxiety postmanipulation (STAIC-s)	29.07 (4.98) 21.00–49.00	30.89 (5.81) 21.00–49.00	27.25 (3.09)*** 12.00–22.00
State anxiety postmanipulation (VAS–parent)	4.61 (2.83) 0.00–10.00	6.30 (2.23) 0.25–10.00	2.93 (2.33)*** 0.00–8.80
Experienced pain intensity (FPS-R)	3.22 (2.20) 0.00–10.00	2.91 (2.03) 0.00–8.00	3.53 (2.34) 0.00–10.00
Experienced pain-related anxiety (CFS)	0.45 (0.71) 0.00–4.00	0.38 (0.65) 0.00–3.00	0.51 (0.77) 0.00–4.00
Trait anxiety (STAIC-t)	33.11 (6.42) 20.00–51.00	32.25 (6.55) 20.00–51.00	33.96 (6.23) 23.00–51.00
Anxiety sensitivity (CASI)	27.65 (5.25) 18.00–41.00	26.96 (5.01) 18.00–40.00	28.33 (5.44) 18.00–41.00
Recalled pain intensity (FPS-R)	3.09 (2.06) 0.00–8.00	2.98 (2.03) 0.00–8.00	3.20 (2.09) 0.00–8.00
Recalled pain-related fear (CFS)	0.70 (0.76) 0.00–4.00	0.65 (0.91) 0.00–4.00	0.75 (0.58) 0.00–2.00

*$p<.05$, **$p<.01$, ***$p<.001$.

Results

Data Analysis

To determine if the experimental manipulation was effective in inducing state anxiety among children, independent samples *t*-tests were conducted between children in the state anxiety induction group and the control group on all state anxiety measures obtained immediately after completion of the TSST-C. Next, a series of between subjects analyses of covariance (ANCOVA) were conducted between the groups on their recalled pain and pain-related fear scores while controlling for initial pain intensity and pain-related fear scores. In order to examine the relative influences of anxiety-related variables on children's recall, bivariate correlations were first conducted between key variables to justify their inclusion in predictive models. Similar to the approach taken by Gedney and Logan (2004), hierarchical linear regression modeling was used to test the ability of state anxiety (STAIC-s) to account for variance in 2-week recall of pain intensity and pain-related fear. Preliminary analyses revealed that girls had higher levels of baseline state anxiety [VAS–child; $M=3.56$, $SD=2.40$; $M=2.63$, $SD=2.28$, respectively; $t(108)=2.08$, $p<.05$], anxiety sensitivity [$M=29.06$, $SD=5.21$; $M=26.47$, $SD=5.03$, respectively; $t(108)=2.65$, $p<.01$] and trait anxiety [$M=34.44$, $SD=6.32$; $M=32.00$, $SD=6.34$, respectively; $t(108)=2.01$, $p<.05$] than boys. Therefore, sex was controlled in the first step of all regression models. Stable anxiety-related variables (trait anxiety and anxiety sensitivity) were entered in step 2,[3] followed by baseline pain intensity and pain-related fear ratings in step 3. Finally, state anxiety (STAIC-s) was entered in step 4 to predict recall scores. Descriptive data for all included measures obtained at baseline, immediately postpain task, and during recall for the total sample and each experimental condition are shown in Table I.

Manipulation Check

Prior to being told which group they were in, children in the state anxiety induction group did not differ from children in the control group in their baseline levels of state anxiety [VAS–child; $t(108)=.61$, $p>.05$, $\eta_p^2=.00$]. They also did not differ in levels of trait anxiety [$t(108)=-1.40$, $p>.05$, $\eta_p^2=.02$) or anxiety sensitivity

---

[3] When trait anxiety and anxiety sensitivity were each entered alone in Step 2 of each regression model, the results did not change and state anxiety continued to be a unique and significant predictor of recalled pain intensity and pain-related fear.

Table II. *Summary of Hierarchical Regression Analyses for State Anxiety Predicting Children's Recalled Pain Intensity*

$N=110$ (Entire Sample)	Variable	β	ΔF	$p \leq$	ΔR^2	Cumulative R^2
Step 1	Sex	.031	.103	.75	.001	.001
Step 2	Trait anxiety, Anxiety sensitivity	.027, .151	1.47	.24	.027	.028
Step 3	Experienced pain intensity	.697	96.68	.001*	.466	.494
Step 4	State anxiety	.158	5.13	.05*	.024	.518

Note. The following measures were used: STAIC-t (trait anxiety), CASI (anxiety sensitivity), FPS-R (experienced pain intensity), STAIC-s (state anxiety) in the regression model. Collectively, this model accounted for 52% of the variance in recalled pain intensity. When the order of steps 3 and 4 were reversed, both variables continued to account for a significant portion of the variance in recalled pain intensity suggesting that state anxiety did not mediate the relationship between experienced pain intensity and recall. *$p < .05$.

($t\ (108) = -1.37, p > .05, \eta_p^2 = .02$). However, following completion of the experimental and control tasks, children in the state anxiety induction group had significantly higher levels of state anxiety than children in the control group as measured by both the child [$t\ (108) = 4.88, p = .000, \eta_p^2 = .18$) and parent [$t\ (108) = 7.75, p = .000, \eta_p^2 = .36$] VAS and the STAIC-s [$t\ (82.32) = 4.10, p = .000, \eta_p^2 = .14$].[4] Furthermore, a 2 (group) × 2 (time) repeated measures analysis of variance (ANOVA) conducted on the baseline and postmanipulation VAS–child scores revealed a significant interaction [$F\ (1, 108) = 22.12, p = .000, \eta_p^2 = .17$]. Subsequent paired samples t-tests revealed that child state anxiety as measured by the VAS–child significantly increased from baseline to postmanipulation for the state anxiety induction group only [$t\ (108) = -5.88, p = .000$]. This suggests that state anxiety was successfully manipulated and was higher among children in the state anxiety induction group as compared to children in the control group.

Impact of Experimentally Manipulated State Anxiety on Pain Memories

To determine the impact of experimentally manipulated state anxiety on children's memories for pain, a series of between-subjects ANCOVAs were conducted between the state anxiety induction and control groups on remembered pain intensity and pain-related fear scores, while controlling for initial pain intensity and pain-related fear scores. Despite successful manipulation of state anxiety among children in the state anxiety induction group, there were no significant differences between children in the experimental and control groups on their memories for pain intensity [$F\ (1, 107) = 0.45, p > .05, \eta_p^2 = .004$] or pain-related fear [$F\ (1, 107) = 0.04, p > .05, \eta_p^2 = .00$].

---

[4] The t-value with unequal variances assumed was used given that Levene's Test for Equality of Variances was significant.

Correlations Between Key Variables

Overall, children who had higher levels of state anxiety (STAIC-s) immediately after exposure to the experimental and control task instructions recalled significantly higher levels of pain intensity ($r = .21, p < .05$) and pain-related fear ($r = .26, p < .01$) than children who had lower levels of state anxiety. Children with higher levels of trait anxiety and anxiety sensitivity recalled higher levels of pain-related fear ($r = .27, p < .01; r = .28, p < .01$, respectively). Trait anxiety and anxiety sensitivity were significantly positively correlated with each other ($r = .64, p < .001$). Experienced pain intensity was significantly positively correlated with experienced pain-related fear ($r = .27, p < .01$) and both experienced pain intensity and pain-related fear were significantly positively correlated with recalled pain intensity ($r = .70, p < .01; r = .32, p < .01$, respectively) and pain-related fear ($r = .49, p < .001; r = .49, p < .01$, respectively). These significant correlations in addition to theoretical and empirical support (e.g., Beck & Clark, 1997; Gedney & Logan, 2006; McNally, 1995; 1999) justify the inclusion of these variables in the regression models.

Influence of Anxiety-Related Variables on Pain Memories

Table II presents results for all groups reporting the effect of sex, stable anxiety-related variables, experienced pain intensity, and state anxiety (STAIC-s) in predicting recalled pain intensity. After controlling for sex, stable anxiety-related variables (trait anxiety and anxiety sensitivity), and experienced pain intensity, state anxiety accounted for a significant portion of variance in recalled pain intensity. As expected, experienced pain intensity was also a unique predictor of recalled pain intensity. Collectively, this model accounted for 52% of the variance in recalled pain intensity.

Table III presents results for all groups reporting the effect of sex, stable anxiety-related variables, experienced pain-related fear and state anxiety (STAIC-s) in predicting

Table III. *Summary of Hierarchical Regression Analyses for State Anxiety Predicting Children's Recalled Pain-Related Fear*

$N = 110$ (Entire Sample)	Variable	β	ΔF	$p \leq$	ΔR^2	Cumulative R^2
Step 1	Sex	.145	2.31	.132	.021	.021
Step 2	Trait anxiety, Anxiety sensitivity	.149, .169	4.61	.012*	.078	.099
Step 3	Experienced pain-related fear	.459	30.20	.001*	.201	.300
Step 4	State anxiety	.222	7.51	.01*	.047	.348

Note. The following measures were used: STAIC-t (trait anxiety), CASI (anxiety sensitivity), FPS-R (experienced pain intensity), STAIC-s (state anxiety) in the regression model. Collectively, this model accounted for 35% of the variance in recalled pain-related fear. When the order of steps 3 and 4 were reversed, both variables continued to account for a significant portion of the variance in recalled pain-related fear suggesting that state anxiety did not mediate the relationship between experienced pain-related fear and recall. *$p < .05$.

recalled pain-related fear. After controlling for sex, stable anxiety-related variables (trait anxiety and anxiety sensitivity), and experienced pain-related fear, state anxiety accounted for a significant portion of variance in recalled pain-related fear. As expected, experienced pain-related fear was also a unique predictor of recalled pain intensity. Stable anxiety-related variables (trait anxiety and anxiety sensitivity) also accounted for a significant portion of the variance in recalled pain-related fear. Collectively, this model accounted for 35% of the variance in recalled pain-related fear.

Discussion

Children's memories for pain have implications for their health throughout life (Chen et al., 2000; Pate et al., 1996). Although the role of trait anxiety in pain memories has been previously investigated (Rocha et al., 2009), far less is known about the role of state anxiety in children's memories for pain. This study represents the first examination of the impact of state anxiety on children's memories for pain. It also extends research by examining the influence of general levels of state anxiety on children's pain memories over and above the contributions of other well established factors implicated in those memories (e.g., experienced pain intensity and pain-related fear, and stable anxiety-related variables). Although state anxiety was successfully manipulated among children who underwent the state anxiety induction task (TSST-C), children in the experimental group did not develop pain memories that were more negative than those of children in the control group. However, irrespective of group assignment, children who reported higher levels of state anxiety recalled higher levels of pain intensity and pain-related fear than children with lower levels of state anxiety. Furthermore, the influence of state anxiety on pain memories persisted over and above the contributions of sex, trait anxiety, anxiety sensitivity and the powerful influence of pain intensity and pain-related fear experienced at baseline. Collectively, these models accounted for a large portion of the variance in children's memories of pain intensity and pain-related fear (52% and 35%, respectively). This extends research on adult acute pain experiences (Gedney & Logan, 2004) to provide a similar model for earlier developmental periods.

There are several possible reasons why children in the state anxiety induction group did not have more negative memories than children in the control group; but, that irrespective of group, state anxiety was a significant predictor of pain memories. First, by comparing experimental groups using ANOVA (i.e., analyzing state anxiety as a categorical variable), there was less power to detect effects as compared to analyzing state anxiety continuously (Aiken & West, 1991). Moreover, the individual variation in state anxiety among children within each experimental group following the manipulation (e.g., higher state anxiety among some children in the control group; lower state anxiety among some children in the state anxiety induction group) was treated as random/error variance in ANOVA. Conversely, in the regression models, the individual variability in state anxiety among children in each group (when treated as a continuous variable) was used to predict individual memory scores, thereby capturing individual variation among children and creating power to detect effects. Second, there were likely other trait variables that were not accounted for in the current study such as individual coping style/ attentional orientation (Krohne, 1993), which could have influenced whether or not individuals exhibited state anxiety in response to experimental instructions. Indeed, the relationship between anxiety and memory is thought to be mediated through attention, and high anxious individuals may differ in their attentional style (e.g., hypervigilant vs. avoidant of pain cues; see Krohne, 1993; Noel et al., in press). This could have introduced additional variability within experimental groups that might have obscured the ability to detect effects using ANOVA. Future research should investigate the impact of individual attentional style among highly anxious children to determine its impact on the development of their pain memories. Finally, regression models, unlike ANOVA, allowed for examination of the *relative* contribution of varying degrees of state anxiety on pain memories that were contextualized among the contributions of other important factors (e.g., sex, experienced pain and pain-related fear, stable anxiety-related variables). The relationship between state anxiety and children's pain memories is likely complex and therefore examination of other factors that impinge on this relationship may be necessary to fully understand it.

The limited research that has previously examined state/preprocedural anxiety and children's pain memories concluded a lack of relationship when assessed in clinical contexts (e.g., venipuncture, dental treatment; Lander et al., 1992; Versloot et al., 2008). However, limitations inherent in these study designs might have precluded accurate assessment of this relationship. For example, among children undergoing dental treatment, preprocedural pain was inferred by parent report of general dental fears that were not necessarily specific to the procedure that children later recalled. Moreover, these parents were not present during the dental treatments and therefore did not directly observe their children in the procedural context. Among children who underwent venipunctures (Lander et al., 1992), it is unclear whether or not state anxiety was measured immediately prior to the pain experience. Moreover, given the unpredictability inherent in clinical settings, it is unlikely that the duration between assessment of state anxiety and pain exposure was consistent across children, which could have introduced measurement error. The present laboratory-based study offers advantages over these previous investigations by enabling standardization of these variables across children. The fact that state anxiety was a significant predictor of more negative pain memories, even over and above the influences of stable anxiety-related variables and experienced pain, suggests that children who perceive themselves as being relatively more anxious immediately prior to a painful experience are at risk for developing negative pain memories. Although children higher in trait anxiety and anxiety sensitivity are more likely to experience relatively higher levels of state anxiety, this is not a perfect relationship and fails to capture the range of children who might exhibit higher levels of state anxiety prior to a painful experience (Tsao, Lu, Kim, & Zeltzer, 2006; Dorn et al., 2003). Children who are relatively less high in trait anxiety or anxiety sensitivity yet who still exhibit higher levels of state anxiety in a procedural context may not be identified *a priori* as being at risk for having negative pain experiences that could later shape their pain memories. Nevertheless, the present research suggests that children who have higher levels of state anxiety are at risk for developing negative pain memories, which could negatively affect their subsequent pain experiences. This implies that identification of, and intervention with, children with relatively higher levels of state anxiety in the immediate pain context may also be important for preventing such longitudinal outcomes.

The relationship between trait anxiety and children's pain memories (Rocha et al., 2009), has been previously documented. Furthermore, there is a wealth of literature documenting the effect of trait anxiety (see review in Mitte, 2008) and anxiety sensitivity (for discussion see Noel et al. 2011) on memory for threatening information among adults. However, this is the first study to examine the relative contributions of stable anxiety-related variables, initial pain experience, and state anxiety to children's pain memories. In addition to state and trait anxiety, the present study demonstrated the importance of anxiety sensitivity in influencing children's memories of pain-related fear. To date, no study has examined the role of anxiety sensitivity (i.e., the fear of anxiety-related symptoms) in children's memories for pain. Anxiety sensitivity is thought to heighten one's susceptibility to experience anxiety which then increases pain perception (Schmidt & Cook, 1999; Stewart & Asmundson, 2006). It is also thought that anxiety sensitivity promotes catastrophic cognitions about pain and the development of fear of pain (Norton & Asmundson, 2004). Indeed, previous research revealed a robust relationship between child anxiety sensitivity and pain-related anticipatory anxiety, which is strongly predictive of children's ratings of laboratory pain intensity (Tsao et al., 2006). The present study suggests that higher levels of anxiety sensitivity in addition to trait anxiety are predictive of more negative memories of pain-related fear but not pain intensity. This also suggests that children's memories of pain-related fear, although related to their memories of pain intensity, encompass a unique aspect of children's remembered pain experience. Memories of pain are multidimensional and involve representations of sensory (i.e., pain intensity), affective (i.e., fear/anxiety), and contextual aspects of the pain experience (Ornstein et al., 1999). Despite this, the majority of research on children's memories for pain has primarily focused on recalled pain intensity as opposed to recalled pain-related fear (for an exception see Noel et al., 2010). Although memories for pain intensity and pain-related fear are related to one another, they reflect different aspects of the pain experience and have different relationships with established predictors of pain and pain memories (e.g., anxiety sensitivity and trait anxiety). Future research should further examine aspects of pain memories beyond the somatosensory representation in order to better capture the complexity inherent in children's memories for pain.

In addition to several strengths, the present research had some potential limitations that highlight avenues for future empirical investigation in this area. First, the children included in the present study were healthy and did not have clinically significant levels of anxiety that warranted diagnosis of an anxiety disorder. As such, the generalizability of these findings to clinical samples of children with high levels of anxiety is currently unknown. Second, the research largely relied on self-report measures reflecting children's subjective perceptions of their own levels of anxiety, pain intensity, and pain-related fear. Future examinations should assess anxiety and pain using a variety of measurement tools, including physiological and behavioral measures, as well as self- and proxy-report completed by different informants (e.g., children, parents, experimenters), as this would likely refine our understanding of the nature of these relationships. Finally, the anxiety-related measures used in the current study assessed children's general levels of anxiety (i.e., their general tendency to perceive threat in their environments), as opposed to anxiety that is specific to pain-related threat. Indeed, similar to the present findings, previous research has shown that both anxiety sensitivity and trait anxiety are not consistently related to healthy children's initial pain ratings following cold pressor pain induction in laboratory settings (Tsao et al., 2004). Moreover, although anticipatory anxiety related to pain has been found to strongly predict children's initial pain reports (Tsao et al., 2004), the measure of state anxiety used in the current study did not assess state anxiety that was specific to pain; rather, children's general levels of anxiety following exposure to task instructions was assessed. The lack of relationship between general state anxiety and experienced pain is consistent with previous research (Arntz, van Eck & Heijmans, 1990; Lander et al., 1992). On the other hand, the relationships between these general anxiety-related variables and children's pain memories were expected and were likely found because higher scores on the anxiety-related measures reflected a tendency for children to develop more catastrophic cognitions, characterized by amplified perceptions of threat. These types of cognitions and associated appraisals could have contributed to negative exaggerations in memory over time as children recalled the pain experience in the interim between the first laboratory visit and the telephone interview. It is also possible that although children were instructed to provide recall ratings based on how they specifically felt about the pain task, their recalled pain ratings could have also reflected their perceptions of the overall emotional context surrounding the pain experience (i.e., the general level of threat that they perceived in their environments before and during the pain task) and not solely the somatosensory or affective experience related to pain. Future investigations should increase the specificity of anxiety constructs for pain contexts through the use of recently developed measures of pain-specific anxiety and fear (e.g., Pediatric Pain Fear Scale, Huguet, McGrath, & Pardos, 2011; Child Pain Anxiety Symptoms Scale, Pagé, Fuss, Martin, Escobar, & Katz, 2010). Such examinations could potentially increase the explanatory power of the models presented herein.

The impact of pain and fear is not over when the painful stimulus is removed. The quality of children's pain experiences can influence the development of their pain memories over time. Although the relationship between children's initial pain experience (e.g., self-reported pain intensity, behavioral distress), trait anxiety, and pain memories has been previously established (Chen et al., 2000; Noel et al., 2010; Rocha et al., 2009), the present study extends this research by showing that state anxiety is also an important and unique predictor of children's memories for pain. This implies that children who report higher levels of state anxiety (irrespective of their natural tendencies to experience anxiety and fear and the quality of their initial pain experiences) will likely develop more negative pain memories. Previous research also suggests that these children may be at risk for experiencing greater distress at subsequent painful experiences (Chen et al., 2000) and developing fear and avoidance of medical care into adulthood (Pate et al., 1996). The present study also extends previous research by showing that anxiety sensitivity in addition to trait anxiety is an important predictor of the development of children's memories for pain-related fear. There is evidence suggesting that a brief cognitive-behavioral intervention designed to reduce anxiety sensitivity among high anxiety sensitive individuals results in concomitant reductions in pain-related fear and anxiety in adults (Watt, Stewart, LeFaivre, & Uman, 2006). Although this has yet to be examined among children, it suggests potential avenues for intervention which could prevent the development of negative pain memories from forming.

Acknowledgments

Noel is a trainee member of *Pain in Child Health*, a Strategic Training Initiative in Health Research of the Canadian Institutes of Health Research (CIHR). C.T. Chambers and P.J. McGrath are supported by Canada Research Chairs. S.H. Stewart was supported through a Killam Research Professorship from the Dalhousie University

Faculty of Science at the time that this research was conducted. We would like to thank the many children and parents who participated in this research. We would also like to thank Dr. Jennifer Parker, Aimee Dort, Bryanne Harris and Laura Slauenwhite for their research assistance, as well as Dr. Christiane Hermann for her valuable insights into the study design and methodology. The authors have no conflicts of interest to disclose.

Funding

This work was supported by a Marion and Donald Routh Student Research Grant from the Society of Pediatric Psychology (Division 54, American Psychological Association), a Trainee Research Award from the Canadian Pain Society, and a Category A Research Award from the IWK Health Centre awarded to Noel. This research was also supported by an operating grant from CIHR and infrastructure funding from the Canada Foundation for Innovation awarded to Chambers. At the time that the research was conducted, Noel was supported by a Frederick Banting and Charles Best Canada Graduate Scholarships Doctoral Award from CIHR, a CIHR Team in Children's Pain Fellowship, and an honorary Killam Predoctoral Scholarship.

Conflicts of interest: None declared.

References

Aiken, L. S., & West, S. G. (1991). *Multiple Regression: Testing and interpreting interactions*. Newbury Park, CA: Sage.

Arntz, A., van Eck, M., & Heijmans, M. (1990). Predictions of dental pain: The fear of an expected evil is worse than the evil itself. *Behaviour Research and Therapy, 28,* 29–41.

Badali, M. A., Pillai, R. R., Craig, K. D., Giesbrecht, K., & Chambers, C. T. (2000). Accuracy of children's and parents' memory for a novel painful experience. *Pediatric Pain Management, 5,* 161–168.

Beck, A. T., & Clark, D. A. (1997). An information processing model of anxiety: Automatic and strategic processes. *Behaviour Research and Therapy, 35*(1), 49–58.

Birnie, K., Noel, M., Chambers, C., von Baeyer, C., & Fernandez, C. (2011). The cold pressor task: Is it an ethically acceptable pain research method in children? *Journal of Pediatric Psychology, 36,* 1071–1081.

Bringuier, S., Dadure, C., Raux, C., Dubois, A., Picot, M., & Capdevila, X. (2009). The perioperative validity of the visual analog anxiety scale in children: A discriminant and useful instrument in routine clinical practice to optimize postoperative pain management. *Anesthesia & Analgesia, 109,* 737–744.

Bruck, M., Ceci, S. J., Francoeur, E., & Barr, R. (1995). "I hardly cried when I got my shot!" Influencing children's reports about a visit to their pediatrician. *Child Development, 66,* 193–208.

Buske-Kirschbaum, A., Jobst, S., Wustmans, A., & Kirschbaum, C. (1997). Attenuated free cortisol response to psychosocial stress in children with atopic dermatitis. *Psychosomatic Medicine, 59*(4), 419–426.

Buske-Kirschbaum, A., von Auer, K., Krieger, S., Weis, S., Rauh, W., & Hellhammer, D. (2003). Blunted cortisol responses to psychosocial stress in asthmatic children: A general feature of atopic disease? *Psychosomatic Medicine, 65*(5), 806–810.

Chen, E., Zeltzer, L. K., Craske, M. G., & Katz, E. R. (1999). Alteration of memory in the reduction of children's distress during repeated aversive medical procedures. *Journal of Consulting and Clinical Psychology, 67,* 481–490.

Chen, E., Craske, M. G., Katz, E. R., Schwartz, E., & Zeltzer, L. K. (2000). Pain-sensitive temperament: Does it predict procedural distress and response to psychological treatment among children with cancer? *Journal of Pediatric Psychology, 25*(4), 269–278.

Dickerson, S.S., & Kemeny, M.E. (2004). Acute stressors and cortisol responses: A theoretical integration and synthesis of laboratory research. *Psychological Bulletin, 130*(3), 355–391.

Dorn, L. D., Campo, J. C., Thato, S., Dahl, R. E., Lewin, D., Chandra, R., & Di Lorenzo, C. (2003). Psychological comorbidity and stress reactivity in children and adolescents with recurrent abdominal pain and anxiety disorders. *Journal of the American Academy of Child and Adolescent Psychiatry, 42,* 66–75.

Eysenck, M. W., Derakshan, N., Santos, R., & Calvo, M. G. (2007). Anxiety and cognitive performance: Attentional control theory. *Emotion, 7*(2), 336–353.

Flor, H., & Birbaumer, N. (1994). Acquisition of chronic pain: Psychophysiological mechanisms. *APS Journal, 3*(2), 119–127.

Gedney, J. J., & Logan, H. (2004). Memory for stress-associated acute pain. *The Journal of Pain, 5*(2), 83–91.

Gedney, J. J., & Logan, H. (2006). Pain related recall predicts future pain report. *Pain, 121*, 69–76.

Gunnar, M. R., Frenn, K., Wewerka, S. S., & Van Ryzin, M. J. (2009). Moderate versus severe early life stress: Associations with stress reactivity and regulation in 10-12-year-old children. *Psychoneuroendocrinology, 34*(1), 62–75.

Gunnar, M. R., Talge, N. M., & Herrera, A. (2009). Stressor paradigms in developmental studies: What does and does not work to produce mean increases in salivary cortisol. *Psychoneuroendocrinology, 34*, 953–967.

Hermann, C., Vogl, D., & Maras, A. (2004). Anticipating stress- subjective, autonomic and endocrinological correlates [Abstract]. *Psychophysiology, 41*, S25–S103.

Hicks, C. L., von Baeyer, C. L., Spafford, P. A., van Korlaar, I., & Goodenough, B. (2001). The faces pain scale-revised: Toward a common metric in pediatric pain measurement. *Pain, 93*(2), 173–183.

Huguet, A., McGrath, P. J., & Pardos, J. (2011). Development and preliminary testing of a scale to assess pain-related fear in children and adolescents. *Journal of Pain, 12*, 840–848.

Krohne, H. W. (1993). Vigilance and cognitive avoidance as concepts in coping research. In H. W. Krohne (Ed.), *Attention and avoidance: Strategies in coping with aversiveness* (pp. 19–50). Toronto, Ontario, Canada: Hogrefe & Huber Publishers.

Lander, J., Hodgins, M., & Fowler-Kerry, S. (1992). Children's pain predications and memories. *Behaviour Research and Therapy, 30*, 117–124.

McCabe, R. E. (1999). Implicit and explicit memory for threat words in high- and low-anxiety-sensitive participants. *Cognitive Therapy and Research, 23*, 21–38.

McKinley, S., Coote, K., & Stein-Parbury, J. (2003). Development and testing of a faces scale for the assessment of anxiety in critically ill patients. *Journal of Advanced Nursing, 41*(1), 73–79.

McMurtry, C. M., Noel, M., Chambers, C. T., & McGrath, P. J. (2011). Children's fear during procedural pain: Preliminary investigation of the Children's Fear Scale. *Health Psychology, 30*(6), 780–788.

McNally, R. J. (1995). Automaticity and the anxiety disorders. *Behaviour Research and Therapy, 33*, 747–754.

McNally, R. J. (1999). Anxiety sensitivity and information-processing biases for threat. In S. Taylor (Ed.), *Anxiety sensitivity: Theory, research, and treatment of the fear of anxiety* (pp. 183–197). Mahwah, NJ: Erlbaum.

Mitte, K. (2008). Memory bias for threatening information in anxiety and anxiety disorders: A meta-analytic review. *Psychological Bulletin, 134*(6), 886–911.

Noel, M., McMurtry, C. M., Chambers, C. T., & McGrath, P. J. (2010). Children's memory for painful procedures: The relationship of pain intensity, anxiety, and adult behaviors to subsequent recall. *Journal of Pediatric Psychology, 35*, 626–636.

Noel, M., Chambers, C. T., McGrath, P. J., Klein, R. M., & Stewart, S. H. (in press). The influence of children's pain memories on subsequent pain experience.

Noel, M., Taylor, T. L., Quinlan, C. K., & Stewart, S. H. (2011). The impact of attention style on directed forgetting among high anxiety sensitive individuals. *Cognitive Therapy and Research*. Advance online publication. doi:10.1007/s10608-011-9366-y.

Norton, P. J., & Asmundson, G. J. G. (2004). Anxiety sensitivity, fear, and avoidance behavior in headache pain. *Pain, 111*, 218–223.

Ornstein, P. A., Manning, E. L., & Pelphrey, K. A. (1999). Children's memory for pain. *Journal of Developmental and Behavioural Pediatrics, 20*, 262–277.

Pagé, M. G., Fuss, S., Martin, A. L., Escobar, E. M. R., & Katz, J. (2010). Development and Preliminary Validation of the Child Pain Anxiety Symptoms Scale in a Community Sample. *Journal of Pediatric Psychology, 35*, 1071–1082.

Pate, J. T., Blount, R. L., Cohen, L. L., & Smith, A. J. (1996). Childhood medical experience and temperament as predictors of adult functioning in medical situations. *Children's Health Care, 25*, 281–298.

Public Health Agency of Canada. (2006). *Canadian Immunization Guide* (7th ed.). Retrieved from http://www.phac-aspc.gc.ca/publicat/cig-gci.

Rocha, E. M., Marche, T. A., & von Baeyer, C. L. (2009). Anxiety influences children's memory for procedural pain. *Pain Research & Management, 14*(3), 233–237.

Rhudy, J. L., & Meagher, M. W. (2003). Negative affect: Effects on an evaluative measure of human pain. *Pain, 104*, 617–626.

Schmidt, N. B., & Cook, J. H. (1999). Effects of anxiety sensitivity on anxiety and pain during a cold pressor challenge in patients with panic disorder. *Behaviour Research and Therapy, 35*, 313–323.

Silverman, W. K., Fleisig, W., Rabian, B., & & Peterson, R. A. (1991). Child anxiety sensitivity index. *Journal of Clinical Child & Adolescent Psychology, 20*, 162–168.

Smith, R. W., Shah, V., Goldman, R. D., & Taddio, A. (2007). Caregivers' responses to pain in their children in the emergency department. *Archives of Pediatrics & Adolescent Medicine, 161*(6), 578–582.

Spielberger, C. D. (1973). *Manual for the state-trait anxiety inventory for children*. Palo Alto, CA: Consulting Psychologists Press.

Stewart, S. H., & Asmundson, G. J. G. (2006). Anxiety sensitivity and its impact on pain experiences and conditions: A state of the art. *Cognitive Behavioural Therapy, 35*, 185–188.

Stinson, J. N., Kavanagh, T., Yamada, J., Gill, N., & Stevens, B. (2006). Systematic review of the psychometric properties, interpretability and feasibility of self-report pain intensity measures for use in clinical trials in children and adolescents. *Pain, 125*(1), 143–157.

Stroud, L. R., Foster, E., Papandonatos, G. D., Handwerger, K., Granger, D. A., Kivlighan, K. T., & Niaura, R. (2009). Stress response and the adolescent transition: Performance versus peer rejection stressors. *Developmental Psychopathology, 21*(1), 47–68.

Sun-Ok, S., & Carr, D. (1999). Pain and memory. *International association for the study of pain. Pain: Clinical Updates, 7*, 1–4.

Taddio, Q., Katz, J., Ilersich, A. L., & Koren, G. (1997). Effect of neonatal circumcision on pain response during subsequent routine vaccination. *Lancet, 349*, 599–603.

Tsao, J. C., Myers, C. D., Craske, M. G., Bursch, B., Kim, S. C., & Zeltzer, L. K. (2004). Role of anticipatory anxiety and anxiety sensitivity in children's and adolescents' laboratory pain responses. *Journal of Pediatric Psychology, 29*(5), 379–388.

Tsao, J. C. I., Lu, Q., Kim, S., & Zeltzer, L. K. (2006). Relationships among anxious symptomatology, anxiety sensitivity, and laboratory pain response in children. *Cognitive Behaviour Therapy, 35*(4), 207–215.

Versloot, J., Veerkamp, J. S. J., & Hoogstraten, J. (2008). Children's self-reported pain at the dentist. *Pain, 137*, 389–394.

von Baeyer, C. L., Piira, T., Chambers, C. T., Trapanotto, M., & Zeltzer, L.K. (2005). Guidelines for the cold pressor task as an experimental pain stimulus for use with children. *Journal of Pain, 6*, 218–227.

von Baeyer, C. L., Marche, T. A., Rocha, E. M., & Salmon, K. (2004). Children's memory for pain: Overview and implications for practice. *Journal of Pain, 5*, 241–249.

Watt, M. C., Stewart, S. H., Lefaivre, M-j., & Uman, L. S. (2006). A brief cognitive-behavioral approach to reducing anxiety sensitivity decreases pain-related anxiety. *Cognitive Behaviour Therapy, 35*(4), 248–256.

Weems, C. F., Hammond-Laurence, K., Silverman, W. K., & Ginsburg, G. S. (1998). Testing the utility of the anxiety sensitivity construct in children and adolescents referred for anxiety disorders. *Journal of Clinical Child & Adolescent Psychology, 27*, 69–77.

Weisman, S. J., Bernstein, B., & Schechter, N. L. (1998). Consequences of inadequate analgesia during painful procedures in children. *Archives of Pediatric and Adolescent Medicine, 152*, 147–149.

Wilby, K., Chambers, C. T., & Perrot-Sinal, T. (2010). *Investigating salivary cortisol as a marker of reactivity during the cold pressor task*. Unpublished manuscript, Department of Psychology, Dalhousie University, Halifax, Canada.

Zonneveld, L. N., McGrath, P. J., Reid, G. J., & Sorbi, M. J. (1997). Accuracy of children's pain memories. *Pain, 71*, 297–302.

A Comparison of Friendship Quality and Social Functioning Among Children With Perinatally Acquired HIV, Children With Persistent Asthma, and Healthy Children of HIV-Positive Mothers

Sarah E. Baker,[1] PHD, Larissa N. Niec,[2] PHD, and Jill Meade,[3] PHD

[1]Center for Human Development and Behavioral Pediatrics, Beaumont Health System, [2]Department of Psychology, Central Michigan University and [3]Carman and Ann Adams Department of Pediatrics, Wayne State University

All correspondence concerning this article should be addressed to Sarah E. Baker, Center for Human Development and Behavioral Pediatrics, Beaumont Health System, 1695 West Twelve Mile Road, Suite 120, Berkley, MI, 48072, USA. E-mail: sarah.baker@beaumont.edu

Received May 10, 2011; revisions received January 15, 2012; accepted January 19, 2012

Objective To examine the friendships and social expectations of children with perinatally acquired HIV and compare them to children with moderate to severe persistent asthma and healthy children of HIV-positive mothers. **Methods** 70 children (ages 8–14 years) were recruited from pediatric allergy and immunology multidisciplinary clinics and hospital-based HIV-support programming. Children completed measures of friendship quality and interpersonal functioning. Caregivers completed a measure of child psychosocial functioning. **Results** Children with asthma, not HIV, demonstrated poorer indicators of friendship and the most negative social expectations of the three groups. Children with HIV maintained best friendships and rated themselves as socially well-adjusted. **Conclusions** Comprehensive multidisciplinary services and ancillary supports may have buffered against stressors and facilitated positive psychosocial outcomes in children with HIV. Children with asthma displayed higher disease activity, possibly contributing to poorer outcomes. Results suggest a need to better understand the protective factors that enhance social functioning in children with HIV.

Key words asthma; friendship; HIV; internal representations.

Peer relations are an important consideration for children with a chronic illness. By influencing perceived support, adherence to treatment regimen, and participation in health-promoting behaviors, peer relationships can play a significant positive role in the lives of children managing a chronic condition or disease (La Greca, Bearman & Moore, 2002). However, concerns about physical appearance, lifestyle modifications due to hospitalizations or intensive treatments, and restriction or interruption of daily activities can interfere with the ability of these children to establish and maintain stable, meaningful friendships. A number of negative short- and long-term consequences are associated with a lack of enriching friendships, including low self-esteem (Ladd & Troop-Gordon, 2003); school adjustment problems (Lopez & DuBois, 2005); psychopathology (Bukowski & Adams, 2005); and misconduct and delinquency (Boivin, Vitaro, & Poulin, 2005). When coupled with the challenges of managing a chronic illness, poor peer relationships can have even greater consequences for children's coping and quality of life.

Children perinatally infected with the human immunodeficiency virus (HIV) may be at higher risk of disrupted peer relations than children with other chronic conditions such as diabetes, cancer, and sickle cell disease. Children living with HIV are at risk for developing cognitive, neuropsychological, sensory–motor, and behavioral deficits associated with the effects of the retrovirus on the central nervous system (CNS) if the disease is not properly treated

(Knight, Mellins, Levenson, Arpadi, & Kairam, 2000; Wolters, Brouwers, & Moss, 1995). Even in HIV-positive children who appear asymptomatic, subtle neurocognitive impairment often exists (Fundaro et al., 1998; Nozyce et al., 2006) and can worsen over time without effective antiretroviral treatment (Franklin et al., 2005). In general, children with CNS-related health conditions have been found to have difficulty developing age-appropriate peer relationships. A review of over 20 years of empirical research on the topic reported that children with CNS conditions, including HIV, were less socially competent and more isolated than physically healthy children and children with non-CNS-related health conditions such as diabetes (Nassau & Drotar, 1997). Possible reasons for this discrepancy include cognitive deficits that interfere with basic social understanding, varying degrees of impairment (with more severe or visible manifestations leading to stigmatization and rejection by peers), and educational and rehabilitation settings that limit social opportunities.

Furthermore, the stigma that continues to be associated with HIV infection may also contribute to social difficulties in this group of children (La Greca et al., 2002). In HIV-positive adults, high levels of internalized HIV-related stigma predict feelings of anxiety, depression, and hopelessness, and also interfere with support seeking from peer, family, and health provider networks (Lee, Kochman, & Sikkema, 2002; Mak et al., 2007). In a meta-analysis of the impact of disclosure on stigma and social support in adults living with HIV, Smith, Rossetto, & Peterson (2008) concluded that both disclosure and social support will continue to be compromised until the stigma surrounding HIV has diminished. While research has not explicitly explored the impact of HIV-related stigma on children living with the disease, it is logical to extrapolate from the adult literature that fear of stigma is likely to have significant implications for disclosure and the quality of their social relationships. Studies of general social functioning in children with HIV indicate that they experience fewer social interactions, lower involvement in activities, and poorer school functioning than their healthy peers (Bose, Moss, Brouwers, Pizzo, & Lorion, 1994). However, children who feel comfortable enough to disclose their HIV status to friends may experience observable health benefits (e.g., increased CD4 percentage) associated with decreased levels of worry and increased access to support in maintaining their health (Sherman, Bonanno, Weiner, & Battles, 2000).

The purpose of this study was to examine the friendship quality and social functioning of children perinatally infected with HIV. Two key elements of children's internal representations of relationships, the affect tone of relationship expectancies (i.e., the extent to which relationships are assumed to be destructive and threatening versus safe and enriching) and emotional investment in relationships (i.e., the ability to relate to others in a meaningful and committed manner), were also examined. The friendships and social expectations of children with perinatally acquired HIV were then compared to those of children with moderate to severe persistent asthma and healthy children born to an HIV-positive mothers. Children with moderate to severe asthma were selected as a comparison group due to the serious but comparatively nonstigmatizing nature of their illness. Similar to children with HIV, children with higher levels of asthma severity must monitor their symptoms, take daily medications, and visit the doctor regularly as part of their disease management regimen, often resulting in considerable burden to the child and family and interfering with opportunities for the child to develop and maintain relationships with peers. Research has demonstrated that behavioral difficulties, particularly internalizing problems such as anxiety, depressive symptoms, and withdrawal, are more pronounced in children with asthma as disease severity increases (McQuaid, Kopel, & Nassau, 2001). Greater asthma severity has also been associated with increased feelings of loneliness in children and less favorable ratings from peers (Graetz & Shute, 1995) as well as higher levels of negative peer sociability (Halterman et al., 2006). However, despite a growing recognition of its potential severity by the general public, asthma is typically not associated with high levels of stigma like other diseases such as HIV. Uninfected children of HIV-positive mothers were included as a second comparison group due to the similar family and environmental stressors experienced (e.g., HIV in a parent) without the added strain of managing a childhood illness. We hypothesized that the children with HIV would demonstrate poorer indicators of friendship quality and social adjustment than the two comparison groups, as reported by both the child and the caregiver.

Method
Participants
Study participants included 70 children (39 males, 31 females) between the ages of 8 and 14 years ($M = 11.39$, $SD = 1.56$) recruited from a multidisciplinary immunology clinic, support programming for families affected by HIV (including uninfected family members), and a high-risk asthma specialty clinic at an urban Midwestern children's hospital. Of the total sample, 21 children were perinatally infected with HIV, 24 children were born to an

HIV-positive mother but were themselves uninfected, and 25 children had a diagnosis of moderate or severe persistent asthma as defined by the National Heart, Lung, and Blood Institute (NHLBI; 2007) guidelines (i.e., a minimum of: daily symptoms, weekly nighttime awakenings, daily use of a short-acting β_2 agonist for symptom control, some limitation in daily activities, $FEV_1 < 80\%$ predicted). There was a statistically significant difference in age among the three groups, $F(2,69) = 6.54$, $p = .003$, with post hoc comparisons indicating that the mean age for the healthy children ($M = 10.33$, $SD = 1.61$) was significantly younger than the HIV group ($M = 11.67$, $SD = 2.11$), 95% CI (−2.64 to −0.03), $p = .04$, as well as the asthma group ($M = 12.16$, $SD = 1.75$), 95% CI (−3.07 to −0.58), $p = .002$. Children were predominantly African American (94%), reflecting the ethnic composition of the population from which the sample was drawn; 3% were Hispanic/Latino and 3% were Caucasian. There were no significant differences in ethnicity or gender among the groups. For the children with HIV, caregivers reported that 57% were fully disclosed to their disease status (i.e., aware that they have HIV and had been educated about transmission and treatment), 14% of children were partially disclosed (i.e., knew that there is a virus in their blood for which they must take medication but did not know the name of the disease), and 29% had not yet been disclosed about their illness. Only one child had disclosed his HIV status to a friend at the time of the study.

Demographic data for the caregivers of children living with HIV differed from that of the two comparison groups. In the HIV group, only 24% of caregivers were biological mothers; for children with asthma and healthy children, biological mothers accounted for 84% of caregivers. Age of caregivers also differed significantly among the groups, $F(2,65) = 9.49$, $p = .000$. Caregivers of children with HIV were significantly older ($M = 49.28$, $SD = 12.76$) than both the caregivers of children with asthma ($M = 39.76$, $SD = 10.98$), 95% CI (1.75 to 17.29), $p = .013$, and healthy children ($M = 35.04$, $SD = 7.54$), 95% CI (6.32 to 22.15), $p = .000$. This was expected, as it is common for children with HIV to live with an extended family member (e.g., grandparent) or other caregiver due to poor maternal health status or following the death of a parent from HIV-related complications. Median household income for the HIV group fell between $20,001 and $30,000 per year; median income for the asthma and healthy groups ranged from $10,001 to $20,000 per year. Demographic information for children and caregivers can be found in Table I.

Caregiver Measures

Demographic Questionnaire

Demographic variables included child and caregiver gender, age, and ethnicity; child grade in school; caregiver relationship to the child; caregiver marital and employment status; and household income. Parents of children with HIV and asthma also reported days missed from school due to illness. For children with HIV, questions about disclosure status were also included. Data regarding immunologic status (i.e., viral load and CD4 percentage) closest in proximity to the date of study completion were obtained from the child's medical record with documented caregiver permission.

Social Adjustment

The Personality Inventory for Children, Second Edition Behavioral Summary (PIC-2, Lachar & Gruber, 2001) is a parent-report instrument consisting of 96 true–false questions about child/adolescent emotional, behavioral, cognitive, and interpersonal functioning. Only the Social Adjustment Composite was used in this study, due to its theoretical correspondence with the construct of friendship quality. Reliability and validity for the PIC-2 fall in the acceptable range (see Lachar, 2007). For the adjustment scales, Cronbach's α coefficients ranged from .75 to .91, with most α-values in the .80 s. The PIC-2 Standard Form and Behavioral Summary have been found to correlate highly with corresponding scores on the early versions of the measure, with teacher report on the Student Behavior Survey (SBS), and with student report on the Personality Inventory for Youth (PIY). The PIC-2 has been used in other studies as a means of assessing child friendship quality via parent report (e.g., Cunningham, Dixon Thomas, & Warschausky, 2007).

Child Measures

Affective Representations of Relationships

The Children's Affective Representations of Relationships Scale (CARRS, Baker & Niec, 2007) was developed from attachment, object relations, and social cognitive foundations to create a brief, collaborative measure of children's internal representations. It consists of 86 statements tapping children's affect tone of relationships, ability to invest emotionally in relationships, and locus of control orientation, printed on cards for children to sort into four piles ranging from "Not at all like me" to "Very much like me". Affect Tone is defined as the extent to which one expects relationships to be destructive and threatening or safe and enriching (example item: "When I'm sad, there's always someone I can talk to"). Emotional Investment is defined as the ability to

Table I. Demographic Data by Group

	Group			Test of Group Differences
	HIV (n = 21)	Asthma (n = 25)	Healthy (n = 24)	
Children				
Age (M, SD)	11.67 (2.11)	12.16 (1.75)	10.33 (1.61)	$F(2,69) = 6.54^{**}$
Grade (M, SD)	6.43 (1.99)	6.80 (1.92)	5.00 (1.84)	$F(2,69) = 5.94^{**}$
Gender (female) (%)	29	40	63	$\chi^2(2) = 5.52$
Race (African American) (%)	90	100	92	$\chi^2(2) = 1.21$
HIV Disclosure Status (%)				
Fully Disclosed	57			
Partially Disclosed	14			
Not Disclosed	29			
Caregivers				
Age (M, SD)	49.28 (12.76)	39.76 (10.98)	35.04 (7.54)	$F(2,65) = 9.49^{***}$
Gender (female) (%)	91	100	96	$\chi^2(2) = 2.53$
Race (African American) (%)	91	100	92	$\chi^2(4) = 4.39$
Relationship to child (%)				$\chi^2(8) = 25.54^{***}$
Biological mother	24	84	84	
Other relative	38	12	0	
Foster parent	5	0	0	
Adoptive parent	29	4	12	
Other caregiver	5	0	4	
Yearly income (median)	$20,001–30,000	$10,001–20,000	$10,001–20,000	$\chi^2(16) = 19.75$

Note. $^{**}p < .01$; $^{***}p < .001$.

relate to others in a meaningful and committed manner (example item: "I would do almost anything for my closest friend"). Locus of control was not a variable of interest for this study and responses to those items were not analyzed. A pilot study conducted with a sample of elementary-age community children provided preliminary support for the CARRS as a measure of children's expectations of relationships and capacity to invest emotionally in others (Baker & Niec, 2007). Correlations between the CARRS Affect Tone and Emotional Investment scales were statistically significant ($p < .01$) and in expected directions. Internal consistency for the Affect Tone scale was very good ($\alpha = .81$); and reliability of the Emotional Investment scale reached the acceptable range ($\alpha = .68$). The scales positively correlated with the Social Cognition and Object Relations Scale, Global Rating Method (Hilsenroth, Stein, & Pinsker, 2004), providing evidence of construct validity.

Friendship Interview
The Friendship Interview (Vandell, 1999) asks children to identify their best friends, rate how each friendship is going (i.e., "great," "good," "not so good," or "bad"), and provide information about where the friends usually interact as well as the frequency of contact between the friends. The interview was modified for disclosed children with HIV to include questions about their disclosure to friends.

Friendship Quality
The Friendship Quality Questionnaire – Revised (FQQ-R, Parker & Asher, 1993) consists of 40 statements that characterize one's best (or closest) friendship. Children were asked to rate how true each statement is for his or her best friendship on a 5-point scale (0 = "not at all true"; 4 = "really true"). The FQQ-R yields six subscales that pertain to different qualitative aspects of friendship: Validation and Caring, Conflict Resolution, Conflict and Betrayal, Help and Guidance, Companionship and Recreation, and Intimate Exchange. The psychometric properties of the instrument are well-established (see Parker & Asher, 1993). The FQQ-R subscales have demonstrated good internal consistency (α-coefficients ranging from .73 for the Conflict Resolution scale to .90 for the Help & Guidance and Validation & Caring scales). The measure has been validated using sociometric rating methods, with lower accepted children demonstrating poorer quality friendships on each of the six FQQ-R subscales than average- and high-accepted children.

Further, the six FQQ-R subscales were found to be strongly predictive of child loneliness (Parker & Asher, 1993).

Receptive Vocabulary

The Peabody Picture Vocabulary Test, Third Edition (PPVT-III, Dunn & Dunn, 1997) is a measure of receptive vocabulary in individuals between the ages of 2 years, 6 months and 90+ years. For the purposes of this study, it was used as a screen for children's intelligence and verbal ability; the validity of the PPVT for this purpose has been widely demonstrated (e.g., Carvajal, Hayes, Miller, Wiebe, & Weaver, 1993). Alpha and split-half reliability coefficients of the PPVT-III range from .86 to .98 for both Forms A and B, while parallel forms reliabilities fall between .88 and .96 with the lower coefficients in the lowest and highest chronological age groups. Correlations with the Wechsler Intelligence Scale for Children, Third Edition (WISC-III) are .91 and .92 for Forms II A and II B, respectively. The validity of the PPVT-III is well-established in the manual and in the literature (e.g., Campbell, Bell, & Keith, 2001).

Psychosocial Functioning

The Behavior Assessment System for Children, Second Edition: Self-Report of Personality (BASC-2 SRP, Reynolds & Kamphaus, 2004) consists of 139 (child version) or 176 (adolescent version) items in a true–false and multiple choice format that measures children's emotions and self-perceptions of daily functioning. It yields 15 primary scales and five composite scales: internalizing problems, inattention/hyperactivity, personal problems, school problems, and the emotional symptoms index. The composite scores have demonstrated internal consistency reliability ranging from 0.84 to 0.96. The BASC-2 SRP has demonstrated convergent validity with the ASEBA Youth Self-Report Form, Conners–Wells Adolescent Self-Report Scale, the Children's Depression Inventory, and the original BASC Self-Report of Personality (Reynolds & Kamphaus, 2004). In this study, the Interpersonal Relations scale, which assesses success in relating to others and the degree of enjoyment experienced within relationships, was used as an indicator of children's social functioning.

Procedure

Upon receipt of Institutional Review Board approval, study advertisements were mailed to families of eligible children aged 8–14 years with HIV and moderate to severe persistent asthma followed in the Division of Allergy, Immunology, and Rheumatology at an urban Midwestern children's hospital. Families were also approached by the first author during their scheduled clinic visits. In the HIV clinic, 81% of families approached completed the study, while 89% of families recruited in the asthma clinic completed all study measures. To recruit uninfected children of HIV-positive mothers, study advertisements were distributed during programs at the hospital designed to address the psychosocial needs of youth affected by HIV. Interested mothers called the first author directly or provided a phone number for later screening.

Data collection took place between April 2008 and August 2009. Consent and assent were obtained upon arrival at the research center; only children who provided assent and had documented parental/caregiver consent were permitted to participate in the study. Children scoring below a standard score of 70 on the PPVT-III were to be excluded from study analyses; however, all children scored at or above this mark and therefore none were excluded. Caregivers completed the demographic questionnaire and the PIC-2 Behavioral Summary individually. Children were taken to a separate room to complete the PPVT-III, Friendship Interview, FQQ-R, CARRS, and the BASC-2 SRP. If children had difficulty reading, the measures were read aloud to them. Each child completed the protocol individually with the experimenter and was given a small token of appreciation (e.g., pencils, stickers, etc.) for participating. Caregivers were compensated $20.00, along with a $5.00 gas card to reimburse travel expenses if needed.

Results
Health and Cognitive Data

Approximately half of the children in the HIV group (48%) had an undetectable viral load (i.e., less than 48 copies of the virus per milliliter of blood) on the test date closest to their study visit. The median viral load for the study sample was 75 copies/ml. One child had not previously been on medication and had a viral load reading of over 24,000 copies/ml on the date of the study visit; although the child was asymptomatic, an antiretroviral medication regimen was initiated at that time.

The median number of school days missed by children with asthma in the past year for illness-related reasons fell between 11 and 15, while the median number of days missed by children with HIV fell between 6 and 10. The association between illness group (asthma or HIV) and days missed was not statistically significant, χ^2 (5, $n = 46) = 9.58$, $p = .09$; however, a medium effect size (Cramer's $V = .46$) indicated a moderate association between the variables.

For the total sample, receptive vocabulary scores on the PPVT-III ranged from 70 to 118 ($M = 92.29$, $SD = 10.27$). There were no significant differences in scores among children with HIV, children with asthma, and healthy children on this measure.

Descriptive Friendship Data

During the Friendship Interview, 31% of children in the total sample named three best friends, 27% reported having two best friends, 29% had one best friend, and 13% reported having no best friend. When children reported no best friend, they were asked to describe their closest friendship, even if they did not consider that individual a "best" friend. Of the 9 children with no best friend, 7 were in the asthma group and 2 were in the HIV group. Results of a two-way ANCOVA that included age as a covariate revealed a significant main effect of group, $F(2,63) = 4.82$, $p = .011$, with a medium effect size (partial $\eta^2 = .13$). Pairwise comparisons revealed that children in the asthma group reported having significantly fewer best friends on average ($M = 1.29$, $SE = 0.21$) than children in the healthy group ($M = 2.20$, $SE = 0.22$), 95% CI (-1.54 to -0.29), $p = .005$, and the HIV group ($M = 2.00$, $SE = 0.24$), 95% CI (-1.34 to -0.09), $p = .026$, based on estimated marginal means.

Hypothesized Differences Among Groups

Descriptive statistics for all study measures are summarized by group in Table II.

Internal Representations of Relationships

Univariate ANCOVAs were performed to determine whether scores on the two CARRS subscales differed based on whether children had HIV, asthma, or no illness, after controlling for the influence of age and gender. Age and gender were included as covariates with illness group based on findings from the literature. When the Affect Tone scale was entered as the dependent variable, the main effect of group was significant, $F(2,63) = 5.56$, $p = .006$, with a large effect size (partial $\eta^2 = .15$). Examination of estimated marginal means for Affect Tone scores by group revealed that on average, it was the asthma group that scored the lowest on the scale ($M = 49.80$, $SE = 1.74$), while the HIV group scored somewhat higher ($M = 53.80$, $SE = 2.00$) and the healthy children scored the highest ($M = 58.60$, $SE = 1.85$). Planned comparisons among the groups indicated that children with asthma differed significantly in their Affect Tone scale responses from healthy children, 95% CI (-14.07 to -3.53), $p = .001$, while children with HIV did not differ significantly in their responses from the healthy group or the asthma group. Additionally, the main effect of age was significant, $F(1,63) = 10.80$, $p = .002$, partial $\eta^2 = .15$, suggesting that child maturity may have impacted scores.

When the Emotional Investment in Relationships scale score was entered as the dependent variable, ANCOVA revealed a significant main effect for group, $F(2,63) = 3.40$, $p = .040$, partial $\eta^2 = .10$, as well as gender, $F(1,63) = 9.15$, $p = .004$, partial $\eta^2 = .13$. The asthma group again scored the lowest on average ($M = 48.41$, $SE = 1.39$), with the HIV group scoring higher

Table II. Descriptive Statistics for Study Measures by Group

Measure	Asthma ($n = 25$) M (SD)	HIV ($n = 21$) M (SD)	Healthy ($n = 24$) M (SD)
CARRS			
Affect tone	50.64 (9.11)	53.62 (8.46)	56.75 (8.96)
Emotional investment	47.92 (9.08)	52.14 (4.61)	53.88 (5.91)
FQQ-R			
Companionship & recreation	0.38 (0.19)	0.50 (0.15)	0.54 (0.16)
Validation & caring	2.83 (0.95)	3.18 (0.48)	3.45 (0.54)
Help & guidance	2.55 (0.82)	2.78 (0.72)	2.94 (0.56)
Intimate disclosure	2.17 (1.04)	2.09 (0.96)	2.85 (0.75)
Conflict resolution	2.60 (1.01)	2.70 (0.97)	3.14 (0.74)
Conflict & betrayal	1.05 (0.69)	1.08 (0.63)	0.82 (0.61)
PIC-2 Social adjustment	55.12 (10.50)	51.14 (15.42)	53.67 (11.72)
BASC-2 Interpersonal relations	47.08 (11.17)	50.62 (9.30)	50.29 (11.73)
PPVT-III	92.16 (10.66)	92.00 (12.15)	92.67 (8.30)

Note. CARRS = Children's Affective Representations of Relationships Scale; values are raw scores. FQQ-R = Friendship Quality Questionnaire – Revised; values range from 0 to 4. PIC-2 = Personality Inventory for Children, Second Edition; values are T-scores (higher = more severe). BASC-2 = Behavioral Assessment System for Children, Second Edition, Self-Report of Personality; values are T-scores (higher = more adaptive functioning). PPVT-III = Peabody Picture Vocabulary Test, Third Edition.

($M = 52.82$, $SE = 1.60$) and the healthy group obtaining the highest scores ($M = 53.30$, $SE = 1.47$). Children with asthma differed significantly from healthy children, 95% CI (−9.09 to −0.70], $p = .023$, and children with HIV, 95% CI (−8.62 to −0.21), $p = .040$ in their ability to invest emotionally in relationships. Additionally, girls ($M = 54.05$, $SE = 1.27$) scored significantly higher than boys ($M = 48.98$, $SE = 1.09$) on this scale, 95% CI (1.72 to 8.42), $p = .004$.

Child Report of Friendship Quality and Social Functioning

Contrary to hypotheses, mean FQQ-R subscale scores for the children with HIV were consistent with those obtained by average- to high-accepted children in the normative sample (Parker & Asher, 1993) and generally reflected satisfactory levels of friendship quality. To test the hypothesis that children with HIV would differ from children with asthma and healthy children in their report of friendship quality, a between-subjects MANCOVA was performed with the six FQQ-R subscales as dependent variables. Again, contrary to expectations, FQQ-R scores did not differ significantly by illness group. In other words, indicators of friendship quality as a whole did not differ based on whether children had HIV, asthma, or no chronic illness.

Hypothesized group differences in more general child-reported social functioning on the BASC-2 SRP Interpersonal Relations Scale were then tested using ANCOVA. The main effect of group was significant, $F(2,63) = 3.39$, $p = .040$, with a medium effect size ($\eta^2 = .10$); there were no interaction effects. Estimated marginal means showed that once again, children in the asthma group scored lowest ($M = 45.56$, $SE = 2.07$), children with HIV scored higher on average ($M = 51.10$, $SE = 2.38$), and healthy children with an HIV-positive mother scored the highest ($M = 53.40$, $SE = 2.19$). Planned pairwise comparisons demonstrated that children with asthma scored significantly lower than healthy children on this measure, 95% CI (−14.09 to −1.59), $p = .015$. Despite this difference, mean scores of children in all three groups fell in the subclinical range with regard to self-reported interpersonal functioning.

Parent Report of Child Social Adjustment

Group differences in caregiver-reported social functioning on the PIC-2 Social Adjustment Composite were assessed using ANCOVA. Results showed no significant main effect $[F(2,63) = 1.15$, $p = .32$, $\eta^2 = .04]$ or interaction effect $[F(2,63) = 0.56$, $p = .57$, $\eta^2 = .02]$, indicating that contrary to the original hypothesis, group differences in social adjustment did not exist based on caregiver report. Caregivers across groups rated their children as generally well-adjusted in the social domain (i.e., mean scores did not fall in the clinically significant range).

Discussion

The purpose of this study was to examine the friendships and social expectations of children with perinatally acquired HIV, an understudied area in the literature. Results were unexpected, in that they showed a trend for the children with asthma, not HIV, to demonstrate poorer self-reported indicators of friendship and the most negative social expectations of the three groups. The children with HIV reported friendship quality on par with established norms, as well as age-appropriate interpersonal functioning. It is worth pointing out that these children were physically healthy, with low-viral loads and fewer illness-related missed school days than their peers with asthma. Their low-viral loads suggest that most of the children were adequately adherent to their antiretroviral medications, reducing not only their risk of perceptible illness but also the potential for associated neurocognitive impairment that can lead to poor social functioning. PPVT-III scores, while somewhat lower than established norms, fell in the average range for the HIV-positive youths and were not significantly different from the scores of children with asthma or healthy children. While the PPVT is only an estimate of cognitive functioning and neurocognitive impairments linked to HIV tend to be more subtle and specific in nature, it is encouraging that scores were comparable to those of uninfected children in this urban setting. It is quite plausible that a combination of overall good health, satisfactory cognitive functioning, and regular school attendance helped these children establish and maintain satisfying friendships with peers despite living with a chronic illness.

While it is encouraging that the children with HIV, as well as healthy children affected by HIV, reported having best friends and experiencing rewarding relationships with peers, the findings that children with asthma may not be faring as well are concerning. Compared with the other two groups, children with moderate to severe persistent asthma in this sample reported significantly fewer best friends, displayed more negative affect as it related to their expectations of others in social contexts, demonstrated less of an ability to invest emotionally in relationships, and reported inferior interpersonal relations. This supports existing research showing poor psychosocial outcomes for youth with more severe forms of asthma (e.g., Calam, Gregg, & Goodman, 2005; Fritz & McQuaid, 2000), particularly in low income urban areas (Weil et al., 1999).

What factors might account for these differences? Although the answer is likely multifaceted, level of disease activity may be one explanation. While HIV and persistent asthma are both potentially life-threatening diseases that require daily management and regular monitoring by a medical team, symptom expression differed between the groups. As noted previously, the children with HIV were physically healthy, usually demonstrating no outward signs of illness. In contrast, the children with asthma had to exhibit symptoms (e.g., wheezing) at least once per day in order to be diagnosed with the moderate or severe persistent form of the disease. Their symptoms would be visible to peers and be more likely to impact their activity level and socialization opportunities. Greater symptom expression would also likely result in more frequent trips to the hospital or clinic, with implications for school attendance and peer interaction. Our findings showed that the children with asthma missed more school due to their illness than those with HIV, suggesting that their opportunities to interact with peers may have been impacted to a greater degree, with implications for the quality of their social functioning.

Lower socioeconomic status may have also played a role. The median yearly household income of the asthma group fell between $10,001 and 20,000 per year, while median income for the HIV group was slightly higher ($20,001–30,000). Although income levels for the asthma and healthy groups were comparable, inadequate resources in conjunction with the burden of high disease severity experienced by the children with persistent asthma could be expected to increase family stress and reduce quality of life. Family stress has been linked to more severe illness presentation in children with asthma via pathways that include less vigilant parenting and illness management practices (Drotar & Bonner, 2009; Kaugars, Klinnert, & Bender, 2004) as well as child emotional states that affect airway inflammation (Wood et al., 2006). It follows that poverty-related family stress and greater disease severity may have accounted for some of the social difficulties reported by the children with asthma in our sample.

It is also possible that an explanation for the observed group differences lies in the systems of care in place for these different populations of children. Federal funding via the Ryan White Care Act has established a structure of supportive services for individuals and families affected by HIV, which in addition to medical care includes case management, mental health services, and advocacy programs. The children in our sample were seen every 2 months in a pediatric specialty clinic by a multidisciplinary team of physicians, nurses, social workers, psychologists, and case managers specializing in HIV/AIDS. They were routinely referred to free hospital-sponsored educational programs, support groups, and camps. Groups and camps, while designed to bring children together in a fun and supportive atmosphere, also included educational activities with social skill-building themes (e.g., communication, problem solving, etc.). Recurring contacts with supportive professionals and the availability of these free services likely translate into greater knowledge of HIV, higher levels of self-efficacy in managing the effects of the virus, and increased accountability that may result in better clinic attendance and enhanced health outcomes (Naar-King et al., 2007). Support services were also available for entire families affected by HIV, allowing mothers with HIV and their uninfected children to increase knowledge while reducing stigma and building social support within the HIV community. In sum, the children with HIV and the healthy children with HIV-positive mothers were "hooked in" to a supportive structure of services that may have buffered against stressors associated with living with a chronic illness in an economically disadvantaged area, and indirectly may have resulted in better psychosocial outcomes. This comprehensive approach is consistent with the "medical home," defined by the American Academy of Pediatrics (2004) as accessible, family-centered, continuous, coordinated, compassionate, and culturally effective care. Unsurprisingly, care within a medical home has been associated with positive outcomes for youth, including better provider relationships, improved family functioning, fewer missed school days, and better physical and mental health than those who do not receive inclusive services (Homer et al., 2008).

In contrast, no such comprehensive, federally funded program exists for children with asthma despite published statistics on asthma-related morbidity and mortality, particularly in urban minority populations. The children with asthma in this study also received care in a pediatric specialty clinic by a multidisciplinary team. However, hospital- and community-based programs were not available to these families to provide additional support in managing illness-related stressors and other life challenges. Kang, Mellins, Ng, Robinson, & Abrams (2008) noted that people living with HIV in poor urban settings are able to access services that improve quality of life over and above what would be attainable for uninfected individuals in the same socioeconomic circumstances. A definite need exists to extend similar services to other at-risk groups; rates of pediatric asthma-related morbidity and mortality clearly identify this group as one in need of additional support.

Limitations and Future Directions

One limitation of this study is sampling. The number of subjects in each group was small, with ages ranging from middle childhood to early adolescence. Because the population of children with HIV is aging and the incidence of perinatal infection in the United States has decreased significantly in recent years, it will be increasingly difficult to obtain adequate sample sizes of younger children from a single site. Collaboration with other pediatric HIV clinics would provide a large enough sample to adequately examine child social functioning at different stages of disclosure to their HIV status. It is also possible that selection bias may partially explain the better child social functioning in the healthy sample. Mothers with HIV who actively attend support groups are likely higher functioning than those who do not, with more emotional resources to cope with the stressors of living with chronic illness; it follows that this may positively impact their children with regard to physical and psychosocial outcomes. Finally, this study did not include a control group of healthy urban children completely unaffected by HIV/AIDS. Future studies of friendship in children with HIV should incorporate a demographically matched sample of children who do not have a biological parent living with HIV in order to identify the effects of various HIV-related stressors on child social functioning. Given these limitations, results should be viewed as preliminary and verified with additional study.

Awareness of illness status varied across the three comparison groups, as well as within the HIV group. Some children with HIV had not yet been fully disclosed to their illness, although all were aware of a medical need to take medicine and see a doctor regularly; this is a function of age and maturity, as children are typically not disclosed to their diagnosis until they reach puberty and this knowledge becomes necessary. Also, some healthy children were not aware of their mother's HIV diagnosis, since child maturity and family preference dictate when this information is disclosed. Different levels of awareness made it difficult to assess the potential impact of stigma on children's social functioning; this relationship should be explored in future studies with somewhat older children. Future research should also include adolescents with perinatally acquired HIV, for whom the decision to disclose their diagnosis begins to have more important implications for both emotional and physical health. Targeting older youth may prove fruitful in exploring the potential health and psychosocial benefits of disclosure to friends.

Results of this study bring encouraging new information to light about the psychosocial functioning of children with perinatally acquired HIV in the era of HAART. Clinically, it is important for practitioners to be aware of the potential for peer relationship difficulties in this group of children and to make the topic of social functioning a routine part of the assessment process. Further research is needed to better understand the factors that promote positive social adjustment in this group of at-risk children, in order to inform and advance interventions for youth living with HIV at the individual, family, and community levels.

Funding

This project was funded in part by a dissertation research support grant from the Central Michigan University College of Graduate Studies.

Conflicts of interest: None declared.

References

American Academy of Pediatrics. (2004). Policy statement: The medical home. *Pediatrics, 113*(Suppl 5), 1545–1547.

Baker, S. E., & Niec, L. N. (2007). Children's representations about self and relationships: What can a card sort tell us about interpersonal functioning? Unpublished thesis manuscript.

Boivin, M., Vitaro, F., & Poulin, F. (2005). Peer relationships and the development of aggressive behavior in early childhood. In R. E. Tremblay, W. W. Hartup, & J. J. Archer (Eds.), *Developmental origins of aggression* (pp. 376–397). New York: Guilford Press.

Bose, S., Moss, H., Brouwers, P., Pizzo, P., & Lorion, R. (1994). Psychologic adjustment of human immunodeficiency virus-infected school-age children. *Journal of Developmental and Behavioral Pediatrics, 15*(3), S26–S33.

Bukowski, W. M., & Adams, R. (2005). Peer relationships and psychopathology: Markers, moderators, mediators, mechanisms, and meanings. *Journal of Clinical Child and Adolescent Psychology, 34*(1), 3–10.

Calam, R., Gregg, L., & Goodman, R. (2005). Psychological adjustment and asthma in children and adolescents: The UK Nationwide Mental Health Survey. *Psychosomatic Medicine, 67*, 105–110.

Campbell, J. M., Bell, S. K., & Keith, L. K. (2001). Concurrent validity of the Peabody Picture Vocabulary Test, Third Edition as an intelligence and achievement screener for low SES African American children. *Assessment, 8*(1), 85–94.

Carvajal, H., Hayes, J. E., Miller, H. R., Wiebe, D. A., & Weaver, K. A. (1993). Comparisons of the vocabulary scores and IQs on the Wechsler Intelligence Scale for Children-III and the Peabody Picture Vocabulary Test-Revised. *Perceptual and Motor Skills, 76,* 28–30.

Cunningham, S. D., Thomas, P. D., & Warschausky, S. (2007). Gender differences in peer relations of children with neurodevelopmental conditions. *Rehabilitation Psychology, 52*(3), 331–337.

Drotar, D., & Bonner, M. S. (2009). Influences on adherence to pediatric asthma treatment: A review of correlates and predictors. *Journal of Developmental and Behavioral Pediatrics, 30,* 574–582.

Dunn, L. M., & Dunn, L. M. (1997). *Peabody Picture Vocabulary Test–Third Edition: Manual.* Circle Pines, MN: American Guidance Services.

Franklin, S., Lim, J. Y., Rennie, K. M., Eastwood, D., Cuene, B., & Havens, P. L. (2005). Longitudinal intellectual assessment of children with HIV infection. *Journal of Clinical Psychology in Medical Settings, 12*(4), 367–376.

Fritz, G. K., & McQuaid, E. L. (2000). Chronic medical conditions: Impact on development. In A. J. Sameroff, M. Lewis, & S. M. Miller (Eds.), *Handbook of developmental psychopathology* (2nd ed., pp. 277–289). (New York: Kluwer Academic/Plenum Press.

Fundaro, C., Miccinesi, N., Baldieri, N. F., Genovese, O., Rendeli, C., & Segni, G. (1998). Cognitive impairment in school-age children with asymptomatic HIV infection. *AIDS Patient Care and STDs, 12*(2), 135–140.

Graetz, B., & Schute, R. (1995). Assessment of peer relationships in children with asthma. *Journal of Pediatric Psychology, 20,* 205–216.

Halterman, J. S., Conn, K. M., Forbes-Jones, E., Fagnano, M., Hightower, A. D., & Szilagyi, P. G. (2006). Behavior problems among inner-city children with asthma: Findings from a community based sample. *Pediatrics, 117,* e192–e199.

Hilsenroth, M. J., Stein, M., & Pinsker, J. (2004). *Social Cognition and Object Relations Scale–Global Rating Method (SCORS-G). Unpublished manuscript,* The Derner Institute of Advanced Psychological Studies, Adelphi University, Garden City, NY.

Homer, C. J., Klatka, K., Romm, D., Kulhthau, K., Bloom, S., Newacheck, P., ... Perrin, J. M. (2008). A review of the evidence for the medical home for children with special health care needs. *Pediatrics, 122,* e922–e937.

Kang, E., Mellins, C. A., Ng, W. Y. K., Robinson, L., & Abrams, E. J. (2008). Standing between two worlds in Harlem: A developmental psychopathology perspective of perinatally acquired human immunodeficiency virus and adolescence. *Journal of Applied Developmental Psychology, 29,* 227–237.

Kaugars, A. S., Klinnert, M. D., & Bender, B. G. (2004). Family influences on pediatric asthma. *Journal of Pediatric Psychology, 29*(7), 475–491.

Knight, W. G., Mellins, C. A., Levenson, R. L., Arpadi, S. M., & Kairam, R. (2000). Brief report: Effects of pediatric HIV infection on mental and psychomotor development. *Journal of Pediatric Psychology, 25*(8), 583–587.

Lachar, D. (2007). Personality inventory for children, second edition (PIC-2), personality inventory for youth (PIY), and student behavior survey (SBS). In S. R. Smith, & L. Handler (Eds.), *The clinical assessment of children and adolescents: A practitioner's handbook* (pp. 289–309). Mahwah, NJ: Lawrence Erlbaum Associates.

Lachar, D., & Gruber, C. P. (2001). *Personality inventory for children, second edition (PIC-2) standard format and behavioral summary manual.* Los Angeles, CA: Western Psychological Services.

Ladd, G. W., & Troop-Gordon, W. (2003). The role of chronic peer difficulties in the development of children's psychological adjustment problems. *Child Development, 74,* 1344–1367.

La Greca, A. M., Bearman, K. J., & Moore, H. (2002). Peer relations of youth with pediatric conditions and health risks: Promoting social support and healthy lifestyles. *Journal of Developmental & Behavioral Pediatrics, 23*(4), 271–280.

Lee, R. S., Kochman, A., & Sikkema, K. J. (2002). Internalized stigma among people living with HIV-AIDS. *AIDS and Behavior, 6*(4), 309–319.

Lopez, C., & DuBois, D. L. (2005). Peer victimization and rejection: Investigation of an integrative model of effects on emotional, behavioral, and academic adjustment in early adolescence. *Journal of Clinical Child and Adolescent Psychology, 34*(1), 25–36.

Mak, W. W. S., Cheung, R. Y. M., Law, R. W., Woo, J., Li, P. C. K., & Chung, R. W. Y. (2007). Examining an attribution model of self-stigma on social support and psychological well-being among people with HIV/AIDS. *Social Science & Medicine, 64,* 1549–1559.

McQuaid, E. L., Kopel, S. J., & Nassau, J. H. (2001). Behavioral adjustment in children with asthma: A meta-analysis. *Developmental and Behavioral Pediatrics, 22*(6), 430–439.

Naar-King, S., Green, M., Wright, K., Outlaw, A., Wang, B., & Liu, H. (2007). Ancillary services and retention of youth in HIV care. *AIDS Care, 19*(2), 248–251.

Nassau, J. H., & Drotar, D. (1997). Social competence among children with central nervous system-related chronic health conditions: A review. *Journal of Pediatric Psychology, 22,* 771–793.

National Heart, Lung, and Blood Institute (NHLBI). (2007). *Expert Panel Report 3: Guidelines for the diagnosis and management of asthma.* Retrieved from http://www.nhlbi.nih.gov/guidelines/asthma/

Nozyce, M. L., Lee, S. S., Wiznia, A., Nachman, S., Mofenson, L. M., Smith, M. E., … Pelton, S. (2006). A behavioral and cognitive profile of clinically stable HIV-infected children. *Pediatrics, 117*(3), 763–770.

Parker, J. G., & Asher, S. R. (1993). Friendship and friendship quality in middle childhood: Links with peer group acceptance and feelings of loneliness and social dissatisfaction. *Developmental Psychology, 29*(4), 611–621.

Reynolds, C. R., & Kamphaus, R. W. (2004). *Behavior assessment system for children, second edition (BASC-2) manual.* Circle Pines, MN: American Guidance Service.

Sherman, B. F., Bonanno, G. A., Weiner, L. S., & Battles, H. B. (2000). When children tell their friends they have AIDS: Possible consequences for psychological well-being and disease progression. *Psychosomatic Medicine, 62,* 238–247.

Smith, R., Rossetto, K., & Peterson, B. L. (2008). A meta-analysis of disclosure of one's HIV-positive status, stigma, and social support. *AIDS Care, 20*(10), 1266–1275.

Vandell, D. L. (1999). *Friendship interview.* Unpublished interview, University of Wisconsin—Madison.

Weil, C. M., Wade, S. L., Bauman, L. J., Lynn, H., Mitchell, H., & Lavigne, J. (1999). The relationship between psychosocial factors and asthma morbidity in inner-city children with asthma. *Pediatrics, 104*(6), 1274–1280.

Wood, B. L., Miller, B. D., Lim, J., Lillis, K., Ballow, M., Stern, T., & Simmens, S. (2006). Family relational factors in pediatric depression and asthma: Pathways of effect. *Journal of the American Academy of Child and Adolescent Psychiatry, 45*(12), 1494–1502.

Wolters, P. L., Brouwers, P., & Moss, H. A. (1995). Pediatric HIV disease: Effect on cognition, learning, and behavior. *School Psychology Quarterly, 10*(4), 305–328.

Friends or Foes? A Review of Peer Influence on Self-Care and Glycemic Control in Adolescents With Type 1 Diabetes

Dianne K. Palladino, BS, and Vicki S. Helgeson, PhD
Department of Psychology, Carnegie Mellon University

All correspondence concerning this article should be addressed to Dianne Palladino, Department of Psychology, Carnegie Mellon University, Pittsburgh, PA, 15213, USA.
E-mail: dkpalladino@cmu.edu

Received July 21, 2011; revisions received December 9, 2011; accepted January 21, 2012

Objective We reviewed studies published from 1990 to 2010 examining the relation of peer influence to diabetes outcomes for adolescents with type 1 diabetes. **Methods** We searched PsychInfo and MedLine databases and personal archives for studies meeting our criteria. 24 articles were included in the final review. **Results** Qualitative studies revealed that teens believe peers have an impact on diabetes behaviors, but quantitative findings are inconclusive. We found more evidence that social conflict was harmful than social support was helpful. Associations were more likely in studies that measured specific support and specific self-care variables. Studies addressing how individual differences interact with social context had promising findings. **Conclusions** The literature linking peer relations to diabetes outcomes is mixed. Future research should consider moderator variables, expand the conceptualization of peer relationships, and consider interactions between person and social context.

Key words adherence; adolescent; friends; glycemic control; peers; self-care; type 1 diabetes.

Among the naturally occurring transitions during adolescence, social changes are some of the most salient. During these years, the social focus of teens moves from an adult-centered view to one that is peer-centered (Fuligni, Barber, Eccles, & Clements, 2001; Larson & Verma, 1999). Adolescents become more involved in extracurricular activities that keep them away from parental supervision and support on an increasing basis (Scholte, van Lieshout, & van Aken, 2001). These changes typically begin during the middle school years, when self-esteem has been found to decline (Wigfield, Eccles, Mac Iver, Reuman, & Midgley, 1991). In fact, peer relationships have been found to be an important factor in determining social competence during childhood and adolescence (Ladd, 2008; Meece & Laird, 2006), and a sense of belonging has been linked to lower levels of depression, less social rejection, and fewer problems in school (Anderman, 2002). It is clear that peer relationships become a prominent factor in the well-being of teens. Peer relationships may play a particularly salient role in the in the life of an adolescent with a chronic disease, especially one with a complicated daily regimen such as diabetes.

Individuals coping with type 1 diabetes (T1D) must manage a complex regimen of blood glucose testing, insulin administration, diet management, and exercise in order to maintain optimal blood glucose levels. Execution of these behaviors is important because failure to successfully manage them can lead to serious short term and long term consequences for teens' health (Hood, Peterson, Rohan, & Drotar, 2009). Research has shown that glycemic control in teens with T1D decreases during adolescence (Greening, Stoppelbein, Konishi, Jordan, & Moll, 2007). This decline has been attributed to physiology (Goran & Gower, 2001) as well as declines in self-care behavior (La Greca, Follansbee, & Skyler, 1990; La Greca, Swales, Klemp, Madigan, & Skyler, 1995). The transition from strong parental involvement to a more peer-focused lifestyle may present challenges to self-care behaviors (Holmes et al., 2006). Peer relationships can be particularly important when an adolescent's chronic disease involves self-care behaviors throughout the day at school or during social events in the presence of others, as with T1D.

Peer relationships may influence diabetes outcomes in a number of ways. The literature shows that social support can be beneficial for health due to its provision of useful information and resources, decreased negative affect and increased self-esteem, and social control (Cohen, 1988). The main effects model emphasizes that these provisions of social support are beneficial for health in general, whereas the stress-buffering model predicts that social support is most beneficial for health under times of stress (Cohen & Wills, 1985). There is also literature suggesting that social relationships may have adverse effects on well-being, including social constraints (Lepore & Helgeson, 1998), social conflict (Rook, Sorkin, & Zettel, 2004), and support attempts that fail (Dakof & Taylor, 1990). In the case of adolescents with T1D, the relation of social support and social conflict from families to diabetes outcomes has been studied extensively (e.g., Berg et al., 2011; Helgeson, Reynolds, Siminerio, Escobar, & Becker, 2008; Ingerski, Anderson, Dolan, & Hood, 2010; Lewandowski & Drotar, 2007). Despite the potential for peers to influence the health of adolescents with diabetes, relatively little research has studied the effect of peer relationships on self-care behaviors and glycemic control.

This systematic review synthesizes findings in research published from 1990 to 2010 that examined the influence of peers on T1D self-care and glycemic control. This article will address: (a) the behaviors peers exhibit that help or hinder self-care and glycemic control and (b) how these behaviors relate to self-care and glycemic control.

We made several distinctions within peer relationships. First, we distinguished between positive and negative peer influences. We refer to the positive relationships as supportive relationships, and the negative relationships as social conflict. Within *supportive relationships* and *conflictual relationships*, we distinguish between general and diabetes specific. *General support* refers to the instrumental, emotional, or informational resources that others provide that are not targeted at diabetes self-care. *Diabetes-specific support* refers to the support from others that is targeted at self-care, such as assisting with blood glucose monitoring. *Social conflict* includes interactions with peers that are negative, conflictual, or problematic in some way. An example of *general conflict* is "showing off or bragging about being better at something," and an example of *diabetes-specific conflict* is "offering food that one is unable to eat."

Finally, some studies did not measure support or conflict, but examined other ways in which peers influence diabetes self-care, such as anticipated peer reactions to diabetes self-care. We refer to these as *other peer influences*.

This review considers articles that evaluate support and conflict, both general and diabetes specific, as well as other peer influences.

Method
Literature Search

We reviewed findings from studies published in English in peer-reviewed journals from 1990 through 2010 that explore the associations of peer relationships to diabetes self-care and glycemic control. We chose 1990 as the starting date to allow for inclusion of as many papers as possible, while also eliminating articles published during a time when diabetes care differed substantially from what it is today due to the tightened self-care recommendations from the Diabetes Control and Complications Trial (DCCT, 1993). In order for an article to be included in this review, the majority of the sample had to include youth with T1D, youth being defined as 18 years old or younger. We reviewed both qualitative studies that described the ways peers affect self-care and quantitative studies that linked peer relationships to self-care and glycemic control.

Exhaustive searches were conducted using both PsychInfo and Medline databases. Search terms included at least one term from each of the following: (a) friend* or peer*; (b) self*care, adherence, compliance, *A1c, or glycemic control; (c) adolescent*, child*, or teen*; and (d) diabetes, diabetic, or IDDM. After reading the abstracts of the 175 articles returned by PsychInfo and 185 articles returned by Medline for relevance and duplication, 53 and 55 were reviewed in detail, respectively. We also retrieved 18 articles from reviewing personal archives and reference lists of recently published review papers. Of the 126 articles reviewed, 24 met the inclusion criteria. Articles most often were excluded because they did not include measures of self-care behaviors or glycemic control (i.e., HbA1c) or the majority of participants were over 18 years old. The final 24 papers are indicated with an 'asterisk' in the reference section.

Results

The first section summarizes qualitative studies that address how adolescents believe peers impact their self-care. The next section reviews the quantitative studies that examine links of supportive peer relationships, social conflict, and other peer influences to self-care and glycemic control. Within the support and conflict sections, studies on general versus diabetes-specific support are distinguished. Finally, within each of those sections, we distinguish between findings on self-care and glycemic control. Unless otherwise noted, all studies are cross-sectional and used a measure of general self-care behavior rather than a measure of individual domains of self-care (e.g., diet). Samples were largely white and studies did not adjust for any covariates in analyses, unless otherwise noted. Nearly half (45%) of the quantitative studies failed to provide any information about socioeconomic status (SES), and the remaining studies used heterogeneous measures, making comparisons based upon SES prohibitive.

The heterogeneity of independent variable measures and the relatively small number of studies reviewed prohibited us from conducting a meta-analysis. However, whenever possible, we provide effect sizes so that comparisons can be made across studies (Table I).

Findings: What Do Peers Do?

The first step to determining what adolescents think is helpful or harmful to diabetes self-management is to ask them. Seven studies provided evidence that teens felt that peers had an influence on their self-care behaviors. Of these, four studies asked teens what they thought would influence self-care, and found that peer influence was a common component (Berlin, 2006; Karlsson, Arman, & Wikblad, 2008; Kyngas, Hentinen, & Barlow, 1998;

Table I. Characteristics and Findings of Studies Linking Peer Relations to Self-Care and Glycemic Control

Authors (year)	N (%F)	Age (years)	XS	Long	Ethnicity (%Caucasian)	Supportive Relationships General	Supportive Relationships Diabetes-specific	Social Conflict General	Social Conflict Diabetes-specific	Other Peer Infl
Self-care										
Skinner & Hampson (1998)[†]	74 (43)	12–18	X		99	✓(.47)/0	✓(.68)/0			
Skinner & Hampson (2000)[†]	52 (46)	12–18		X	100	✓(.85/.90)/0	0/0			
Helgeson et al. (2007)	132 (53)	10–14	X	X	91	0		0		
Helgeson, Lopez et al. (2009)	76 (50)	13–16	X	X	90	✓[a,d]/0		✓[a]/0		
Hains et al. (2007)	102 (60)	10–18	X		81			0		✓(1.22)
La Greca et al. (1995)	74 (39)	11–18	X		84			0		
Naar-King et al. (2006)	96 (54)	10–17	X		24			0		
Pendley et al. (2002)	68 (62)	8–17	X		88			0		
Greco et al. (2001)	21 (48)	10–18		X	81			0		
Bearman & La Greca (2002)	74 (40)	11–18	X		83		✓[a]/0			
Kyngäs & Rissanen (2001)	1061 (50)	13–17	X		NR		✓(.41)			
Kyngäs et al. (1998)	51 (45)	13–17	X		NR		✓[c]/0			
Thomas et al. (1997)	67 (49)	8–17	X		79					✓(1.30)
Drew et al. (2010)	252 (54)	10–15		X	94					✓(−.58)
Grey et al. (1998)	65 (57)	13–20		X	92					0
Glycemic control										
Kager & Holden (1992)	64 (67)	7–15	X		94	0				
Helgeson et al. (2007)[‡]	132 (53)	10–14	X	X	91	0		✓[b]✓[a]		
Helgeson, Siminerio et al. (2009)[‡]	132 (53)	10–14	X	X	93	✓*,[a]/0		✓[a]/0		
Helgeson, Lopez et al. (2009)	76 (50)	13–16	X	X	90	0		✓[b]/0		
Smith et al. (1991)	37 (32)	11–18	X		NR		0			
DeDios et al. (2003)	55 (40)	M = 17	X		NR		0			
Pendley et al. (2002)	68 (62)	8–17	X		88		✓(1.15)/0			
Lehmkuhl & Nabors (2008)	81 (39)	8–14	X		100		✓[b]			
Hains et al. (2007)	102 (60)	10–18	X		81		✓*,[d]/0			✓[d]
Thomas et al. (1997)	67 (49)	8–17	X		79					0
Drew et al. (2010)	252 (54)	10–15		X	94					✓(.47)
Grey et al. (1998)	65 (57)	13–20		X	92					✓(.38)

Note. XS = cross-sectional; Long = longitudinal; Oth Peer Infl = other peer influences; effect sizes shown in the form of Cohen's d
✓association found; ✓* association found in unexpected direction; 0, no association found; [†,‡],studies are linked; NR = not reported.
[a]Beta from MLM or HLM models—cannot calculate effect sizes.
[b]Standardized beta not ± 0.50, cannot convert to d (Peterson & Brown, 2005).
[c]Inferential statistics not run—only averages reported.
[d]More complicated relation reported in text.

Schlundt et al., 1994). Schlundt et al. (1994) asked teens about obstacles to dietary adherence and found that several could be attributed to the actions or the presence of peers. Of the 10 clusters of obstacles identified in the study, two were directly related to peers (i.e., peer interpersonal conflict, eating at school), and three were likely to involve peers (i.e., competing priorities due to fear of social repercussions, social events and holidays, social pressures to eat inappropriate foods). A second study asked teens how they cared for themselves, what factors supported their care, and what factors hindered their care (Kyngas et al., 1998). Three categories arose from the interview responses that described peer relationships: dominant (teens like to live like their peers and are tempted to break healthcare regimens), silent support (peers adjust to the limitations of the teen with T1D), and irrelevant (peers have no influence on self-care). The third study asked open-ended questions about the context of diabetes-related problems that have occurred since beginning to use an insulin pump (Berlin, 2006). The most frequent context in which problems were reported by teens was in social situations with peers. A fourth study found that emotional support in the form of acceptance and encouragement from peers resulted in Swedish teens feeling secure incorporating self-care behaviors into their daily routines (Karlsson et al., 2008).

One study directly asked adolescents how peers influence how they take care of themselves, and if there were ways in which peers could be more supportive of diabetes self-care (Lehmkuhl et al., 2009). Although teens most frequently said that their self-care was not affected by the presence of peers and that peers' support behaviors were satisfactory, participants identified a number of ways in which peers could be more helpful: provide verbal reminders, monitor symptoms of hyper/hypoglycemia, and refrain from drawing attention to their diabetes.

Two other studies used a semi-structured interview, the Diabetes Social Support Interview (DSSI; La Greca, Auslander et al., 1995), to ascertain ways in which teens ages 11–18 years found peers to be helpful. Responses to open-ended questions, such as, "*In what ways do your family/friends provide support for [diabetes care tasks],*" were coded into categories of diabetes-specific instrumental (i.e., behaviors that providing assistance or resources for solving a problem) and emotional (i.e., behaviors that provide comfort, affirmation, or communicate caring) support. Teens reported that family members provided higher levels of diabetes-specific instrumental support than peers, whereas peers provided more diabetes-specific emotional support (e.g., companionship, acceptance) than parents. Support in the form of companionship from peers was most frequently mentioned in the contexts of exercise and diet. When teens with T1D did report diabetes-specific instrumental support from friends, it was more likely to be for insulin administration and blood glucose monitoring than for diet and exercise.

Pendley et al. (2002) used the DSSI to examine whether the kind of support received from peers depended on adolescent age. Older adolescents (ages 13–17 years) reported more diabetes-specific instrumental support for taking insulin, testing blood glucose and diet and more emotional support from peers than younger children (ages 8–12 years). Interestingly, there were no differences between the two age groups in the kinds of support received from family.

These qualitative studies indicate that teens with T1D consider peers to have influence on their self-care behavior, but it is not clear whether this influence is positive or negative. In the next sections, we examine whether existing research supports teens' beliefs by reviewing the literature on the association of peer relationships to self-care and glycemic control. The descriptive characteristics and overall study findings are shown in the top half of Table I for self-care and in the bottom half of Table I for glycemic control.

Supportive Relationships and Diabetes Outcomes
General Support

Self-care. Three studies presented in four published reports examined the relation of general support to self-care, one of which resulted in separate cross-sectional and longitudinal reports. This study found a cross-sectional relation of general support to stronger dietary adherence, but not to insulin administration or blood glucose testing (Skinner & Hampson, 1998). In addition, a baseline measure of combined family and friend support predicted improvements in dietary self-care 6 months later, but did not predict changes in insulin administration or blood glucose monitoring after adjusting for illness duration, SES, and gender (Skinner, John, & Hampson, 2000). Increases in combined friend and family support over the 6 months also were associated with improvements in dietary self-care. The fact that investigators combined friend and family support into one variable, however, makes it impossible to determine whether friend support had a unique impact on self-care.

The second study did not find an association between a measure of general support and self-care behavior cross-sectionally or longitudinally using multilevel modeling after 1 year controlling for BMI, pubertal stage, and SES (Helgeson, Reynolds, Escobar, Siminerio, & Becker, 2007). A third study found no cross-sectional relation of general support to self-care, but the number of enjoyable interactions with friends using ecological momentary assessment aggregated over 4 days was positively associated with self-care, especially for girls (Helgeson, Lopez, & Karmack, 2009). This study provided a different way to assess general peer support. Rather than relying on retrospective reports, proximal measures of social interactions over several days may have provided a more accurate representation of teens' social lives.

Glycemic Control. Three studies (four reports) examined the association of general support to glycemic control. One study found no correlation of general support to glycemic control (Kager & Holden, 1992). A second study found no association of general support to glycemic control cross-sectionally or longitudinally 1 year later using multilevel modeling and controlling for BMI, pubertal stage, and SES (Helgeson et al., 2007). In contrast, a follow-up study of the same sample showed that peer support was related to *poor* glycemic control over four annual assessments using multilevel modeling controlling for age, pubertal status, treatment delivery method, baseline SES, and baseline BMI (Helgeson, Siminerio, Escobar, & Becker, 2009). However, lagged analyses over 4 years that controlled for the same variables showed that peer support did not predict changes in glycemic control. Finally, the previously described ecological momentary assessment study of social interactions did not find a relation of an aggregate measure of enjoyable interactions over 4 days or retrospectively reported general support to glycemic control (Helgeson, Lopez et al., 2009).

Summary. Even though significant effects were strong to moderate, overall evidence to link general support to self-care is weak. With the exception of the one finding in the direction opposite of predictions, there was no evidence that general peer support was related to glycemic control, despite the variety of design approaches that were employed.

Diabetes-specific Support

Self-care. Nine studies (10 reports) examined the relation of diabetes-specific support to self-care. One study found no correlation of peer support to anticipated self-care difficulties (Hains et al., 2007). Three studies found no association of diabetes-specific support to self-care using MANOVA (La Greca, Auslander et al., 1995), multiple regression with controls for age with a mostly minority sample (Naar-King, Podolski, Ellis, Frey, & Templin, 2006), or multiple regression with controls for diabetes duration (Pendley et al., 2002). In addition, an intervention using a small sample ($n=21$) with a wide age range (10–18) of adolescents aimed at increasing peer support and peer diabetes knowledge had no effect on self-care (Greco, Pendley, McDonell, & Reeves, 2001).

One study reported mixed findings. Diabetes-specific support from peers was correlated with good blood glucose monitoring, but not diet and insulin administration cross-sectionally (Skinner & Hampson, 1998), and neither a combined measure of family and friend diabetes-specific support nor changes in this measure were associated with changes in self-care behaviors over 6 months using multiple regression controlling for illness duration, SES, and gender (Skinner et al., 2000). As noted previously, the use of a combined measure of friend and family support in this follow-up study precludes our ability to draw strong conclusions.

In contrast, three studies found a link between diabetes-specific peer support and self-care. Using a quantitative adaptation of the DSSI, one study linked support for blood glucose testing on the Diabetes Social Support Questionnaire (DSSQ) to more frequent blood glucose testing, but did not link support for insulin administration or diet to their respective self-care behaviors when adjusting for age in multilevel modeling analyses (Bearman & La Greca, 2002). In addition, diabetes-specific support was not related to a general index of adherence. The second, a study of Finnish teenagers with one of four different chronic diseases (asthma, epilepsy, juvenile rheumatoid arthritis, diabetes), used logistic regression to show that adolescents who felt that peers supported their diabetes self-care behaviors were 2.11 times more likely to adhere to those behaviors (Kyngas & Rissanen, 2001). However, these investigators did not conduct separate analyses within specific disease groups. Finally, a study of Finnish teens examined the association of different categories of diabetes-specific support from peers to self-care. Peer support that was categorized as silent or irrelevant was associated with better self-care than peer support that was categorized as dominant (Kyngas et al., 1998). These findings are difficult to interpret, however, because no inferential statistics were used to determine whether there were group differences in compliance.

Glycemic Control. Five studies examined the relation of diabetes-specific support to glycemic control. One study found no correlation between more positive diabetes-related interactions with peers and glycemic control (Smith, Mauseth, Palmer, Pecoraro, & Wenet, 1991). Two studies found no relation of diabetes-specific support to glycemic control (de Dios, 2003), one of which controlled for adherence and diabetes knowledge using multiple regression analysis (Pendley et al., 2002). However, the latter study also employed an indirect measure of diabetes-specific support by asking teens to identify peers who would participate in a "support team" for an intervention aimed at improving family and peer involvement in diabetes self-care (Pendley et al., 2002). Teens who chose a larger number of peers had better glycemic control. A large effect size for this relation indicated a strong association.

One study measured teens' satisfaction with school support for diabetes (including peer support) and found that higher satisfaction predicted improved glycemic control over 6 months using regression, but only for those teens with better glycemic control at baseline (Lehmkuhl & Nabors, 2008). The last study employed structural equation modeling, found no direct association of support to glycemic control, but found that support moderated the association between diabetes-related stress and glycemic control (Hains et al., 2007). Surprisingly, as peer support increased, the link of diabetes-related stress to poor glycemic control grew stronger.

Summary. Of the 9 studies, 4 found relations between diabetes-specific peer support and self-care. Those four had heterogeneous designs relative to each other compared to the five that did not find relations. Two of the studies that found relations were quite different from the others—one included teens with diseases other than diabetes, and one used descriptive statistics from a primarily qualitative measure. Thus, even considering moderate effects for two of these four findings, the link of diabetes-specific support to self-care is relatively weak.

Although more complicated designs were more likely to find relations of diabetes-specific support to glycemic control, the overall evidence is weak. The majority of the studies found no effects but the few that did find effects had moderate to large effect sizes. Significant relations typically linked supportive peer relations to good glycemic control, with two exceptions that found a detrimental relation. These two studies have little in common, and are indistinguishable from other studies, thus offering no explanation for their unexpected findings.

Social Conflict and Diabetes Outcomes
General Conflict
Self-care. Two studies examined peer conflict as a predictor of self-care. One found no relation of peer conflict to self-care behaviors cross-sectionally or longitudinally using multilevel modeling over 1 year controlling for BMI, pubertal stage, and SES (Helgeson et al., 2007). The second study had mixed findings. Peer conflict was associated with worse self-care behavior cross-sectionally, but an ecological momentary assessment of peer conflict revealed that an aggregate measure of upsetting peer interactions over 4 days was not related to self-care behavior (Helgeson, Lopez et al., 2009).

Glycemic Control. These same two studies (three reports) also examined the relation of peer conflict to glycemic control. Both found an association of higher levels of peer conflict to poor glycemic control. In a cross-sectional study, conflict with peers was associated with poor glycemic control, especially for girls (Helgeson, Lopez et al., 2009). However, the ecological momentary assessment portion of the study did not reveal a relation of an aggregate measure of upsetting peer interactions over 4 days to glycemic control. In a second study, conflict with peers was associated with poor glycemic control cross-sectionally at baseline, and predicted a decline in glycemic control over 1 year using multilevel modeling with controls for BMI, pubertal stage, and SES (Helgeson et al., 2007). In a follow-up report of this same sample, multilevel modeling showed that peer conflict was unrelated to glycemic control over a 4-year period in concurrent analyses, but that peer conflict predicted deterioration in glycemic control in lagged analyses over the same 4 years (Helgeson, Siminerio et al., 2009).

Diabetes-Specific Conflict
Although qualitative studies found that teens with T1D mentioned diabetes-specific conflict as detrimental to self-care, we could not locate any studies that examined the relation of diabetes-related conflict to self-care or glycemic control.

Summary. The existing studies, while small in number, suggest that general peer conflict may adversely affect self-care and metabolic control. The two studies that support this conclusion used different designs, but were conducted by the same laboratory. Thus replication is needed before strong conclusions can be drawn. We did not locate any studies that examined diabetes-specific conflict in connection to self-care or glycemic control.

Other Peer Influences and Diabetes Outcomes
Self-care. Four studies examined associations of other peer influences to self-care behavior, three of which found a relation. The first used an innovative design in which teens ages 8–17 years were asked how they would respond to vignettes of situations that posed self-care dilemmas (Thomas, Peterson, & Goldstein, 1997). Across the five vignettes, older teens stated they would be more likely to choose less adherent behaviors in the face of social

pressures in spite of a more accurate understanding of appropriate self-care behaviors than younger teens. The second study examined vulnerability to peer influence by asking teens how they imagined peers would react to the execution of their self-care behaviors in social situations. When teens anticipated negative reactions from peers, they were more likely to say that they would have trouble with self-management (Hains et al., 2007).

The third study investigated the role of peer influence by measuring an individual difference variable called extreme peer orientation (EPO) that reflects whether teens were more or less vulnerable to peer influence. This study used regression analysis to find that teens who scored high on EPO reported worse self-care behaviors (Drew, Berg, & Wiebe, 2010).

The fourth study examined whether adolescents can learn skills that would help them face challenging situations around peers. When randomly assigned to an intervention group that involved coping skills training for resolution of diabetes-related social dilemmas or a control group, there was no evidence that the intervention group improved testing or insulin administration over 3 months (Grey et al., 1998). The investigators did not examine other self-care behaviors that could have been affected by the training, such as diet and exercise.

Glycemic Control. The same four studies also examined links to glycemic control. Three of the four found a relation. The vignette study found no relation of responses to situations that posed challenges to diabetes to glycemic control (Thomas et al., 1997). In contrast, the study that examined teen perceptions of peer reactions (Hains et al., 2007) found an indirect link to glycemic control. Specifically, teens who expected negative reactions from peers regarding their self-care anticipated self-care difficulties, which were associated with increased diabetes-related stress, which, in turn, was linked to worse glycemic control. Third, the intervention to address social dilemmas showed a benefit for glycemic control (Grey et al., 1998).

Finally, the study that examined vulnerability to peer influence found a link of EPO to poor glycemic control (Drew et al., 2010). EPO was also found to mediate the relation between strong parental relationships and glycemic control, such that good relationships with parents were associated with good self-care behavior and good glycemic control in the presence of lower EPO. These findings suggest that a balance between the importance placed on family versus peer relationships may be one key to optimal diabetes outcomes in this age group.

Summary

Taken collectively, these four studies provide the strongest links of peer relationships to self-care and glycemic control in the literature reviewed, with effect sizes in the moderate to strong range. Each study considers attributes or skills of teens in conjunction with their environment.

Discussion

Previous reviews have acknowledged the importance of examining social support and its influence on diabetes and other health outcomes (La Greca, Bearman, & Moore, 2002; Wysocki & Greco, 2006), but this is the first review to our knowledge to focus exclusively on peer relationships and their link to self-care and glycemic control in adolescents with T1D. Previous reviews have concluded that peer support has a positive impact on adolescent disease outcomes (La Greca et al., 2002; Wysocki & Greco, 2006). The qualitative studies included in this review provide clear evidence that teens with T1D believe peers influence their self-care behavior, but this review found a weak relation between peer support and self-care, and mixed evidence linking peer support to glycemic control.

The majority of studies examining the association of peer support with self-care found no link of general or diabetes-specific support to global self-care indices. Although our intention at the outset of this review was to examine the relation of different kinds of peer support to self-care and glycemic control, specifically distinguishing between emotional and instrumental support, studies failed to distinguish between the two within the context of general or diabetes-specific support. Of the studies that did find a relation between support and self-care, all associated higher levels of support with better self-care behaviors. Two of the five found an association with a specific self-care behavior (e.g., diet, blood glucose monitoring) rather than with a global index of self-care behaviors. Four of the five found a link of diabetes-specific support to self-care. Together, these findings suggest that links of support to self-care require consideration of diabetes-specific predictor variables and specific aspects of self care. It also may be the case that certain types of support have a stronger influence on specific self-care behaviors, as argued previously by La Greca (1995). For example, reminding teens to test their blood sugar (i.e., diabetes-specific instrumental support) may be more strongly related to blood glucose monitoring, and helping teens feel good about themselves despite dietary restrictions (i.e., diabetes-specific emotional support) may be more strongly linked to diet.

Evidence for a link between peer support and glycemic control among adolescents is mixed. The majority of the studies found no relation between peer support and glycemic control. Of the two studies that found a beneficial association, one found that satisfaction with school support predicted an improvement in glycemic control, but only for those who had better glycemic control at baseline (Lehmkuhl & Nabors, 2008), and the other linked the number of peers selected to participate in an intervention to better glycemic control (Pendley et al., 2002). These measures of support are unique relative to the other support measures used. In addition, two studies indicated that peer support was associated with poor rather than good glycemic control, one of which found a direct link (Helgeson, Siminerio et al., 2009), and one of which showed an indirect link in which peer support intensified the negative relation between diabetes-related stress and glycemic control (Hains et al., 2007). Consequently, it is difficult to conclude that peer support is beneficial in terms of glycemic control.

Despite the fact that there were fewer studies that examined the negative compared to the positive side of peer relationships, more consistent evidence relates peer conflict, rather than support, to diabetes outcomes. Interestingly, it was general conflict rather than diabetes-related peer conflict that was examined in these studies. The two studies that linked general conflict to poor glycemic control are especially important, because both were longitudinal.

Why would general peer conflict be associated with poor diabetes outcomes? First, conflict with peers can lead to increased levels of interpersonal stress for teens, who are already involved in a wide variety of challenges from school and other activities. Stress can detract from self-care and directly or indirectly affect glycemic control. Research has shown that stress is associated with poor self-care and poor glycemic control among youth with diabetes (Helgeson, Escobar, Siminerio, & Becker, 2010). Second, peer conflict could be a reflection of low social competence. Youth who are less skilled at negotiating and adapting to their social environment may face more difficulties in their relationships. Social competence has been linked to better health among adolescents in general (Mechanic & Hansell, 1987) and to better self-care in teens with diabetes (Miller & Drotar, 2006); it also mitigates the detrimental relation of stress to metabolic control (C. L. Hanson, Henggeler, & Burghen, 1987). Therefore, teens who lack the advantage of social competence may be more prone to health-related difficulties. Third, adolescents experiencing conflict may be reluctant to discuss their diabetes with peers (Jacobson et al., 1986), which could lead to neglect of self-care around peers. Newly diagnosed teens who said they did not plan to share their diabetes with their friends at baseline had poorer self-care behavior and poorer adjustment 3 months later (Greco et al., 2003). In contrast, teens who had more peers in school who were aware of their diagnosis reported fewer concerns about diabetes self-management in the presence of peers (Salamon, 2010). Fourth, in the case of severe conflict (i.e., bullying), teens may be neglectful of their diabetes self-care in public situations to avoid being singled out (Susman-Stillman, Hyson, Anderson, & Collins, 1997).

We do not know, however, whether general peer conflict or diabetes-specific conflict are more strongly related to diabetes health outcomes because, surprisingly, not a single study examined the relation of diabetes-specific conflict with peers to self-care or glycemic control. Despite the fact that qualitative research indicated peers can present challenges to self-care behaviors, researchers have not used an instrument that taps diabetes-specific conflict to explore its association to diabetes outcomes. Although instruments measuring diabetes-related family conflict, such as the Diabetes Family Conflict Scale (DFCS; Hood, Anderson, Butler, & Laffel, 2007; Rubin, Young-Hyman, & Peyrot, 1985), are widely used in pediatric research, no instrument exists that specifically taps diabetes-related peer conflict. Some measures of diabetes-related support include conflict items, such as the Diabetes Family Behavior Scale (DFBS; McKelvey et al., 1993) and the Diabetes Family Behavior Checklist (DFBC; Schafer, McCaul, & Glasgow, 1986), but they do not examine the conflict items separately from the support items. The Diabetes Stress Questionnaire (DSQ; Salamon, 2010) is a recently developed measure of diabetes-related stress that teens may experience in social situations, but to date it has not been examined with respect to self-care or glycemic control.

The strongest overall evidence that peer relationships are linked to diabetes outcomes arose from studies that considered both the personalities of youth and the context of the situations they faced. Teens may be more or less influenced by peers for reasons that have little to do with peers, but more to do with their own dispositions and coping skills and styles. The key to assisting teens to cope effectively with social situations must consider the adolescent's cognitive framing of social challenges in conjunction with the social environment. Three studies considered how the dispositions or cognitions of adolescents with T1D interacted with the social environment. Peer relationships were linked to poor self-care behaviors when those relationships were examined in the context of social situations that pose challenges to self-care for older, more knowledgeable teens (Thomas et al., 1997), when an individual difference variable was developed that tapped hyper-responsiveness to peer relationships (Drew et al., 2010), and when the respondent's perception of peer reactions was taken into consideration (Hains et al., 2007). Similar findings appeared for glycemic control. Interestingly, an intervention that trained newly-diagnosed adolescents with T1D to deal with difficult diabetes-related social situations led to steeper improvements in glycemic control over time compared to controls.

Together, the findings relating peer influence to diabetes self-care and glycemic control are inconclusive. Although the majority of studies showed no relation, there were some notable patterns in the findings. When a relation of peer support to self-care was found, it was more likely to be positive and to involve diabetes-specific support and specific self-care behaviors. Associations of peer support to glycemic control were provocative, in that there were equal numbers of beneficial and harmful relations. Drawing overall conclusions from these studies is difficult, however, because many more studies assessed self-care behavior than glycemic control. Peer conflict, on the other hand, was more consistently related to poor self-care and poor glycemic control, but fewer studies examined peer conflict and none examined diabetes-specific conflict. Finally, when considering participant dispositions and cognitions in social context, peer influence was typically linked to poor diabetes outcomes. The next section addresses limitations that may have contributed to these mixed findings and provides recommendations for how future research can extend knowledge regarding peer influence on teens with T1D.

Limitations of Past Research and Future Directions

Future research on the impact of peers on diabetes outcomes might benefit from different ways of conceptualizing peer relationships. One potentially important distinction is the one between friends and peers. The distinction between friends and peers has been studied in the developmental literature (Berndt, 2002; La Greca & Harrison, 2005). Despite recommendations that this distinction be considered in pediatric health research (La Greca et al., 2002), the differential influence of friends versus peers rarely has been examined in the context of T1D. Only one study explicitly distinguished between friends and peers (Hains et al., 2007), and only for a portion of the measures used. When asked how participants thought friends and peers would react to their self-care behaviors, the distinction did not make a difference. However, these researchers did not distinguish between friends and peers when examining peer support. Peers are individuals of the same age, grade, or social status as the teen, whereas classifying a peer as a friend suggests a person who the teen likes, trusts, and spends time. It may not be friends who pose challenges to diabetes self-care, but other classmates and acquaintances with whom the teen has substantial contact. Since the closeness of friendships changes throughout adolescence, however, it may be difficult for teens to distinguish friends from peers.

Another way of conceptualizing peer relationships is to examine the characteristics of teens' social networks. Recall that one study showed that teens who chose a greater number of peers to participate with them in an intervention had better glycemic control (Pendley et al., 2002). This finding suggests that simply being embedded in a larger social network is beneficial to diabetes health. However, it is also possible that larger social networks could lead to more peer pressure and detrimental influence on self-care and, subsequently, poor glycemic control, especially if teens are overly concerned with peer acceptance as was found in the case of EPO (Drew et al., 2010). Recall the two studies that linked peer support to poor glycemic control (Hains et al., 2007; Helgeson, Siminerio et al., 2009). Peer support in these studies could have reflected embedding in a social network that made it difficult to resist peer influence. Future research should assess characteristics of peer social networks including network size, diversity, and strength to ascertain their associations with diabetes outcomes.

Peer relationships should also be considered in the context of the family environment. Research has shown that strong parent–adolescent relationships are more likely to be linked to good self-care and glycemic control when teens do not place excessive importance on peer acceptance (Drew et al., 2010). Research has also shown that friendships of teens with chronic diseases are protective from negative effects of poor parental relationships, but that there are limits to the role that parental relationships can play in alleviating negative effects of problematic relationships with friends (Herzer, Umfress, Aljadeff, Ghai, & Zakowski, 2009). This synergistic influence of friends and family relationships on teens' well-being suggests that peer influence should be examined within the context of the quality of familial relationships.

Future research that examines the association of peer relationships to diabetes outcomes also would benefit from an examination of several variables that have implications for teens' relationships—specifically age, gender, and SES. Since peer relationships change over the course of adolescence (Berndt, 1979; McNelles & Connolly, 1999), the implications of peer relationships for diabetes self-care also may change with age. Older teens report more support from peers than children (Pendley et al., 2002), but also are more vulnerable to peer influences than children (Thomas et al., 1997). Researchers typically studied children and adolescents across a wide variety of ages (i.e., 10–18 years) without determining whether age moderated links of peer relations to diabetes outcomes. Findings based upon youth across multiple stages of development may fail to identify a stage of social development in which peers have an important influence.

Gender is another variable that should be considered more prominently in future research. Studies show that girls report more diabetes-specific support (Bearman & La Greca, 2002; La Greca, Auslander et al., 1995; Skinner & Hampson, 1998; Skinner et al., 2000) and more general support (Helgeson, Reynolds, Shestak, & Wei, 2006; Skinner & Hampson, 1998; Skinner et al., 2000) than boys. However, it is not clear whether sex affects the role that peer relationships play in self-care and glycemic control. The one study that examined this issue found that peer conflict was more strongly associated with poor glycemic control among girls than boys (Helgeson, Lopez et al., 2009).

Peer influence on teens with T1D may also depend upon SES. Lower SES has been associated with poorer health (e.g., smoking, pooer diets, less physical activity; M. D. Hanson & Chen, 2007; Matthews, Gallo, & Taylor, 2010; Wilkinson, 1992). In the context of diabetes, teens from lower SES households may experience less frequent adult supervision than those from more affluent households, leading them to be more susceptible to peer influence (Evans, 2004). Simply adjusting analyses for SES is not enough to capture its important influence on health (Adler et al., 1994). None of the studies that we reviewed examined whether findings held across different SES groups.

Finally, two other methodological limitations may have contributed to the lack of clear findings. First, all but one of the studies reviewed (Naar-King et al., 2006) employed relatively homogeneous samples of adolescents with regard to race, ethnicity, and SES. This lack of representative samples limits the generalizability of the findings. Minority races and cultures place greater importance on family and community than whites (Ajrouch, Antonucci, & Janevic, 2001; Siddiqui, Mott, Anderson, & Flay, 1999), and this difference could result in lower rates of peer influence among minority teens. Second, the majority of study designs were cross-sectional, limiting the ability to draw conclusions about causality. It is important to determine if peer relationships impact diabetes-related behaviors, if diabetes-related behaviors impact peer relationships, or if third variables influence the relationship.

The study of peer influences on self-care and glycemic control in adolescents with T1D is at an exciting crossroads. Qualitative studies have established that teens believe peers influence their self-care, but quantitative studies have yet to provide conclusive evidence as to the nature of this influence. Clear methodological limitations, the lack of measurement specificity, and the paucity of research addressing the problematic aspects of peer relationships are problems that can be remedied. Different conceptualizations of peer support, such as discerning friends from peers, and more carefully examining peer network characteristics, provide many opportunities for further investigation. Learning to navigate their social environments while coping with the requirements of a chronic disease is an important developmental task for teens with T1D, and may have an important impact on health outcomes. Whether the peers of teens with T1D are friends or foes with regard to their impact on diabetes outcomes remains to be determined.

Funding

This work was supported by the National Institutes of Health/The National Institute of Diabetes and Digestive and Kidney Diseases (grant number R01 DK60586 to V.H.).

Conflicts of interest: None declared.

References

Adler, N. E., Boyce, T., Chesney, M. A., Cohen, S., Folkman, S., Kahn, R. L., & Syme, S.L. (1994). Socioeconomic status and health: The challenge of the gradient. *American Psychologist, 49*(1), 15–24.

Ajrouch, K. J., Antonucci, T. C., & Janevic, M. R. (2001). Social networks among blacks and whites: The interaction between race and age. *The Journals of Gerontology Series B: Psychological Sciences and Social Sciences, 56B*(2), S112–S118.

Anderman, E. M. (2002). School effects on psychological outcomes during adolescence. *Journal of Educational Psychology, 94*(4), 795–809.

*Bearman, K. J., & La Greca, A. M. (2002). Assessing friend support of adolescents' diabetes care: The diabetes social support questionnaire-friends version. *Journal of Pediatric Psychology, 27*(5), 417–428.

Berg, C. A., King, P. S., Butler, J. M., Pham, P., Palmer, D., & Wiebe, D. J. (2011). Parental involvement and adolescents' diabetes management: The mediating role of self-efficacy and externalizing and internalizing behaviors. *Journal of Pediatric Psychology, 36*(3), 329–339.

*Berlin, K. S., Davies, W. H., Jastrowski, K. E., Hains, A. A., Parton, E. A., & Alemzadeh, R. (2006). Contextual assessment of problematic situations identified by insulin pump using adolescents and their parents. *Families, Systems, & Health, 24*(1), 33–44.

Berndt, T. J. (1979). Developmental changes in conformity to peers and parents. *Developmental Psychology, 15*(6), 608–616.

Berndt, T. J. (2002). Friendship quality and social development. *Current Directions in Psychological Science, 11*(1), 7–10.

Cohen, S. (1988). Psychosocial models of the role of social support in the etiology of physical disease. *Health Psychology, 7*(3), 269–297.

Cohen, S., & Wills, T. A. (1985). Stress, social support, and the buffering hypothesis. *Psychological Bulletin, 98*(2), 310.

Dakof, G. A., & Taylor, S. E. (1990). Victims' perceptions of social support: What is helpful from whom? *Journal of Personality and Social Psychology, 58*(1), 80–89.

DCCT. (1993). The effect of intensive treatment of diabetes on the development and progression of long-term complications in insulin-dependent diabetes mellitus. *New England Journal of Medicine, 329*(14), 977–986.

*de Dios, C., Avedillo, C., Palao, A., Ortiz, A., & Agud, J. L. (2003). Family and social factors related to emotional well-being in adolescents with Diabetes Mellitus Type 1. *European Journal of Psychiatry, 17*(3), 182–192.

*Drew, L. M., Berg, C., & Wiebe, D. J. (2010). The mediating role of extreme peer orientation in the relationships between adolescent–parent relationship and diabetes management. *Journal of Family Psychology, 24*(3), 299–306.

Evans, G. W. (2004). The environment of childhood poverty. *American Psychologist, 59*(2), 77–92.

Fuligni, A. J., Barber, B. L., Eccles, J. S., & Clements, P. (2001). Early adolescent peer orientation and adjustment during high school. *Developmental Psychology, 37*(1), 28–36.

Goran, M. I., & Gower, B. A. (2001). Longitudinal study on pubertal insulin resistance. *Diabetes, 50*, 2444–2450.

Greco, P., Harris, M., Milkes, A., Sadler, M., Mertlich, D., & Jones, J. (2003). Revealing the diagnosis of diabetes to friends: The beginnings of social support. *Diabetes, 52*, A414.

*Greco, P., Pendley, J., McDonell, K., & Reeves, G. (2001). A peer group intervention for adolescents with type 1 diabetes and their best friends. *Journal of Pediatric Psychology, 26*(8), 485–490.

Greening, L., Stoppelbein, L., Konishi, C., Jordan, S. S., & Moll, G. (2007). Child routines and youths' adherence to treatment for type 1 diabetes. *Journal of Pediatric Psychology, 32*, 437–447.

*Grey, M., Boland, E., Davidson, M., Yu, C., Sullivan-Bolyai, S., & Tamborlane, W. V. (1998). Short-term effects of coping skills training as adjunct to intensive therapy in adolescents. *Diabetes Care, 21*(6), 902–908.

*Hains, A. A., Berlin, K. S., Hobart Davies, W., Smothers, M. K., Sato, A. F., & Alemzadeh, R. (2007). Attributions of adolescents with type 1 diabetes related to performing diabetes care around friends and peers: The moderating role of friend support. *Journal of Pediatric Psychology, 32*(5), 561.

Hanson, C. L., Henggeler, S. W., & Burghen, G. A. (1987). Social competence and parental support as mediators of the link between stress and metabolic control in adolescents with insulin-dependent diabetes mellitus. *Journal of Consulting and Clinical Psychology, 55*(4), 529–533.

Hanson, M. D., & Chen, E. (2007). Socioeconomic status and health behaviors in adolescence: A review of the literature. *Journal of Behavioral Medicine, 30*(3), 263–285.

Helgeson, V. S., Escobar, O., Siminerio, L., & Becker, D. (2010). Relation of stressful life events to metabolic control among adolescents with diabetes: 5-Year longitudinal study. *Health Psychology, 29*(2), 153–159.

*Helgeson, V. S., Lopez, L. C., & Karmack, T. (2009). Peer relationships and diabetes: Retrospective and ecological momentary assessment approaches. *Health Psychology, 28*(3), 273–282.

*Helgeson, V. S., Reynolds, K. A., Escobar, O., Siminerio, L., & Becker, D. (2007). The role of friendship in the lives of male and female adolescents: Does diabetes make a difference? *Journal of Adolescent Health, 40*(1), 36–43.

Helgeson, V. S., Reynolds, K. A., Shestak, A., & Wei, S. (2006). Brief report: Friendships of adolescents with and without diabetes. *Journal of Pediatric Psychology, 31*(2), 194–199.

Helgeson, V. S., Reynolds, K. A., Siminerio, L., Escobar, O., & Becker, D. (2008). Parent and adolescent distribution of responsibility for diabetes self-care: Links to health outcomes. *Journal of Pediatric Psychology, 33*(5), 497–508.

*Helgeson, V. S., Siminerio, L., Escobar, O., & Becker, D. (2009). Predictors of metabolic control among adolescents with diabetes: A 4-year longitudinal study. *Journal of Pediatric Psychology, 34*(3), 254–270.

Herzer, M., Umfress, K., Aljadeff, G., Ghai, K., & Zakowski, S. G. (2009). Interactions with parents and friends among chronically ill children: Examining social networks. *Journal of developmental and behavioral pediatrics, 30*(6), 499–508.

Holmes, C. S., Chen, R., Streisand, R., Marschall, D. E., Souter, S., & Swift, E. E. (2006). Predictors of youth diabetes care behaviors and metabolic control: A structural equation modeling approach. *Journal of Pediatric Psychology, 31*, 770–784.

Hood, K., Anderson, B. J., Butler, D. A., & Laffel, L. M. (2007). Updated and revised diabetes family conflict scale. *Diabetes Care, 30*(7), 1764–1769.

Hood, K., Peterson, C. M., Rohan, J. M., & Drotar, D. (2009). Association between adherence and glycemic control in pediatric type 1 diabetes: A meta-analysis. *Pediatrics, 124*(6), e1171–e1179.

Ingerski, L. M., Anderson, B. J., Dolan, L. M., & Hood, K. K. (2010). Blood glucose monitoring and glycemic control in adolescence: Contribution of diabetes-specific responsibility and family conflict. *Journal of Adolescent Health, 47*(2), 191–197.

Jacobson, A., Hauser, S., Wertlieb, D., Wolfsdorf, J., Orleans, J., & Vieyra, M. (1986). Psychological adjustment of children with recently diagnosed diabetes mellitus. *Diabetes Care, 9*(4), 323–329.

*Kager, V. A., & Holden, E. W. (1992). Preliminary investigation of the direct and moderating effects of family and individual variables on the adjustment of children and adolescents with diabetes. *Journal of Pediatric Psychology, 17*(4), 491–502.

*Karlsson, A., Arman, M., & Wikblad, K. (2008). Teenagers with type 1 diabetes- a phenomenological study of the transition towards autonomy in self-management. *International Journal of Nursing Studies, 45*, 562–570.

*Kyngas, H., Hentinen, M., & Barlow, J. H. (1998). Adolescents' perceptions of physicians, nurses, parents and friends: Help or hindrance in compliance with diabetes self-care? *Journal of Advanced Nursing, 27*(4), 760–769.

*Kyngas, H., & Rissanen, M. (2001). Support as a crucial predictor of good compliance of adolescents with a chronic disease. *Journal of clinical nursing, 10*(6), 767–774.

*La Greca, A. M., Auslander, W. F., Greco, P., Spetter, D., Fisher, E. B., & Santiago, J. V. (1995). I get by with a little help from my family and friends: Adolescents' support for diabetes care. *Journal of Pediatric Psychology, 20*(4), 449–476.

La Greca, A. M., Bearman, K. J., & Moore, H. (2002). Peer relations of youth with pediatric conditions and health risks: Promoting social support and healthy lifestyles. *Developmental and Behavioral Pediatrics, 23*(4), 271–280.

La Greca, A. M., Follansbee, D., & Skyler, J. S. (1990). Developmental and behavioral aspects of diabetes management in youngsters. *Children s Health Care, 19*(3), 132–139.

La Greca, A. M., & Harrison, H. M. (2005). Adolescent peer relations, friendships, and romantic relationships: Do they predict social anxiety and depression? *Journal of Clinical Child and Adolescent Psychology, 34*(1), 49–61.

La Greca, A. M., Swales, T., Klemp, S., Madigan, S., & Skyler, J. (1995). Adolescents with diabetes: Gender differences in psychosocial functioning and glycemic control. *Children s Health Care, 24*(1), 61–78.

Ladd, G. W. (2008). Social competence and peer relations: Significance for young children and their service-providers. *Early Childhood Services: An Interdisciplinary Journal of Effectiveness, 2*(3), 129–148.

Larson, R. W., & Verma, S. (1999). How children and adolescents spend time across the world: Work, play, and developmental opportunities. *Psychological Bulletin, 125*(6), 701–736.

*Lehmkuhl, H., Merlo, L. J., Devine, K., Gaines, J., Storch, E. A., Silverstein, J. H., & Geffken, G. (2009). Perceptions of type 1 diabetes among affected youth and their peers. *Journal of Clinical Psychology in Medical Setting, 16*(3), 209–215.

*Lehmkuhl, H., & Nabors, L. (2008). Children with diabetes: Satisfaction with school support, illness perceptions and HbA1c levels. *Journal of Developmental Physical Disabilities, 20*, 101–114.

Lepore, S. J., & Helgeson, V. S. (1998). Social constraints, intrusive thoughts, and mental health after prostate cancer. *Journal of Social and Clinical Psychology, 17*(1), 89–106.

Lewandowski, A., & Drotar, D. (2007). The relationship between parent-reported social support and adherence to medical treatment in families of adolescents with type 1 diabetes. *Journal of Pediatric Psychology, 32*(4), 427–436.

Matthews, K. A., Gallo, L. C., & Taylor, S. E. (2010). Are psychosocial factors mediators of socioeconomic status and health connections? *Annals of the New York Academy of Sciences, 1186*(1), 146–173.

McKelvey, J., Waller, D. A., North, A. J., Marks, J. F., Schreiner, B., Travis, L. B., & Murphy, J. N. (1993). Reliability and validity of the diabetes family behavior scale (DFBS). *The Diabetes Educator, 19*(2), 125–132.

McNelles, L. R., & Connolly, J. A. (1999). Intimacy between adolescent friends: Age and gender differences in intimate affect and intimate behaviors. *Journal of Research on Adolescence, 9*(2), 143–159.

Mechanic, D., & Hansell, S. (1987). Adolescent competence, psychological well-being, and self-assessed physical health. *Journal of Health and Social Behavior,* 364–374.

Meece, D., & Laird, R. D. (2006). The importance of peers. In F. A. Villarruel, & T. Luster (Eds.), *The Crisis in Youth Mental Health: Critical Issues and Effective Programs*(Vol. 2, p. 2006). Westport, CT: Praeger Publishers.

Miller, V. A., & Drotar, D. (2006). Decision-making competence and adherence to treatment in adolescents with diabetes. *Journal of Pediatric Psychology, 32*(2), 178–188.

*Naar-King, S., Podolski, C. L., Ellis, D. A., Frey, M. A., & Templin, T. (2006). Social Ecological Model of Illness Management in High-Risk Youths With Type 1 Diabetes. *Journal of Consulting and Clinical Psychology, 74*(4), 785–789.

*Pendley, J. S., Kasmen, L. J., Miller, D. L., Donze, J., Swenson, C., & Reeves, G. (2002). Peer and family support in children and adolescents with type 1 diabetes. *Journal of Pediatric Psychology, 27*(5), 429–438.

Peterson, R. A., & Brown, S. P. (2005). On the use of beta coefficients in meta-analysis. *Journal of Applied Psychology, 90*(1), 175–181.

Rook, K., Sorkin, D., & Zettel, L. (2004). Stress in social relationships: Coping and adaptation across the life span. *Growing together: Personal relationships across the life span,* 210–239.

Rubin, R. R., Young-Hyman, D., & Peyrot, M. (1985). Parent-child responsibility and conflict in diabetes care. *Diabetes, 38*(Suppl. 2), 28A.

Salamon, K. S., Hains, A. A., Fleischman, K. M., Davies, W. H., & Kichler, J. (2010). Improving adherence in social situations for adolescents with type 1 diabetes mellitus: A Pilot Study. *Primary Care Diabetes, 4,* 47–55.

Schafer, L. C., McCaul, K. D., & Glasgow, R. E. (1986). Supportive and nonsupportive family behaviors: Relationships to adherence and metabolic control in persons with type I diabetes. *Diabetes Care, 9*(2), 179.

*Schlundt, D. G., Pichert, J. W., Rea, M. R., Puryear, W., Penha, M. L. I., & Kline, S. S. (1994). Situational obstacles to adherence for adolescents with diabetes. *The Diabetes Educator, 20*(3), 207–211.

Scholte, R. H., van Lieshout, C. F., & van Aken, M. A. (2001). Perceived relational support in adolescence: Dimensions, configurations, and adolescent adjustment. *Journal of Research on Adolescence, 11*(1), 71–94.

Siddiqui, O., Mott, J., Anderson, T., & Flay, B. (1999). The application of Poisson random-effects regression models to the analyses of adolescents' current level of smoking. *Preventive medicine, 29*(2), 92–101.

*Skinner, T., & Hampson, S. E. (1998). Social support and personal models of diabetes in relation to self-care and well-being in adolescents with type I diabetes mellitus. *Journal of Adolescence, 21*(6), 703–715.

*Skinner, T., John, M., & Hampson, S. E. (2000). Social support and personal models of diabetes as predictors of self-care and well-being: A longitudinal study of adolescents with diabetes. *Journal of Pediatric Psychology, 25*(4), 257–267.

*Smith, M. S., Mauseth, R., Palmer, J. P., Pecoraro, R., & Wenet, G. (1991). Glycosylated hemoglobin and psychological adjustment in adolescents with diabetes. *Adolescence, 26*(101), 31–40.

Susman-Stillman, A., Hyson, D. M., Anderson, F. S., & Collins, W. A. (1997). Adolescent psychosocial development and adherence to treatment for insulin-dependent diabetes mellitus. *Creating the compliant patient, 33,* 73–101.

*Thomas, A. M., Peterson, L., & Goldstein, D. (1997). Problem solving and diabetes regimen adherence by children and adolescents with IDDM in social pressure situations: A reflection of normal development. *Journal of Pediatric Psychology, 22*(4), 541–561.

Wigfield, A., Eccles, J. S., Mac Iver, D., Reuman, D. A., & Midgley, C. (1991). Transitions during early adolescence: Changes in children's domain-specific self-perceptions and general self-esteem across the transition to junior high school. *Developmental Psychology, 27*(4), 552–565.

Wilkinson, R. G. (1992). Income distribution and life expectancy. *British medical journal, 304*(6820), 165–168.

Wysocki, T., & Greco, P. (2006). Social support and diabetes management in childhood and adolescence: Influence of parents and friends. *Current Diabetes Reports, 6*(2), 117–122.

Call for Submissions
Journal of Pediatric Psychology:
Special Issue on *Adherence*
Guest Editor: Lori J. Stark, Ph.D., ABPP
Due Date 11/01/12

"Drugs don't work in patients who don't take them!" Former U.S. Surgeon General C. Everett Koop.

Background

Adherence is defined as "…the extent to which a person's behavior -- taking medications, following a diet, and/or executing lifestyle changes, corresponds with agreed recommendations from a health care provider" (World Health Organization, 2003, pp. 3-4). Research with a wide range of chronic conditions in children and adolescents has indicated that nonadherence to treatment is pervasive (as high as 50% for some conditions). Nonadherence can take many forms including not filling prescriptions to skipping or missing doses and can be intentional (e.g., deciding not to take a medication because of side effects) or unintentional (e.g., forgetting). Poorer adherence has been documented for regimens that are more time-consuming and complex, and rates of nonadherence in pediatric chronic illness populations, especially among adolescents (Rapoff, 2010), are even higher than those in adult populations. Potentially serious health consequences can result from nonadherence. For example, incomplete adherence to immunosuppressive drugs has been linked to heart, kidney, and liver transplant failures (Ettemger et al. 1991). Nonadherence can influence clinical decisions about care, resulting in increases or changes in medication when none are needed. Nonadherence has been estimated to result in billions of dollars of excess medical care annually (The Task Force for Compliance, 1994). Despite the clinical importance of nonadherence and the significance of its impact on health care delivery, the assessment and treatment of adherence problems in pediatric chronic diseases have received surprisingly little attention (Rapoff, 2010). Moreover, few studies have evaluated the impact of interventions designed to promote adherence to medical treatment in childhood chronic diseases using randomized controlled trials (Rapoff, 2010).

Details

The aim of this special issue is to highlight innovative approaches to the treatment or prevention of pediatric nonadherence. We anticipate studies will focus on a range of health conditions and topics including innovative approaches to assessing adherence and understanding causes of nonadherence. However, priority will be given to studies focused on interventions to improve adherence in pediatric health conditions and research examining the translation and dissemination of interventions previously demonstrated to be efficacious in clinical trials. In this regard, a broad range of research methodologies will be considered for the special issue, including single case or small-n designs, randomized clinical trials, qualitative methodologies, and demonstration studies. Regardless of topic or methodology, a premium will be placed on the manuscript's demonstration of innovation. We expect manuscripts to highlight implications of the research for practitioners and/or policy makers.

Submissions for this special issue will be accepted until November 1, 2012.

Papers should be prepared in compliance with *JPP*'s Instructions to Authors (http://jpepsy.oxfordjournals.org/) and submitted through the ScholarOne Manuscript Central™ submission portal (http://mc.manuscriptcentral.com/jpepsy). Manuscripts will be peer reviewed. Please direct all inquiries about the suitability of manuscripts for the special issue to Lori.Stark@CCHMC.org .

Call for Submissions
Journal of Pediatric Psychology:
Special Issue on Innovative Treatment and Prevention Programs
for Pediatric Overweight and Obesity
Guest Editors: David M. Janicke, Ph.D. and Ric G. Steele, Ph.D.

Background
Despite significant clinical research directed at the problem, obesity remains a preeminent health problem in pediatric populations in the United States and abroad. The most current epidemiological data indicate that upwards of 17% of children and adolescents are obese, and that more than 30% of children and adolescents are overweight (Ogden et al., 2010). These aggregated data mask significant health disparities across medically underserved and racially or ethnically diverse groups. Recent reviews of the literature (e.g., Kitzmann et al., 2010; Luttikhuis et al., 2009) indicate that behaviorally-based individual and family-based interventions can be efficacious, yet the literature continues to be plagued with barriers to the successful translation of efficacious studies into clinical practice. Issues such as non- or incomplete treatment adherence, non-completion of therapy, poor maintenance of treatment effects, and unknown efficacy of interventions for medically underserved or culturally diverse populations limit the applicability of the current literature to cases most often seen in practice.

Details
The aim of this special issue is to highlight innovative approaches to the treatment or prevention of pediatric overweight and obesity. We anticipate that studies will focus on a range of topics, including, but not limited to: interventions that employ eHealth, mHealth, or telehealth technologies; intervention or prevention programs specifically designed for medically underserved or ethnically or culturally diverse samples; studies examining ecological systems-based intervention/prevention efforts such as school, or community based programs; empirical studies of policies that are designed to address obesity/overweight at the community or population level; and research examining the translation and dissemination of interventions previously demonstrated to be efficacious in clinical trials. A broad range of research methodologies will be considered for the special issue, including single case or small-n designs, randomized clinical trials, qualitative methodologies, and demonstration studies. Regardless of topic or methodology, a premium will be placed on the manuscript's demonstration of innovation. We expect manuscripts to highlight implications of the research for practitioners and/or policy makers.

Submissions for this special issue will be accepted until October 1, 2012.

Papers should be prepared in compliance with *JPP*'s Instructions to Authors (http://jpepsy.oxfordjournals.org/) and submitted through the ScholarOne Manuscript Central™ submission portal (http://mc.manuscriptcentral.com/jpepsy). Manuscripts will be peer reviewed. Papers that are not appropriate for inclusion in this special issue may be rerouted (with the authors' knowledge and consent) for consideration for publication in *JPP* as regular papers. Please indicate in the cover letter accompanying your manuscript that you would like to have the paper considered for the Special Issue on Innovative Treatment and Prevention Programs for Pediatric Overweight and Obesity.

Please direct all inquiries to David M. Janicke at djanicke@phhp.ufl.edu or Ric G. Steele at rsteele@ku.edu.

Society of Pediatric Psychology
Division 54, American Psychological Association

Please visit our website **https://www.societyofpediatricpsychology.org/** for complete membership information and to join.

Our membership benefits include:

- Subscription to the *Journal of Pediatric Psychology*
- Representation and advocacy for pediatric psychology
- Option to join the SPP member listserv, with postings about job openings, discussions of clinical issues, referral requests, etc.
- Option to join the SPP student listserv addressing training and early career issues
- Programming specific to pediatric psychology at the annual APA meeting
- Subscription to the SPP newsletter, *Progress Notes*
- Opportunities to be involved and volunteer in SPP
- Various awards and grants for students and psychologists at all career stages
- Opportunity to participate in various Special Interest Groups with SPP
- Participation in the SPP mentoring program---as mentee or mentor
- Access to online member directory and option to be listed in the directory

Society of Clinical Child and Adolescent Psychology
Division 53, American Psychological Association

Come join us! Visit our website **https://www.clinicalchildpsychology.org/** for complete membership information. Here are just a few of the reasons to join Division 53.

Our Journal
The *Journal of Clinical Child and Adolescent Psychology* is a leading child psychopathology and treatment journal.

Quest BehavioralPro
Division 53 members are provided behavioral health information for clinical practice, teaching, and research purposes from Quest Health Systems, Inc.

Our Newsletter
InBalance is published 3 times a year offering topical features, news of interest, and important policy-related information.

Our Listservs
A members-only listserv provides a forum for scientific and professional topics. The announce-only listserv alerts you to Division developments. Students may join either of these listservs as well as a Student Only listserv.

Convention Activities
We sponsor several APA Convention activities: symposia, workshops, poster sessions, and a social hour that allow you to network, learn, exchange information, and stay abreast of current clinical and research topics in our field.

Continuing Education
CE credits that can be obtained at the APA annual convention and at sponsored regional conferences designed to advance evidence-based assessment and treatment of children and adolescents.

Task Forces
SCCAP task forces investigate issues pertinent to child mental health policy, treatment, and diagnostics.